ORGANOMETALLIC SYNTHESES

Volume 1

Transition-Metal Compounds

Organometallic Syntheses

Edited by

JOHN J. EISCH
DEPARTMENT OF CHEMISTRY
THE CATHOLIC UNIVERSITY OF AMERICA
WASHINGTON, D. C.

R. BRUCE KING
MELLON INSTITUTE
PITTSBURGH, PENNSYLVANIA

---

1. Transition-Metal Compounds, R. BRUCE KING, 1965
2. Non-Transition-Metal Compounds, JOHN J. EISCH, *in preparation*

ORGANOMETALLIC SYNTHESES

SYNTHESES

Volume 1
Transition-Metal Compounds

By

R. Bruce King

MELLON INSTITUTE
PITTSBURGH, PENNSYLVANIA

1965

ACADEMIC PRESS   New York and London

ACADEMIC PRESS INC.
111 Fifth Avenue, New York, New York 10003

United Kingdom Edition published by
ACADEMIC PRESS INC. (LONDON) LTD.
Berkeley Square House, London W.1

LIBRARY OF CONGRESS CATALOG CARD NUMBER: 65-18428

PRINTED IN THE UNITED STATES OF AMERICA

Foreword

Compounds containing carbon–metal bonds have come to occupy a prominent position in many phases of modern chemical research. During the past fifteen years these organometallic compounds have served as key reagents in masterly major synthetic achievements, both in organic chemistry as well as inorganic chemistry. Moreover, because of their variegated patterns of molecular structure, organometallic compounds are themselves the test subjects in many recent physicochemical studies. These latter investigations continue to furnish an ever-deepening understanding of chemical bonding. Thus, researchers of diverse backgrounds are faced with the problem of preparing pure organometallic compounds in a reliable fashion. Due to the specialized techniques involved in handling substances which are often poisonous, flammable, and sensitive to moisture and air, chemists engaging in such preparative work for the first time need guidance. Although several procedures for the commoner organometallic compounds (e.g., Grignard reagents; alkyls of mercury, tin, and zinc; and ferrocene) have been included from time to time in the excellent compilations, "Organic Syntheses" and "Inorganic Syntheses," many desired procedures must be ferreted out of the voluminous research literature. Descriptions of essential techniques and apparatus, uncovered incidental to another research goal, often are difficult to trace by available literature indices.

The editors have decided, accordingly, to initiate a series devoted to furnishing clear and reliable procedures for the preparation of important organometallic types. To this end, the first volume of this series will compile accurate descriptions for various transition-metal compounds, together with a general discussion of special laboratory techniques necessary in such experimentation (reactions under pressure or requiring ultraviolet irradiation; procedures for the purification, identification, and analysis of products; safety precautions; etc.). This will be followed by a second volume dealing with nontransition-metal compounds, which will offer suitable procedures for this type, as well as a discussion of the purification of sensitive liquids, inert atmosphere provision, sample transfer and analytical techniques, etc. Thereafter, the editors, acting in concert with an editorial board of prominent organometallic chemists, will serve as a screening committee for contributed procedures. Periodically the accepted and substantiated contributions will be published in further volumes of the series.

The editors solicit the cooperation of the many workers in organometallic chemistry in making the continuation of this series a success.

v

Organometallic chemists are invited to submit reliable synthetic procedures to the editors. Appropriate contributions might consist of original procedures for the preparation of novel organometallic types or of modifications in existing procedures giving superior results. Manuscripts in the area of transition-metal compounds are to be submitted to R. B. King and those involving nontransition-metal types to J. J. Eisch. The format to be followed in preparing such contributions is that used in Volume I of the series. In general, procedures are sought which have proved trustworthy in the hands of two or more independent researchers. Therefore, novel synthetic procedures originating from a given research group will be checked in an independent, cooperating laboratory. Active organometallic chemists throughout the world have offered to participate in such checking of procedures. This excellent *esprit de corps* promises to make this phase of the venture more stimulating than onerous, promoting as it does an international exchange of research results.

The editors would like to acknowledge the fruitful discussions with the editorial board and with many of their research colleagues concerning the feasibility and format of this new series. The staff of Academic Press has aided the successful completion of this endeavor by its wealth of editorial insight. Finally, the editors and editorial board are gratified by the enthusiasm with which this series has been greeted. They look forward to the continued interest and cooperation of their colleagues in forging this new research tool.

JOHN J. EISCH
R. BRUCE KING

Preface

Since the discovery of ferrocene in 1951 there has been a great expansion in transition-metal organometallic chemistry. Many compounds with unusual structures, reactions, and physical properties have been discovered. Such compounds are of interest both in various areas of basic chemistry and in certain applications, notably catalysis and metal deposition.

Preparative techniques in transition-metal organometallic chemistry are of obvious importance to anyone desiring such a compound which is not commercially available. Although conventional in many respects, such preparative techniques present certain unusual features due to the characteristic chemical and physical properties of the materials used. Therefore, detailed descriptions in one book of the best available procedures for the preparation of important transition-metal organometallic compounds as well as a general discussion of the important experimental techniques in this area of chemistry appeared very useful. The present volume is the result of my efforts to achieve this goal.

Part I of this volume contains a brief general description of the most important experimental techniques in transition-metal organometallic chemistry. I discuss only the most essential features of the experimental techniques not only for brevity but also because less important details may be highly variable depending on the facilities of the laboratory, the commercial availability of various items, the temperament of the investigator, the purpose of the experiment, and many other factors. Inclusion of these less important details would contribute more to the confusion of the inexperienced reader than to the enlightenment of the experienced one. References to more detailed discussions of many experimental techniques are frequently given to aid the reader wishing a much more thorough exposition on a given experimental technique.

Part II of this volume contains a detailed description of satisfactory syntheses of over sixty transition-metal organometallic compounds. Among these sixty compounds are all of the neutral biscyclopentadienyl compounds, neutral cyclopentadienylmetal carbonyls, and neutral metal carbonyls without other ligands for which an adequately tested preparation is available. In some cases (e.g. ferrocene and ruthenocene) I refer to a procedure in "Inorganic Syntheses" or "Organic Syntheses" without repeating the procedure in this volume since I know of no materially better preparation. In other cases (e.g., iron pentacarbonyl and nickel tetracarbonyl) the compound appears to be available commercially throughout the world so that its synthesis in the laboratory is not required.

The remaining specific preparations discussed in Part II are generally compounds with which I have had some personal experience. I include these preparations both because the compounds are interesting and because I feel especially qualified from my research experience to discuss them. This somewhat subjective selection process naturally leaves a few gaps in the coverage of interesting transition-metal organometallic compounds with which I have had no personal experience. I hope to fill these gaps in future volumes of "Organometallic Syntheses" by contributions from workers throughout the world who have had experience with syntheses of important transition-metal organometallic compounds not discussed in this volume.

All of the syntheses in this volume have been carried out in a manner closely related to that described here by at least two independent laboratories. About two-thirds of the procedures were derived from the literature and repeated under my close supervision at various times during the last six years. The remaining third of the procedures are described in the literature in similar form by at least two different laboratories. For this reason the procedures described in this volume should be reliable. I would appreciate hearing of any persistent difficulties in repeating the procedures given in this volume. If any worthwhile modifications, improvements, or corrections of any procedures given here are made, they will be discussed in future volumes of this series. Unsolicited synthetic procedures for transition-metal organometallic compounds to be included in Volume III and subsequent volumes of "Organometallic Syntheses" are welcome. They should conform to the format of the procedures in this volume. Many such procedures will be checked in an independent laboratory and all procedures will be refereed before acceptance for publication.

For convenience the syntheses described in Part II are divided into several sections according to the general type of compound obtained as the product of interest. References and other footnotes are numbered consecutively within a given section to avoid large numbers and cross-reference to other sections. Footnote numbers encountered in the text thus refer to the corresponding footnote in that section alone.

I would like to acknowledge the helpful discussions with my co-editor, Professor J. J. Eisch, as well as with various members of the editorial board and other organometallic chemists. Finally I would like to acknowledge the cooperation of my wife and family and the help of several members of the Mellon Institute during various phases of my work on this volume.

R. BRUCE KING

Pittsburgh, Pennsylvania
March, 1965

Contents

PART I

General Techniques in Transition-
Metal Organometallic Chemistry

A. Techniques for Carrying Out Reactions

1. Reactions in Open Systems at Atmospheric Pressure

Most reactions in transition-metal organometallic chemistry are carried out at atmospheric pressure in open systems because of convenience and general availability of equipment. The reaction vessel is generally a one- to five-necked flask[1] with ground joints[2,3] in the necks (Fig. 1) or a Schlenk tube (Fig. 2). Depending upon the reaction, provisions must be made for heating, cooling, admission of gases, stirring, and addition of reagents. Most of these techniques are very similar to those in general use in organic chemistry,[4] and, therefore, will only be outlined briefly here.

Heating is most commonly provided by an electrically operated heating mantle[5] or an oil bath heated by an electric hot plate. In either case, the heat may be controlled by use of a continuously variable transformer ("Variac") to vary the electrical input. Of these two alternatives, the heating mantle is more convenient and effectively used when the desired reaction temperature is the same as the boiling point of the solvent.[6] If

---

[1] One- and three-necked flasks are most frequently used.

[2] Ground glass standard taper joints have been used so universally in the leading laboratories doing research in organometallic transition-metal chemistry that it is not known to what extent the less expensive but less convenient cork and rubber stoppers may be used in reactions involving these organometallic compounds. It should be pointed out, however, that many of the commonly used solvents in this type of chemistry (e.g., tetrahydrofuran and benzene) readily attack and swell rubber stoppers.

[3] Various commercial types of stopcock grease may be used to lubricate the joints. Teflon sleeves may be used in place of a lubricant.

[4] General discussions of laboratory techniques in organic chemistry are given in K. B. Wiberg, "Laboratory Technique in Organic Chemistry." McGraw-Hill, New York, 1960, and L. F. Fieser, "Experiments in Organic Chemistry," 3rd Ed., Heath, Boston, Massachusetts, 1955.

[5] Suitable heating mantles are available from Glas-Col Apparatus, Co., Terre Haute, Indiana.

[6] Often a solvent for a reaction is selected so that its boiling point is the desired reaction temperature.

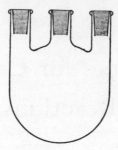

FIG. 1. Diagram of a three-necked reaction flask.

the desired reaction temperature is below the boiling point of the solvent (e.g., the preparation of $C_3H_5Fe(CO)_3I$, page 176), then an oil bath should be used since more precise control of the temperature is possible. For mild heating (30° to 50°) (e.g., the preparation of $Hg[Fe(CO)_3NO]_2$, page 165), a less messy water bath may be used in place of the oil bath. However, at higher temperatures the evaporation rate of the water is inconveniently high. Baths of sand, graphite, molten metal, and fused salts are useful at temperatures above those recommended for oil baths but are very rarely required in organometallic chemistry. Free flames are not recommended for heating organometallic reaction mixtures owing to uneven heating and the fire hazard arising from the great flammability of most organometallic reaction mixtures.

When an oil or water bath is used, its temperature may be readily measured by immersion of a thermometer in the bath. Occasionally (e.g.,

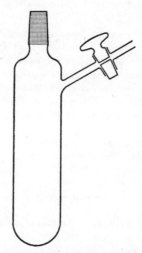

FIG. 2. Illustration of a Schlenk tube.

the preparation of $[C_5H_5Fe(CO)_2]_2$, page 114), it is important to know the temperature of the reaction mixture. For this purpose a thermometer may be inserted through a closed connection in one of the necks of the reaction flask until the bulb is below the level of the reaction mixture.

Cooling the reaction mixture is generally accomplished by a pan or pail surrounding the reaction flask and containing the desired coolant. Commonly used coolants are ice for temperatures around 0° and Dry Ice for temperatures around −80°. Common salt may be added to lower the freezing point of the ice. If Dry Ice is used, a liquid freezing below −80° such as acetone, methanol, or hexane should be added to improve heat conduction from the flask to the bath. In all cooling baths in pans or pails most of the coolant is wasted by cooling the surrounding air. The life of cooling baths may be considerably prolonged by using a vacuum flask[7] (Dewar flask) instead of the pan or pail to improve insulation of the bath from the surrounding air. However, Dewar flasks that are sufficiently large to surround flasks of capacity larger than 500 ml. are very expensive.

In most reactions, a solvent is used which has an appreciable vapor pressure at the reaction temperature. In order to prevent losses of the solvent, a water-cooled *reflux condenser* (Fig. 3) should be inserted into the neck of the flask leading to the outlet of the system. The common

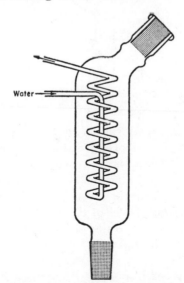

Water —

FIG. 3. Illustration of a water-cooled reflux condenser.

[7] For safety in the event of implosion, these vacuum flasks should either be covered completely with electrical tape or placed in a metal shield.

practice of carrying out organometallic reactions in a slow stream of nitrogen to prevent intake of air increases the amount of solvent lost and the importance of a good reflux condenser.

Occasionally, as in reactions with liquid ammonia or sulfur dioxide as solvents, a solvent or other important material boiling below room temperature is present. Naturally, in this case a water-cooled reflux condenser is of no value. A reflux condenser cooled to ~−78° with Dry Ice (Fig. 4) is required to prevent loss of materials boiling between about −50° and room temperature.

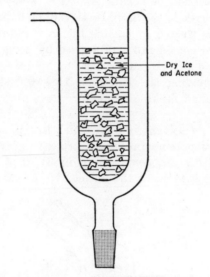

Dry Ice and Acetone

FIG. 4. Diagram of a reflux condenser cooled with Dry Ice and acetone.

Generally, the presence of the oxygen of the air is detrimental in organometallic reactions by causing oxidation of the reactants and/or products. Such reactions are therefore conducted in an atmosphere of pure *nitrogen*.[8] The source of nitrogen is connected through a mineral oil or mercury bubbler (Fig. 5) to the reaction flask by means of an inlet tube ending well *above* the liquid level of the reaction mixture. Alternatively, the bubbler may be connected to the outlet of the reaction system. If the bubbler is connected to the nitrogen *inlet*, it indicates directly the rate

[8] For preparative purposes, the best grade of commercial tank nitrogen is generally adequate without further purification. If further purification of tank nitrogen is desired it may be accomplished by passage of the gas through sodium benzophenone ketyl, triisobutylaluminum, active copper heated to 200° or BTS-Katalysator (Badische Anilin- und Sodafabrik, Ludwigshafen, Germany).

of flow of the nitrogen into the system. However, if the bubbler is connected to the *out*let of the system, it indicates the combined rate of the nitrogen flow into the system and the evolution of any gases during the reaction. This difference points out the major advantages and disadvantages of connecting the nitrogen bubbler to the outlet rather than the inlet of the system. Thus, a bubbler connected to the outlet permits direct observation of any gas evolution during the reaction.[9] However, a greater variety of materials will pass through the bubbler necessitating much more frequent cleaning of the nitrogen bubbler and replacement of the liquid therein.

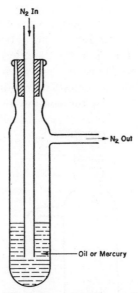

Fɪɢ. 5. Illustration of a nitrogen bubbler.

In conducting a reaction under a nitrogen atmosphere, it is necessary to replace the air with nitrogen after assembling the system but before beginning the reaction. This may be accomplished simply by passing a rapid stream of nitrogen through the system for several minutes. However, a more efficient procedure, especially useful with very air-sensitive materials such as sodium cyclopentadienide, is to evacuate the system with a water-aspirator and to refill the system to atmospheric pressure with pure nitrogen. To insure as complete absence of oxygen as possible, this procedure of evacuating and refilling with nitrogen may be repeated several times.

---

[9] Gas evolution from the reaction may be confirmed by temporarily interrupting the nitrogen flow and then observing the bubbler.

The use of a nitrogen atmosphere is so frequent in carrying out reactions in transition-metal organometallic chemistry that all such reactions should be carried out under nitrogen unless specifically stated otherwise. Occasionally, helium or argon may be used instead of nitrogen for an inert atmosphere; however, none of the presently known reactions in transition-metal organometallic chemistry are apparently affected by elemental nitrogen.

Many times it is necessary or desirable to add gradually one or more reactants to the reaction mixture during the reaction rather than to charge the reaction flask with the entire quantity of each reactant before the reaction. For example, in preparing a solution of 1 mole of sodium cyclopentadienide in 1 liter of tetrahydrofuran, if the entire appropriate amounts of sodium, cyclopentadiene, and tetrahydrofuran are charged into the reaction flask and stirred, the reaction will become so vigorous that the reaction mixture will become very warm and spurt out of the top of the reflux condenser. However, excellent results are obtained by adding the cyclopentadiene dropwise to the sodium in the tetrahydrofuran. In

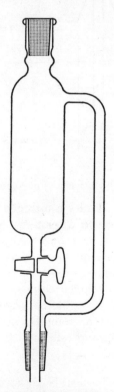

Fig. 6. Diagram of a pressure-equalized dropping funnel.

such a preparation, it is necessary to have a *dropping funnel* attached to the system to permit gradual addition of the cyclopentadiene. To insure a reliable rate of addition a dropping funnel with a pressure equalization tube (Fig. 6) is recommended.

Finally, *stirring* is desirable or necessary for most organometallic reactions of transition metal derivatives. If the mixture is not particularly difficult to stir, a magnetic Teflon-covered stirring bar operated by a variable-speed rotating magnet placed below the reaction flask may be used. This type of stirring system has the advantage that no special connection is required through the neck of the reaction flask. If this type of magnetic stirring system is operated too rapidly, there is some danger of the relatively heavy stirring bar breaking the flask.

In larger scale reactions or in reactions requiring stirring of mixtures with relatively large quantities of suspended solid material, especially metals such as sodium, lithium, or magnesium, magnetic stirring is often too weak. In these cases, it is best to use a stirring blade of appropriate size attached to the end of a shaft inserted through the center neck of the flask and driven by an electrically or air-operated motor at the other end (Fig. 7). The neck containing the stirring assembly should be sealed

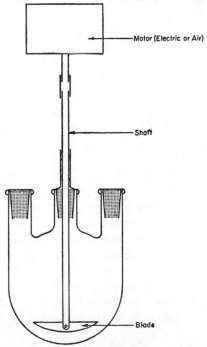

FIG. 7. Illustration of a reaction flask equipped for motor stirring.

with an appropriate fitting to prevent losses of solvent vapors through this opening. Most fittings of this type do not hold a vacuum satisfactorily. Thus, the entire stirrer assembly is best removed and replaced with a stopper during any steps of preparations requiring a vacuum such as solvent removal. This precaution is especially important with air-sensitive materials. One hazard of motor-operated stirring is ignition by a spark from the motor of solvent fumes emerging from the reflux condenser. This danger may be minimized by using an efficient reflux condenser and using either an air-operated or explosion-proof electrically operated motor to drive the stirrer.

2. Reactions in Closed Systems

When one of the reactants is a gas at the reaction temperature, it is frequently necessary to carry out the reaction in a closed system. The three general categories of reaction vessels of this type are (a) rocking, rotating, or stirred autoclaves or shaker tubes, (b) Hoke bombs, and (c) sealed glass vessels such as Carius tubes or bulbs.

Autoclaves made of stainless steel are indispensable in transition-metal organometallic chemistry for preparing metal carbonyl derivatives requiring the use of carbon monoxide under pressures sufficiently high to exclude use of Hoke bombs or Carius tubes. Perhaps the greatest limitation on laboratory use of the autoclave is the weight of the reaction vessels that is necessitated by the thick walls that will safely withstand the required pressure. Thus an autoclave of 1400-ml. internal capacity without liner and 1000-ml. internal capacity with liner weighs about 23 kg. It is about the largest standard size readily manipulated by the average man. Industrial operations requiring use of autoclaves weighing 50 kg. or more provide block-and-tackle arrangements for lifting the autoclaves.

Autoclave installations vary considerably in various institutions. It should be emphasized that almost any autoclave system withstanding safely the necessary pressures of carbon monoxide and capable of being heated to the necessary reaction temperature may be used for carrying out carbon monoxide reactions under pressure. The contamination of the product with iron pentacarbonyl formed by reaction of the carbon monoxide with the iron in the stainless steel of the autoclave is generally insignificant, especially since iron pentacarbonyl differs considerably in volatility and solubility from most carbonyl derivatives prepared from carbon monoxide under pressure. If the danger of iron pentacarbonyl contamination of the product is particularly serious, the autoclave may be plated with copper or silver.

Details of all of the specialized techniques in construction, use, and maintenance of autoclave systems for carrying out high-pressure reactions although not readily available to the chemist[10] are nevertheless well beyond the scope of this book. Instead, a few details on the use of a 1-liter rocking autoclave[11] will be given. This type of autoclave is recommended for a laboratory that has no high-pressure equipment and it will enable the chemist to prepare carbonyl derivatives in reasonable quantities by reactions requiring carbon monoxide under pressure but at minimum (although still considerable) cost.

The reaction vessel (Fig. 8) weighing about 23 kg. with head consists

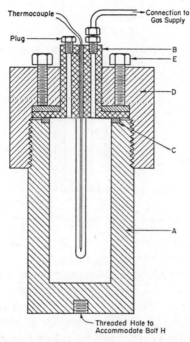

FIG. 8. Diagram of a high-pressure reaction vessel (cross section).

of a stainless steel tube (A) with a top (B) containing a hole for a gas inlet tube and another hole for a thermocouple. To minimize leakage, a copper gasket (C) should be used between the top (B) and the reaction

[10] One source of information on high-pressure techniques is H. Adkins, "Reactions of Hydrogen with Organic Compounds over Copper-Chromium Oxide and Nickel Catalysts," pp. 29–45. Univ. of Wisconsin Press, Madison Wisconsin, 1937.

[11] The equipment described here may be purchased from American Instrument Company, 8030 Georgia Avenue, Silver Spring, Maryland for about $2900 (1963) including the autoclave, liner, rocker, air-operated compressor, and estimated installation costs.

vessel (A) itself.[12] The top part of the stainless steel tube (A) is threaded to accommodate a head (D) containing several bolts (E) which when tightened after assembly seal the system. In addition, a liner of stainless steel, copper, or glass (F) with a "pinhole" fitting snugly into the reaction vessel may be used (Fig. 9). The use of the liner (F) is especially valuable for messy reaction mixtures.[13]

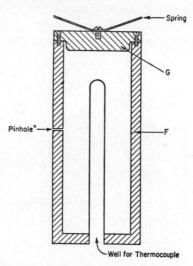

FIG. 9. Illustration of a liner for high-pressure reaction vessel (cross section).

In carrying out a reaction with this type of system, the liner (F) is charged first with the desired reaction mixture using a stream of nitrogen if necessary to protect the reaction mixture from hydrolysis or oxidation.[14] The top of the liner with the metal spring (G) is then attached with the appropriate screws. The closed liner is then inserted into the open autoclave (A) so that the top of the liner (G) is at the bottom of the autoclave; care must be taken that the reaction mixture does not spill from the pinhole. The copper gasket (C) and the top (B) are placed on the top of the autoclave (A). The threads of the reaction

---

[12] Although it is possible to obtain a tight seal in a new autoclave without using a copper gasket by tightening the bolts (E), to a much greater extent, such a practice is injurious to the autoclave and emphatically not recommended.

[13] Even when the liner is used, the autoclave will become somewhat dirty due to a small portion of the reaction mixture emerging from the pinhole either mechanically or by volatilization. However, the heavy autoclave is much easier to clean when the liner is used than when it contains the entire reaction mixture.

[14] If the reaction mixture is air-sensitive, the pinhole may be covered with tape until immediately before loading the liner into the autoclave to minimize air leakage into the pinhole.

vessel (A) are then lubricated with some pipe thread grease or mineral oil and the head (D) is then screwed on until tight. The head is then loosened by about a half turn, and the bolts (E) are then tightened with a torque wrench. The autoclave is then inserted into the rocker and held there by tightening a bolt (H) that goes through the bottom of the rocker into the bottom of the autoclave. The gas inlet tube is then attached to the top of the autoclave followed by the thermocouple. The connection of the autoclave to the high-pressure system is now complete. If the autoclave is behind a barrier and the controls are in front of the barrier as recommended for safety reasons, it should no longer be necessary for personnel to be behind the barrier if everything works properly.

The autoclave is then flushed with the necessary gas. After venting this gas, the autoclave is then charged with the necessary amount of carbon monoxide or other gas for the reaction. Many times, the required gas pressure for the reaction is greater than that present in the tank. In these cases, it is necessary to use a compressor to build up the tank pressure to the required pressure. The traditional type of compressor for this purpose fills a thick-walled metal vessel with the gas at tank pressure and then pumps oil with an electric motor into this vessel to decrease its volume and therefore increase the pressure of the gas inside. This gas at higher pressure is then admitted to the autoclave increasing the pressure of the gas therein. This cycle of operations is sometimes repeated as often as four or five times until the pressure in the autoclave reaches the desired pressure. With a compressor, it is necessary to be very careful that the oil is not pumped too far; otherwise, some oil will eventually be introduced into the autoclave contaminating the reaction mixture. The author has several times found pump oil to be the major "reaction product" after carrying out a high-pressure reaction using such a compressor.

Recently, an air-operated compressor has been developed[15] which is not only less expensive and more convenient to use than the previously described compressor but which prevents all contact between the oil and the gas being compressed. This compressor requires a compressed air line near the high-pressure system for its operation.

After the gas has been introduced into the autoclave to the required pressure, the autoclave is then heated to the desired reaction temperature for the desired period of time. It is convenient to have an electronic temperature control device attached to the system to insure maintenance

---

[15] The air-operated compressor described here may be purchased from American Instrument Company, 8030 Georgia Avenue, Silver Spring, Maryland for around $1000 (1963).

of the reaction temperature in the desired range. After the reaction period is over, the heat is turned off and the autoclave is allowed to cool to room temperature. Because of the mass of the system, this process normally takes several hours. It may be expedited by directing a stream of air from a compressed air line onto the autoclave. When the autoclave has reached room temperature or at least a temperature at which it may be handled, rocking is stopped and the gases are vented. Since carbon monoxide is very toxic, it should be released into a well-ventilated area. The autoclave is then opened and the contents are removed for isolation of the product by reversing the previously described loading process.

Stainless steel *Hoke bombs*[16] (Fig. 10) are particularly suitable for reactions requiring gases conveniently charged from a vacuum system. The Hoke bomb fittings are also readily adaptable for connection to a high-pressure system for introduction of carbon monoxide under pressure.

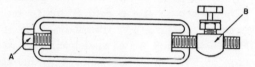

FIG. 10. Diagram of a Hoke bomb (cross section).

However, it must be borne in mind that the maximum safe operating pressure of a Hoke bomb is around 100 atmospheres. This and the difficulty of stirring or shaking reaction mixtures in Hoke bombs make them less desirable than autoclaves for reactions with carbon monoxide under pressure. The use of Hoke bombs for simply carrying out reactions with liquids above their boiling points (e.g., the preparations of $C_6H_8Fe(CO)_3$, page 129, and of $C_3F_7Fe(CO)_4I$, page 177) should be pointed out.

In order to use a Hoke bomb, valve B is closed. Plug A is then removed, and solid and liquid reagents are introduced into the bomb through this opening. The plug is then replaced using a Teflon suspension or tape to insure a tight seal. The bomb is then cooled in a $-78°$ or $-196°$ bath (Dry Ice or liquid nitrogen, respectively) and evacuated through valve B. After charging any gases from the vacuum system, valve B is closed and the bomb is allowed to warm to room temperature. It is then heated in an oven to the desired reaction temperature. If the reaction involves potentially explosive materials, the oven should be in a barricaded area. A large oil bath may also be used for heating Hoke bombs in certain cases.

---

[16] Hoke bombs (stainless steel cylinders, high-pressure series) are manufactured by Hoke, Inc., 1 Tenakill Park, Cresskill, New Jersey.

After the reaction period is over, the bomb is removed from the oven. After cooling to room temperature, valve B is then opened to bring the internal pressure to atmospheric. Depending upon the reaction, the pressure in the bomb may be either higher or lower than atmospheric; in the latter case, it may be desirable sometimes to admit nitrogen to the bomb to prevent oxidation of the contents by the incoming air. Plug A may then be removed, the contents discharged, and the bomb rinsed with an appropriate solvent.

The final alternative for pressure reactions is a sealed thick-walled glass *Carius tube* (Fig. 11). The maximum safe working pressure for a

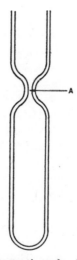

Fig. 11. Illustration of a Carius tube.

Carius tube depends on the skill of the operator in sealing the tube but in any case it is less than that of a Hoke bomb. Explosions are therefore more frequent when using Carius tubes than when using Hoke bombs. However, flying particles of glass are less dangerous than flying particles of metal making explosions with Carius tubes less serious than explosions with metal equipment. An obvious advantage of Carius tubes over Hoke bombs is the ability to observe the reaction mixture while the reaction is taking place.

In order to load a Carius tube, solid and liquid reagents are charged through the open neck. The tube is then connected to a vacuum system and cooled to $-78°$ or $-196°$.[17] Because of the thick glass of these tubes,

---

[17] Because of the proximity of a free flame during sealing of the Carius tube, the cooling bath should be nonflammable for safety considerations.

it is necessary to do this cooling gradually to prevent breakage. After evacuation and distilling in any gaseous reagents, the tube is sealed at the constriction A. The tube is then carefully annealed around the seal with a luminous flame. This step is critical and even after careful annealing, some tubes crack. The tube is then removed from the cooling bath and allowed to warm to room temperature. Finally, it is heated in an oven to the desired reaction temperature. It should be pointed out that sealed Carius tubes should be handled not only with the usual recommended laboratory eye protection but also with tongs or thick gloves.

After the reaction period is over, the Carius tube is allowed to cool to room temperature and finally in a $-78°$ or $-196°$ bath. The tube is most conveniently opened by heating the seal with a hot flame until the pressure differential forces a hole in the molten glass. The tube may then be warmed up to room temperature and the contents discharged.

At this point, a few general comments on *high-vacuum technique*[18] in transition-metal organometallic chemistry are in order. Most transition-metal organometallic compounds are not sufficiently volatile to be transferred readily in a vacuum system. However, certain carbonyl hydrides such as $HMn(CO)_5$ (page 158) and certain nitrosyl carbonyls such as $Mn(CO)_4NO$ (page 164) are best purified by trap-to-trap distillation in a vacuum system and best handled by transfer within the vacuum system. Other, less volatile, compounds such as certain lower-molecular-weight diene-iron tricarbonyl derivatives, the perfluoroalkyl nickel derivatives C_5H_5NiCOR,[19] and certain alkylmanganese pentacarbonyl derivatives $RMn(CO)_5$ may be distilled in a vacuum system occasionally with modifications of certain techniques (continuous pumping, etc.). Finally, volatile degradation products of transition-metal organometallic derivatives may be studied with the aid of high-vacuum techniques. A good example of this is the carbon monoxide analysis in metal carbonyls by degradation with iodine at elevated temperatures followed by measurement of the carbon monoxide produced. In this case, carbon monoxide cannot be condensed in a vacuum system and thus requires a Sprengel or Töpler pump for its transfer.

A vacuum system used for transition metal organometallic derivatives will generally become dirty rapidly from decomposition products. Re-

---

[18] For a more detailed discussion on high-vacuum technique, see R. T. Sanderson, "Vacuum Manipulation of Volatile Compounds." Wiley, New York, 1948.

[19] D. W. McBride, Ph.D. Thesis, Harvard University, 1962 (F. G. A. Stone, Research Adviser). This thesis, available inexpensively in microfilm or Xerox form from University Microfilms Inc., Ann Arbor, Michigan, describes a suitable vacuum system for handling organonickel compounds which should also be appropriate for other metal carbonyl derivatives with similar properties.

moval of these materials may usually be accomplished with strong nitric acid but it is somewhat inconvenient. In many cases, the presence of these decomposition products in moderately small quantities is not detrimental to use of the vacuum system for transfer of transition-metal derivatives. It is advisable to handle transition-metal organometallic derivatives in a vacuum system that is not used for other purposes and to use as simple a system as possible to minimize cleaning.

3. Photochemical Reactions

Occasionally (e.g., the preparation of $Fe_2(CO)_9$, page 93), ultraviolet irradiation is useful in reactions of metal carbonyl derivatives. These reactions may be carried out in the obvious manner of exposing the reaction mixture to the radiation from an ultraviolet lamp.[20] Quartz equipment should be used where feasible because of its more efficient transmission of ultraviolet irradiation. Occasionally, after prolonged use, quartz reaction tubes used for irradiation reactions of transition-metal organometallic derivatives will acquire a nearly invisible coating of metal oxide which will greatly impede transmission of ultraviolet irradiation to the reaction mixture making the tubes useless for further reactions.

The ultraviolet lamps used for photochemical reactions also generate an appreciable amount of heat. In some cases (e.g., the preparation of $Fe_2(CO)_9$), it is important that the reaction mixture does not become too hot; consequently, the reaction mixture should not be placed too close to the lamp.

Ultraviolet irradiations may also be carried out with an ultraviolet lamp of special construction inserted in one neck of a reaction flask.[21] With this type of system, the transmission of irradiation to the reaction mixture is much more efficient but the lamp is more accessible to breakage or contamination from the reaction mixture. However, this technique facilitates heating or cooling of the reaction mixture during irradiation.

---

[20] The eyes may be harmed by looking at the irradiation from ultraviolet lamps. Prolonged exposure of the skin to a strong ultraviolet lamp can cause a sunburn.

[21] Apparatus for ultraviolet irradiation using this technique may be purchased from Nester/Faust Manufacturing Corporation, Box 565, 2401 Ogletown Road, Newark, Delaware, or Englehard-Hanovia, Inc., Slough, Bucks, England (U.S. branch: 100 Chestnut St., Newark 5, New Jersey).

B. Techniques for Isolating and Purifying Products

1. Crystallization

Since most organometallic transition-metal compounds are solid at room temperature, *crystallization* is commonly used for isolation and purification of products. Crystallization consists of changing either the temperature or solvent composition of a solution of a solid substance in order to decrease the solubility of the solute so that it separates from the solution in the solid phase. Both *temperature-differential* and *solvent-differential* techniques find application in transition-metal organometallic chemistry.

There are two basic types of *temperature-differential* crystallization for the common types of compounds more soluble in hot solvents than cold solvents.[1] The first technique consists of dissolving the solid material in a solvent above room temperature and allowing the filtered solution to cool to room temperature and product to crystallize. This technique although frequently used with excellent results in the crystallization of many types of compounds must be applied with caution in the crystallization of transition-metal organometallic compounds. Many of these compounds possess limited thermal stability and are likely to be at least partially decomposed by the warm solvent.[2] Even if this is not a difficulty, the enhanced sensitivity of many transition-metal organometallic compounds to oxygen especially in solution at the elevated temperatures used for the crystallization makes more rigorous protection against air oxidation necessary. These difficulties make this crystallization technique risky in the study of organometallic derivatives which are either new or of uncertain stability.

The second technique of temperature-differential crystallization consists of dissolving the solid material in a solvent at room temperature

---

[1] No transition-metal organometallic compounds that are less soluble in hot solvents than in the corresponding cold solvents have been described.
[2] Warm chlorinated solvents such as chloroform or carbon tetrachloride are likely to be reactive with transition-metal organometallic compounds.

and cooling the filtered solution below room temperature generally in a —78° (Dry Ice) bath. If the compound is moderately air- and water-stable, the crystals which separate can then be filtered by suction in the usual manner. Since the solution is never heated above room temperature, this technique is especially suitable for the crystallization of many compounds of questionable stability.

When using this second temperature differential crystallization technique, solvent selection is determined not only by the solubility of the compound to be crystallized but also by the freezing point of the solvent. Thus, in the most common form of this technique in which the solution is cooled in a —78° bath, benzene, water, cyclohexane, or carbon tetrachloride cannot be used as solvents since they freeze well above —78°. In practice, this crystallization technique is most commonly used for the crystallization from saturated aliphatic hydrocarbon solvents (pentane, hexane, ligroin, etc.) of materials appreciably soluble in these solvents at room temperature.

This second temperature differential crystallization technique is also occasionally useful for the purification of compounds such as butadiene-iron tricarbonyl (page 128) which are liquid at room temperature but which freeze well above —78°. In these cases, the crystallization may be conducted in the usual manner until the product has separated from the solution cooled in the —78° bath. In some cases, when the melting point of the product is only slightly below room temperature and the product is insensitive to water and air-stable for at least several minutes, the crystals may be removed by suction filtration in the usual manner provided that the crystals are removed quickly from the filter to a suitable storage container before they melt. However, in this isolation procedure, ice condenses onto the cold crystals contaminating the final product with water which must subsequently be removed in a drying step. More generally, in the crystallization of liquids by this technique, the supernatant liquid is removed from the crystals at —78° as completely as possible with a syringe or pipette (preferably under nitrogen). The residue is freed from the remaining solvent by allowing it to warm to room temperature in a rapid stream of nitrogen; the crystals melt in the process. The resulting liquid may then be removed with a pipette or syringe. When using this technique of crystallization, it is preferable to use relatively low-boiling solvents such as pentane to facilitate the removal of final traces of solvent in the nitrogen stream.

There are also two basic types of *solvent-differential* crystallization. The first consists of dissolving at room temperature the solid material to be crystallized in a minimum quantity of a solvent in which it is appreciably soluble. The filtered solution is then treated with an excess of a second solvent miscible with the first solvent but in which the solute is insoluble. The solid material since it is sparingly soluble in the solvent mixture separates out again. It is then removed by filtration and, if necessary, washed with an additional portion of the second solvent. There are several difficulties in the application of this crystallization technique. First, upon addition of the second solvent, the precipitation of the product is often so rapid that a fine powder[3] rather than well-formed crystals are obtained. This fine powder often adsorbs significant amounts of impurities. Second, it is sometimes difficult to find two miscible solvents so that it is possible to prepare a solution of the compound in the better solvent and to reprecipitate the compound by addition of a poorer solvent. An example of this type of solvent differential crystallization technique is the crystallization of certain ionic organometallic compounds (e.g., $[C_5H_5Mn(CO)_2NO][PF_6]$, page 163) by dissolving in a minimum of acetone and reprecipitating the product from the filtered solution by addition of excess diethyl ether.

The second technique of solvent-differential crystallization consists of dissolving the material to be crystallized at room temperature in a solvent in which it is appreciably soluble. The filtered solution is then treated with a second solvent *less volatile* than and miscible with the first solvent, but in which the solute is insoluble. Ideally, the quantity of the second poorer and less volatile solvent should be insufficient to cause immediate precipitation. The solvent is then removed by distillation from the solution generally at room temperature in a water-aspirator vacuum. Since the poor second solvent is less volatile than the good first solvent, the solvent mixture slowly becomes enriched during the evaporation process in the poor solvent and eventually crystals of the solute separate. When crystallization appears to be complete, the evaporation process is discontinued; the crystals are removed by filtration, washed with the poor solvent or other appropriate solvent, and dried. This second type of solvent-differential crystallization because of the slower crystallization generally gives larger and better-formed crystals than the first type. This second type of solvent-differential crystallization is often useful for crystallizing the many transition-metal organometallic compounds sparingly soluble in saturated aliphatic hydrocarbons but readily soluble in polar organic solvents. A frequently used solvent mixture at least in the author's laboratory is dichloromethane as the "good" solvent and hexane as the "poor" less volatile solvent.

---

[3] Sintered-glass funnels used for the filtration of the fine precipitates obtained in this manner should generally be of "fine" porosity to eliminate passage of the precipitate through the filter.

During crystallization processes, there are three principal degrees of precautions which may be taken against air oxidation. First, some transition-metal organometallic compounds are so air-sensitive that exposure of the solution or even the solid material to air for even the few minutes to an hour required for carrying out a crystallization will cause complete or at least very extensive destruction of the compound by air oxidation. With these very air-sensitive compounds it is necessary to carry out the entire crystallization process under nitrogen or other inert gas with deaerated solvents.[4] Generally, Schlenk tubes (page 4) and related attachments are useful for the filtration processes. Second, many transition-metal organometallic compounds including most of the compounds discussed in this book are sufficiently slowly oxidized by air in solution so that only very minor amounts are lost during the time required to carry out a crystallization. However, the rate of air oxidation is still sufficient so that, upon filtering the solution in the presence of air, noticeable oxidation of the first portions of the filtrate will occur before the filtration is complete thus contaminating the crystals finally obtained with oxidation products generally metal oxides.[5] These compounds like the very air-sensitive compounds may be crystallized entirely under nitrogen in deaerated solvents. However, little is lost and much gained in convenience by carrying out the crystallization of these slightly air-sensitive compounds in air except for collecting and handling the filtered solution under nitrogen to prevent formation of the small quantities of oxidation products which will contaminate the finally obtained crystals. Third, a few transition-metal organometallic compounds such as ferrocene are so completely stable in air even in solution that the use of an inert atmosphere at any stage of the crystallization process is without benefit.

The two major considerations determining selections of solvents for crystallizations are solubility of the solute in the solvent and reactivity of the solute with the solvent. In general, neutral transition-metal organometallic compounds are insoluble in water, readily soluble in polar organic solvents such as dichloromethane, chloroform, tetrahydrofuran,

---

[4] Solvents may be deaerated by bubbling a rapid stream of nitrogen through them for several minutes. In very critical cases, a flask containing the solvent can be evacuated until the solvent bubbles vigorously, then nitrogen is admitted, and the process is repeated several times.

[5] A relatively large volume of air is required to destroy a compound by oxidation. Thus in a case in which 1 mole of oxygen will destroy 1 mole of compound, about 110 ml. of air is required to destroy completely 1 mmole of compound. Thus, unless either oxidation or the circulation of the surrounding air is rapid, the oxygen supply of the air immediately surrounding the air-sensitive compound will soon be depleted by the oxidation of relatively minor quantities of the compound.

and acetone and in aromatic hydrocarbons, and soluble to a variable extent in saturated aliphatic hydrocarbons and alcohols. Ionic transition-metal organometallic compounds are soluble to a variable extent in water, soluble in many Lewis base organic solvents such as acetone or dimethyl-formamide (but often insoluble in diethyl ether), generally, but not always, insoluble in halogenated organic solvents, and insoluble in hydro-carbon solvents. Many halogenated solvents such as carbon tetrachloride often react with transition-metal organometallic compounds and some-times form halogenated derivatives. However, most of these compounds are stable to chloroform and particularly dichloromethane for the periods of time required for crystallizations. A crude rule to follow in this respect is that the rate of reaction of a transition-metal organometallic compound with chloroform in the absence of air is comparable to the rate of oxidation by air of a pentane or benzene solution of the compound. Basic solvents notably pyridine but occasionally dimethylformamide, dimethyl-sulfoxide, etc., often react with transition-metal organometallic com-pounds displacing various ligands especially carbon monoxide. Finally, for reasons not clearly established, the rate of oxidation of many com-pounds dissolved in polar solvents particularly alcohols is greater than the rate of oxidation of the same compounds dissolved in nonpolar solvents.

Other significant considerations in the selection of a solvent for crystallization are volatility, freezing point, and toxicity. It is convenient to use a solvent readily evaporated at room temperature in a water-aspirator vacuum (15 to 50 mm.). Common solvents in this category include pentane, diethyl ether, dichloromethane, tetrahydrofuran, chloro-form, and acetone and to a lesser extent benzene, hexane, methanol, ethanol, and 1,2-dimethoxyethane. A high freezing point, as previously discussed limits the applications of certain solvents for crystallization at low temperatures. Relatively high toxicity is unfortunately a limiting factor in the use of benzene, an excellent and unreactive solvent for most neutral transition-metal organometallic compounds and removable in a good water-aspirator vacuum.

2. Volatilization

Volatilization processes are traditionally divided into two categories: *sublimation* (conversion of a solid to its vapor followed by condensation of the vapor back to the solid phase) and *distillation* (conversion of a liquid to its vapor followed by condensation of the vapor back to the liquid phase). The techniques and apparatus used for each process are distinctly different. However, in transition-metal organometallic chemis-try, the techniques and apparatus used for sublimation rather than the standard techniques of distillation are sometimes used for the purification of liquids by volatilization because of the rarity and sensitive nature of many compounds. Several times, the author has purified liquid materials by volatilization in a sublimation apparatus without ever having present a solid phase. Also, in transition-metal organometallic chemistry, almost all volatilization processes are carried out in a vacuum most frequently of 0.02 to 0.5 mm. obtained by a properly working oil pump protected by −78° or −196° traps.

A variety of types of apparatus commonly known as *sublimers* (Figs. 12–16) have been used for sublimations. In all of these sublimers, the sample to be sublimed is charged into an area provided with a source of heat. If there is danger of mechanical transfer of solid particles onto the probe, the sample is covered with glass wool. After evacuation of the sublimer,[6] the sample is heated to the necessary sublimation temperature.[7] Each type of sublimer provides an area for the vapor to condense back to the solid or occasionally liquid phase. Often, this is a cold finger or *probe* which may be cooled with either stationary or running water, wet ice, or Dry Ice. The sublimation is generally continued until no more sublimate is collected. The residue is then removed from the source of heat, and after cooling to room temperature,[8] the stopcock leading to the source of vacuum is closed and the sublimer is disconnected from the vacuum. Nitrogen is then admitted to the evacuated sublimer and the sublimate removed.

The most generally useful and convenient sublimer with a tubular probe is depicted in Fig. 12. The top of the exterior of the probe may either be left open for introduction of water, ice, or Dry Ice (Fig. 12a) or closed with hose connections for running water (Fig. 12b). The upper

---

[6] In most sublimations, the sublimer is continuously evacuated during the sublimation in order to obtain the best possible vacuum with the available equipment ("dynamic system"). Occasionally, with very volatile compounds, the sublimer is evacuated and the source of vacuum is then shut off in order to minimize sublimation of the compound beyond the probe into the vacuum system, trap, or pump ("static system").

[7] Occasionally, in order to minimize decomposition of certain compounds, it is preferable to insert the sublimer into a bath preheated to the desired sublimation temperature.

[8] After the sublimation is complete and the sublimer has cooled to room temperature, nitrogen (or air in some cases) should be admitted promptly to the sublimer to break the vacuum. If an evacuated sublimer is allowed to stand too long at room temperature after a completed sublimation, the sublimate that collected on the probe will begin to sublime away from the probe onto the walls of the sublimer which will complicate removal of the sublimate without contamination from the residue.

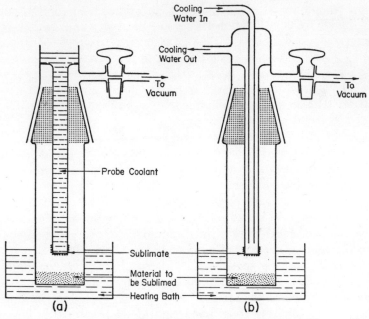

FIG. 12. Diagram of a vacuum sublimation apparatus (a) with a probe cooled by running water (b).

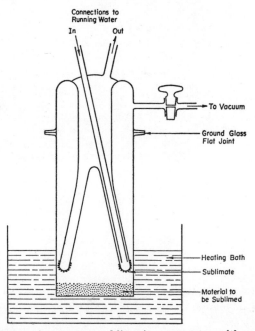

FIG. 13. Diagram of a vacuum sublimation apparatus with conical probe.

practical limit for a single charge in this type of sublimer is 2 to 15 g. of sublimate depending on the size of the sublimer and the density of the sublimate. For sublimation of larger quantities of material, a sublimer with a conical probe (Fig. 13) may be used. For very large scale sublimations (~50 g. or more) a giant sublimer (Fig. 14) may be constructed from a resin kettle and a round bottom flask.

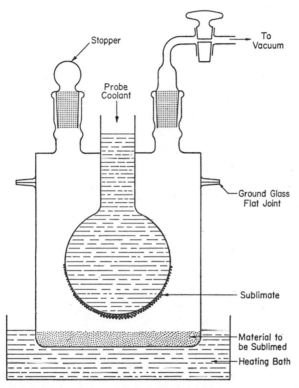

FIG. 14. Illustration of a large vacuum sublimation apparatus made from a resin kettle.

The sublimers illustrated in Figs. 12–14 permit sublimations of various quantities and with various probe coolants. However, it is impossible to remove the sublimate in the complete absence of air without using a cumbersome and expensive nitrogen-filled glove box (page 55). Figure 15 illustrates a sublimer in which the sublimate may be transferred to a Schlenk tube without exposure to air. It is especially well-suited for the sublimation of very air-sensitive materials such as biscyclopentadienyl-vanadium (page 64). In using sublimers of this type, the residue should always be covered with glass wool to prevent contamination of the sublimate with the residue during removal of the former.

The most generally useful probe coolant is stationary water. Although the water will heat up even to 70° during sublimations at relatively high temperatures, the probe will still remain cooler than the sublimer walls

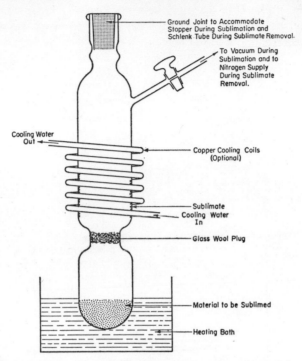

FIG. 15. Diagram of a vacuum sublimation apparatus for air-sensitive compounds.

which will cause the sublimate to condense on the probe as desired. More volatile impurities will gradually sublime past the desired sublimate beyond the probe.[9]

However, in some cases, the sublimate is sufficiently low melting so that a stationary water-cooled probe will heat above its melting point causing the sublimate to melt and drip off the probe back onto the residue. In other cases, the sublimate is so volatile that the stationary water-cooled probe will become sufficiently warm so that the desired sublimate, like the volatile impurities previously discussed, will volatilize beyond the probe at an appreciable rate into the upper parts of the

[9] Use of a water-cooled probe in this manner permits fractional sublimation; the more volatile component gradually migrates to the upper portion of the sublimer. This technique is particularly useful in separating the very volatile hexacarbonyls of chromium, molybdenum, or tungsten from the less volatile materials formed in some of their reactions.

sublimer or possibly even the vacuum system itself. In either of these cases, the probe must be cooled to a greater extent either with *running* water, ice, or Dry Ice (generally mixed with acetone or other low-melting cheap liquid). For compounds crystallizing readily at room temperature, it is generally satisfactory to substitute running cold water from the tap for the stationary water. For compounds either melting below room temperature or readily supercooled below their melting points, ice or Dry Ice may be used as a probe coolant.[10] The lower the temperature to which the probe is cooled, the greater the chance of contamination of the sublimate with more volatile impurities which cannot volatilize beyond the cool probe. Thus, the major factors determining selection of a probe coolant are melting point and volatility of the sublimate on the one hand, and the presence of more volatile impurities on the other.

Many "sublimations" of low-melting solid materials are actually conducted in sublimers as illustrated in Figs. 12–14 in which the compounds melt before they volatilize.[11] In other cases, a liquid may be sublimed in these sublimers collecting the sublimate as a solid on a probe cooled to $-78°$ with Dry Ice and acetone. In a few cases (e.g., $C_2H_5SCH = CH_2Fe_2(CO)_6$),[12] a liquid may even be purified by volatilization in these sublimers collecting the product as a *liquid* on the $-78°$ probe. The high viscosity of some liquids at these very low temperatures prevents them from dripping back into the residue. In purifications of liquids by sublimation, the sublimer illustrated in Fig. 12a is most appropriate.[13]

In cases in which the sublimate is a solid at room temperature, it can be removed from the probes of the sublimer by a spatula in the obvious manner. In cases in which the sublimate is a liquid at room temperature, the sublimer is dismantled after completing the sublimation and admitting nitrogen. The coolant is immediately dumped out of the probe and the top portion is placed so that the probe is inserted into a small beaker (Fig. 16). Water at room temperature is immediately poured into the

---

[10] Use of Dry Ice in the probe of a sublimer is somewhat troublesome since it evaporates rapidly. In many cases, fresh Dry Ice must be added to the probe at least every hour. Thus, in most laboratories, it is not feasible to run a sublimation with a Dry Ice cooled probe overnight.

[11] Many times, when subliming a compound that melts below the sublimation temperature, the liquid residue spatters onto the probe and contaminates the sublimate. This effect can be eliminated by covering the residue in the bottom of the sublimer with a layer of glass wool before assembling the sublimer.

[12] R. B. King, P. M. Treichel, and F. G. A. Stone, *J. Am. Chem. Soc.* **83**, 3600 (1961).

[13] By providing a drip tip on the probe directed toward a tube leading to a receiver, a sublimer as illustrated in Figs. 12a and 12b may be converted to a *molecular still*.

probe[14] to warm the sublimate to room temperature rapidly before it can collect much moisture from the air. As it warms to room temperature, the sublimate melts and drips off the probe into the beaker. When all of the sublimate has dripped into the beaker, the beaker is then inclined so that all of the liquid product collects at one edge. The liquid is then removed from the beaker to the desired storage container with a small

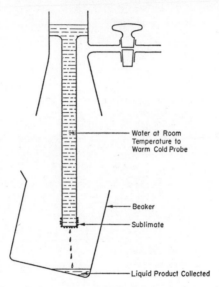

FIG. 16. Illustration of the removal of liquid from the probe of a sublimer.

pipette or syringe. Even under the most favorable conditions, the liquid products removed from a sublimer probe in this manner collect moisture from the air which must be removed in a subsequent drying step. This may be accomplished by drying briefly in a vacuum desiccator over phosphorus pentoxide or other efficient desiccant. Prolonged evacuation of many volatile liquids, however, may lead to appreciable losses through evaporation.

One of the severe disadvantages of purification of volatile liquids by volatilization in the previously described sublimer is the necessity to expose the cold sublimate to air and moisture during its removal from the probe. This makes the purification of volatile liquids that are either sensitive to air or water or are not readily freed from the water introduced as an impurity impossible by this technique. A modified sublimer could be constructed similar to that illustrated in Figs. 12 or 13 but

---

[14] The water must be poured into the probe rapidly but *cautiously*. Spilled water will fall into the beaker and contaminate the product.

having a drip tip on the bottom of the probe so that the liquid condensing
on the probe would collect on the drip tip and drip into a tube leading to
an appropriate receiver. Such a "molecular distillation" apparatus has
been constructed for other purposes, but this rather cumbersome setup
has apparently not yet been used for purifying transition-metal organometallic compounds. Instead, volatile liquid transition-metal organo-

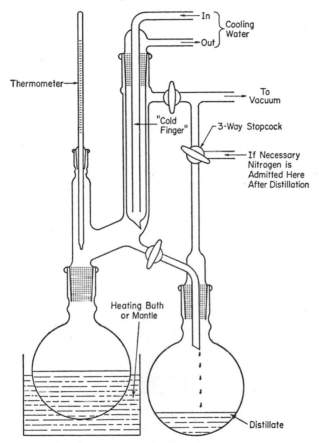

FIG. 17. Diagram of a typical vacuum distillation apparatus.

metallic compounds that are sufficiently abundant to be distilled in the
conventional manner are so purified. A typical distillation apparatus
completely similar to those used in more conventional organic chemistry
is illustrated in Fig. 17. These distillations are carried out in the usual
manner remembering that the significant air sensitivity of many transition-metal organometallic compounds suggests admission of pure nitrogen
rather than air to the evacuated apparatus before changing fractions,

removing product, etc. Most liquid compounds described in this book are purified by such a conventional distillation; however, relatively few other transition-metal organometallic compounds are available in sufficient quantities to permit distillation in this manner.

Finally, distillation in a high-vacuum system may be used for the purification of volatile transition-metal organometallic compounds especially those that are too rare or unstable for distillation in the more usual manner. A setup as illustrated in Fig. 18 is especially useful for some of

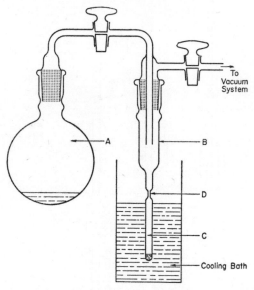

Fɪɢ. 18. Illustration of the attachment to a vacuum system for high-vacuum distillation of small quantities of liquids.

these distillations. Here, the liquid contained in Flask A, which may be, for example, a liquid residue remaining after solvent evaporation from a solution, is distilled at room temperature and high vacuum into the special receiver B, which is designed to permit accumulation of the distillate eventually in the bottom of C which may then be sealed off at D in order to give the desired product stored in a sealed tube. Receiver B is best cooled to a temperature that is sufficient to condense, in high vacuum, the material being distilled but will allow as many more volatile potential impurities as possible to pass into the vacuum system. A −22° bath (carbon tetrachloride frozen with liquid nitrogen) is often useful for this purpose. During a distillation of this type, the compound is never exposed to air. An example of compound conveniently purified by this type of distillation is manganese tetracarbonyl nitrosyl, page 164. In some cases, several trap-to-trap distillations in a vacuum system are desirable for complete removal of impurities before final distillation into the special receiver B illustrated in Fig. 18.

3. Chromatography

The third major technique for the purification of transition-metal organometallic compounds is *chromatography*, which is almost always carried out by the fractional adsorption and elution of the components in a solution on a column of aluminum oxide (alumina). The characteristic colors of many transition-metal organometallic compounds facilitate their identification when adsorbed on an alumina column. However, chromatography is an expensive method of purification requiring relatively large quantities of solvents and a rather expensive ($5–$15 per kilogram) special grade of alumina. Because of the high cost of large scale chromatography, very few syntheses requiring its use have been included in this volume.[15] Moreover, some otherwise reasonably stable transition-metal organometallic compounds decompose sometimes completely on attempted chromatography on an alumina column. Despite these limitations, column chromatography is important in transition-metal organometallic chemistry and will be discussed briefly in this volume.

Column chromatography is carried out in a long glass tube of appropriate dimensions[16] with a plug of glass wool and a stopcock[17] at the bottom and a ground glass joint to which a dropping funnel can be fitted at the top (Fig. 19). A slurry of alumina in the desired solvent (generally pentane or benzene) is poured into the top of the column while a layer of solvent is always kept above the alumina. The alumina is allowed to settle; the process may be hastened by tapping the column

---

[15] The synthesis of [C$_5$H$_5$NiCO]$_2$ (page 119) in this book uses filtration through a small alumina column to eliminate (C$_5$H$_5$)$_3$Ni$_3$(CO)$_2$. However, the separation in this case is accomplished more by filtration and selective decomposition than by selective absorption as in true chromatography. The weight of alumina per gram of reaction mixture used for this operation is much less than the weight of alumina per gram of reaction mixture necessary in true chromatography. Chromatography in a more usual form is used in the preparation of C$_5$H$_5$CoC$_8$H$_{12}$ (page 131) to remove ethylcyclohexane from the reaction mixture.

[16] For separation of most mixtures from reactions carried out on a 0.01–0.02 mole scale, a 2 × 50 cm. column of alumina is recommended. For separation of most mixtures from reactions carried out on a 0.05–0.1 mole scale, a 5 × 50 cm. column of alumina is recommended.

[17] In order to eliminate grease which is readily leached out by the large quantities of solvent, a stopcock with a Teflon plug is recommended.

with a cork ring or other soft, solid object.[18] When the alumina has reached the desired height, the solvent is drained through the stopcock at the bottom until about 3 mm. of solvent cover the alumina. The

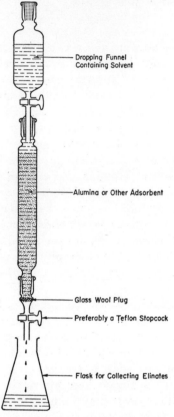

Fig. 19. Diagram of a chromatography column.

solution to be chromatographed, which should be as concentrated as possible and filtered if suspended material is present, is then poured into the top of the column and allowed to run through the column. Depending on the size of the column and the nature of the solution to be chromatographed, the rate of flow of liquid from the bottom of the column may

---

[18] When using pentane or diethyl ether as a solvent for a chromatography column, bubbles on the column are often a problem because of the high volatility of pentane. These may be reduced in quantity by tapping the column with a soft object. In critical cases, chromatography requiring saturated hydrocarbon solvents should be carried out with the less volatile hexane or cyclohexane although these solvents are less conveniently evaporated from eluates.

range from a thin stream to about one drop every 3 seconds. A slower rate of flow is undesirable because it lengthens the time necessary to complete the chromatography which increases the amount of decomposition of compounds that slowly decompose on exposure to alumina. If the rate of flow through the column is too slow, it may sometimes be speeded up by stirring up the top 5 mm. of alumina with a spatula or by tapping the side of the column with a stick or cork ring.

After all of the solution to be chromatographed has been introduced and allowed to flow into the column until a layer of about 3 mm. of liquid remains above the top of the alumina, pure solvent is introduced into the column in 10- to 25-ml. portions until all of the compound has been washed into the column. About three portions should be sufficient. The column is then *developed*[19] with an appropriate solvent to separate the components into individual bands. Each band is then *eluted*[19] with an appropriate solvent. If air-sensitive, the eluates may be collected in a flask flushed out with nitrogen. If the eluates contain any particles of alumina or insoluble decomposition products, they are then filtered collecting the filtrate under nitrogen if air-sensitive. The solvent is removed from the filtrate in a water-aspirator vacuum. Residues of the individual components remain which may either be washed on a filter with a solvent in which the compound is insoluble and/or purified further by crystallization or sublimation.

Sometimes transition-metal organometallic compounds decompose upon attempted chromatography on alumina. In some cases, this decomposition can be eliminated or markedly reduced by deactivating the alumina by adding up to 15% of water. In other cases, alumina of a different acidity should be used. More frequently useful is a *deaerated* alumina column. This may be obtained by preparing an alumina column in the usual manner first and then allowing several hundred milliliters of solvent to flow through the column while bubbling a rapid stream of nitrogen through the solvent at the top of the column. A more rigorous procedure is to deaerate the alumina by heating several hours above 200° in vacuum and then admitting pure nitrogen. The solvent is deaerated either by bubbling nitrogen through it for several minutes or by evacuating a container of the solvent until it begins to boil and then refilling

---

[19] *Developing* refers to washing the column with a solvent (the *developer*) to cause the material initially adsorbed at the top of the column to move down the column gradually and to separate into bands or zones corresponding to the various components. *Elution* refers to washing the column with a solvent (the *eluent*) in order to remove the material on the zone at the bottom of the column from the column. The solution emerging from the bottom during elution is known as the *eluate*.

with nitrogen. The chromatography column is then prepared in the usual manner but under nitrogen and the deaerated alumina and solvent are used. Finally, adsorbents other than alumina such as silica gel and Florisil are available and suitable for chromatography. Compounds unstable to alumina may be stable to these other adsorbents.

The five solvents most frequently used by the author for column chromatography of transition-metal organometallic derivatives are pentane (or other volatile saturated aliphatic hydrocarbon), benzene,[20] diethyl ether, dichloromethane (or chloroform), and acetone.[21] The eluting power increases in the order given with pentane as the poorest eluent and acetone as the best eluent. Other workers have also used ethyl acetate, tetrahydrofuran, and alcohols as solvents for chromatography.

In selecting the solvent to be used for a given chromatogram, the weakest readily available eluent in which the material to be chromatographed is stable and soluble should be used for preparing the column and the initial development. In transition-metal organometallic chemistry this generally means using a saturated aliphatic hydrocarbon such as pentane, hexane, or petroleum ether if the material to be chromatographed is soluble in these solvents; most such compounds, which are insoluble in saturated aliphatic hydrocarbons, are readily soluble in benzene, which should then be used to prepare the column and for the initial development. If the initial solvent is not a sufficiently powerful eluent for complete development and elution of all of the components of interest,[22] more powerful eluents may gradually be introduced until development and elution is complete. However, a weaker eluent should never be

---

[20] Benzene in quantities required for chromatography is toxic and obnoxious. Unfortunately, chromatography is frequently best carried out with an aromatic hydrocarbon as solvent, developer, and/or eluent. Inexpensive aromatic hydrocarbons other than benzene (e.g., toluene) are too high-boiling for convenient removal from eluates.

[21] Acetone has a tendency to condense to higher-boiling materials (often recognized by odor) on treatment with alumina. This does not appear to interfere with the use of acetone for the chromatography of transition-metal organometallic compounds. In any case, acetone is only infrequently necessary for the chromatography of organometallic compounds since most such compounds which can be eluted from an alumina column can be eluted satisfactorily with a weaker eluent than acetone such as dichloromethane or benzene. Acetone does have the advantage of being relatively inexpensive.

[22] Often a zone (generally brown or black) will remain at the top of the column even on treatment of the column with acetone. This generally arises from decomposition products. If no mobile bands are observed on an attempted chromatogram even after treatment of the column with acetone, it may generally be concluded that the compound under investigation is unstable to chromatography.

used after a strong eluant. Finer gradations of eluting power may be obtained by mixing two solvents of different eluting power in various proportions. Mixtures of benzene and a saturated aliphatic hydrocarbon are frequently used in the chromatography of transition-metal organometallic compounds.

Two other generally important chromatographic techniques are vapor-phase chromatography and thin-layer chromatography. The application of vapor-phase chromatography to transition-metal organometallic compounds is severely limited by the instability of most compounds of this type at temperatures at which the vapor pressures are sufficiently high. Thin-layer chromatography is suitable for the relatively rapid analysis of crude reaction mixtures on the basis of spots produced on the chromatography plates. However, in most cases, the additional time and materials required for column chromatography as compared with thin-layer chromatography are well rewarded by the chance to isolate sufficient quantities of the products of interest for characterization.

C. Techniques for Identifying Products

1. Melting Point

Some solid transition-metal organometallic compounds such as ferrocene, $C_5H_5Mn(CO)_3$, $Mn_2(CO)_{10}$, and cycloheptatriene-molybdenum tricarbonyl like many purely organic compounds exhibit definite melting points sometimes with accompanying decomposition. The standard technique of melting-point determination by heating a capillary of the compound in an oil bath containing a thermometer is suitable for these compounds. If the compound is somewhat air-sensitive, and an ordinary open capillary is used, it is advisable to pack the capillary to a depth of at least 5 mm. Although the top portion of the sample may decompose because of the small quantity of air present in the capillary, the bottom, more protected portion of the sample will melt reasonably close to the true melting point. However, for melting points of the greatest precision or of compounds so air-sensitive that they cannot be exposed to air, the determination should be carried out in a sealed evacuated capillary. Melting point determination of transition-metal organometallic compounds by placing the samples on a cover glass on an electrically heated hot stage (e.g., the Fisher-Johns apparatus) is not recommended as a general practice as the sample is much more poorly protected against air oxidation and evaporation than a sample at the bottom of a capillary.

Many transition-metal organometallic compounds especially ionic derivatives such as $[C_5H_5Mn(CO)_2NO][PF_6]$ (page 163) do not melt on heating but decompose into solid and gaseous materials. The only noticeable change that is found on heating these materials is generally a change in color often over a rather broad and ill-defined temperature range. If both a compound and its decomposition products are black or other similar color, no visible change may occur upon heating the compound even though extensive decomposition may be taking place.

2. Infrared Spectroscopy

Infrared spectroscopy is frequently very useful in transition-metal organomeallic chemistry both in establishing the presence of certain

ligands, such as terminal and bridging carbonyls and nitrosyls, fluoro-
carbons, and hydrocarbons, in various compounds, and in establishing the
nature of an unknown material that is either identical to or closely
related to a known compound.

Infrared spectra may be obtained in the gas, liquid, or solid phases.
Relatively few transition-metal organometallic compounds are sufficiently
volatile for gas-phase spectra; these few compounds include $HMn(CO)_5$
(page 158) and $Mn(CO)_4NO$ (page 164). With a heated cell gas-phase
spectra of a few other compounds such as $C_5H_5Mo(CO)_3CH_3$ have been
obtained.[1] The technique for gas-phase spectra of transition-metal organometallic compounds is similar to that used to obtain other gas-phase
spectra and will not be described in detail here. Basically, a glass cell
about 5 to 10 cm. long with sodium chloride windows is attached to a
vacuum system, evacuated, and then the desired vapor is admitted until
the desired pressure is reached. The loaded cell is then disconnected
from the vacuum system and inserted in the beam of the spectrometer in
order to obtain the spectrum. The intensity of the spectrum may be
varied by changing the pressure of the vapor in the cell.

Infrared spectra of *liquid* materials may be run by placing a drop
or two of the liquid on a sodium chloride plate, placing another sodium
chloride plate on top of the liquid and the first sodium chloride plate,
and finally clamping the resulting "sandwich" into a suitable holder.
The whole assembly is placed in the beam of the spectrometer and the
spectrum then obtained.

A related technique may be used to obtain infrared spectra of *solutions* of liquid or solid compounds. In this case, a specially constructed
cell[2] of known thickness is used. In general, cells with sodium chloride
windows are used although when samples reacting with sodium chloride
are to be investigated, cells with windows of other materials such as
"Irtran-2" (inert to water)[3] are available.[4] The cell is loaded with the
solution of interest and then placed in the beam of the spectrometer.

In all cases, solvents used for infrared spectra also absorb in some

[1] T. S. Piper and G. Wilkinson, *J. Inorg. Nucl. Chem.* 3, 104 (1956).
[2] Suitable cells for solution spectra may be obtained from Limit Research Corp.,
Darien, Connecticut, Instrument Division, Barnes Engineering Company, 30
Commerce Road, Stamford, Connecticut, or various infrared spectrometer manu-
facturers such as Perkin-Elmer, Beckman, or Baird.
[3] "Irtran 2" is a hard durable material insoluble in water and all organic solvents
useful in the 5000–770 cm.$^{-1}$ range. It is manufactured by the Eastman Corp. Suitable crystals and cells for infrared work made of "Irtran 2" may be purchased from
the Instrument Division, Barnes Engineering Co. (ref. 2).
[4] Other water-insoluble cell materials which may be used include the fluorides of
calcium and barium.

region of the infrared spectrum. In order to eliminate these solvent absorptions from the observed spectrum, a second cell identical to the one containing the solution is loaded with pure solvent identical to that used for the solution and placed in the second beam of the spectrometer.[5] The circuitry of the instrument is designed so that the absorption from the cell containing the pure solvent cancels the absorption from the solvent in the cell containing the solution so that the observed spectrum corresponds entirely to that of the solute.

Although the use of the previously described double-beam spectrometer eliminates solvent absorptions from the spectrum, the spectrometer is much less sensitive in the regions in which a solvent absorption is being canceled out. Thus, it is still necessary to select solvents free of infrared absorption in the desired regions. If a reliable complete spectrum (5000–650 cm.$^{-1}$) of a compound in solution is desired, two spectra should be obtained in solvents which absorb in different regions. A useful solvent pair for many transition-metal organometallic compounds is carbon disulfide and tetrachloroethylene.

Many solid compounds are too insoluble or unstable in appropriate solvents for their spectra to be obtained in solution. In these and other cases in which the use of solvents is best avoided, infrared spectra may be obtained in the *solid* state either in the form of a *mull* or *pellet*.

In order to obtain the spectrum of a solid by mulling, several milligrams of the sample are ground in an agate mortar with a few drops of the mulling agent which may be either pure white mineral oil ("Nujol"), Halocarbon oil, or hexachlorobutadiene depending upon the region of the spectrum to be investigated. The resulting mull is placed with a clean "policeman" (glass rod with a flattened rubber tip) on a sodium chloride plate and a second sodium chloride plate placed on top of the sample and the first sodium chloride plate as when running a spectrum of a pure liquid. Again the "sandwich" is clamped into a suitable holder, the assembly is placed in the beam of the spectrometer, and the spectrum is taken.

The spectrum of the mull thus obtained not only contains the spectrum of the solid material but also of the mulling agent. It is necessary to select a mulling agent that does not absorb in the region of interest in the spectrum. As in the case of solution spectra, a reliable complete spectrum of a solid may only be obtained if spectra of mulls in two different mulling agents absorbing in different regions (such as Nujol and Halo-

---

[5] Cancelling out of solvent absorptions cannot be done in this manner using a single-beam rather than a double-beam spectrometer. However, most spectrometers in use today are of the double-beam variety.

carbon oil) are obtained. Since the thickness of the film of mull on the sodium chloride plates is ill defined by the previously described technique, it is not possible to eliminate readily the spectrum of the mulling agent by placing a second set of sodium chloride plates with a film of pure mulling agent in the second beam of a double-beam spectrometer.

In order to obtain the spectrum of a solid as a pellet, several milligrams of the solid are ground with 50 to 200 times its weight of dry potassium bromide.[6] Although the grinding may be carried out in an agate mortar, the use of a dental amalgamator[7] is preferable in minimizing exposure of the mixture to the moisture of the air. The mixture is then transferred to a stainless steel die[8] (Fig. 20) designed to permit

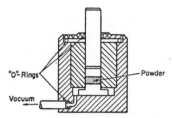

Fig. 20. Illustration of an evacuable die for preparing KBr pellets (cross section).

evacuation. The sample is evened out; the top part of the die is replaced; the die is connected to the vacuum pump and is evacuated to at least 1 mm. While continuing the evacuation, pressure is put on the die with a hydraulic press up to 2000 kg/cm² and maintained there for at least 30 seconds. The pressure is released followed by the vacuum. The die is then dismantled and the pellet removed. It is transferred to a suitable pellet holder, placed in the beam of the spectrometer, and the spectrum taken. In taking the spectrum of a potassium bromide pellet, it is almost always necessary to adjust the "balance" control of the spectrometer so that the transmission is maximum and even then the transmission may be less than in spectra taken in most other media.

---

[6] Specially prepared and finely powdered potassium bromide is commercially available (Harshaw Chemical Company, Cleveland, Ohio, $15./100 g.). The finely powdered potassium bromide rapidly absorbs water from the air. Water may be removed from potassium bromide by drying in an oven for several hours above 130°. Potassium iodide has also been used for preparing pellets for infrared spectra[2] but apparently offers no advantage over the less-expensive bromide.

[7] A suitable dental amalgamator may be purchased from Spex Industries Inc., Hollis 23, New York.

[8] Suitable dies for the preparation of potassium bromide pellets are commercially available from the Research and Industrial Instruments Co., 30 Langton Road, Brixton, London, S.W. 9, England, or its subsidiary Limit Research Corporation, 557 Post Road, Darien, Connecticut.

Even with the purest potassium bromide available, potassium bromide pellets almost invariably contain some water detectable by an absorption at ~3430 cm.$^{-1}$ and a much weaker absorption at ~1620 cm.$^{-1}$ Thus, the potassium bromide pellet technique is not recommended for water-sensitive compounds. In addition, some compounds react with potassium bromide under pressure.[9] Although this is rarely a difficulty with transition-metal organometallic compounds similar to those in this book, it is necessary to be aware of this possibilty and to check doubtful spectra by repetition in a mull or solution.

The various techniques used for preparing transition-metal organometallic compounds for infrared spectra are summarized in Table I.

TABLE I

INFRARED SAMPLE PREPARATION TECHNIQUES USED IN TRANSITION-METAL ORGANOMETALLIC CHEMISTRY

Phase of compound	Phase of sample	Technique	Limitations
(A) Gas	Gas	Gas-phase spectra	Compound must be volatile.
(B) Liquid	Liquid	Liquid film	Extremely strong bonds may be off scale.
	Liquid	Solution	Compound and solvent must be miscible and not react. Solvent must not absorb in region of interest.
(C) Solid	Liquid	Solution	Compound must be soluble and not react with solvent. Solvent must not absorb in region of interest.
	Solid	Mull (Nujol, Halocarbon oil, etc.)	Compound must not react with mulling agent. Mulling agent must not absorb in region of interest.
	Solid	Pellet (KBr)	Compound must be stable to water and halide ions.

Interpretation of the infrared spectra obtained by any of these methods may be a complex matter and a general discussion is beyond the scope of the book. The characteristic frequencies of many of the organic functional groups encountered in purely organic as well as organometallic compounds are discussed in detail by Bellamy.[10] In this book, only a few of the characteristic infrared frequencies peculiar to transition-metal organometallic compounds will be briefly noted.

[9] V. W. Meloche and G. E. Kalbus, *J. Inorg. Nucl. Chem.* **6**, 104 (1958).
[10] L. J. Bellamy, "The Infrared Spectra of Complex Molecules," Methuen, London, 1958.

In neutral compounds, terminal metal carbonyl groups exhibit one or more very strong bands in the 2100–1800-cm.$^{-1}$ range. In anionic metal carbonyl derivatives, terminal carbonyl frequencies as low as 1645 cm.$^{-1}$ (in $[C_5H_5V(CO)_3]^{2-}$) may be found. The abundance of data discussed in detail elsewhere[11] suggests that an increasing negative charge on the metal atom lowers the metal carbonyl frequency. Terminal metal nitrosyl groups similarly exhibit one or more very strong bands in the 1850–1650-cm.$^{-1}$ range.

Bridging metal carbonyl groups exhibit very strong bands in the 1850–1650-cm.$^{-1}$ range. Thus, in almost all cases, infrared spectra clearly distinguish between bridging and terminal metal carbonyl groups. Relatively limited data suggest that bridging metal nitrosyl groups exhibit very strong absorption around 1500 cm.$^{-1}$.[12]

Acyl carbonyl groups in compounds of the types $RCOMn(CO)_5$, $RCOFe(CO)_2C_5H_5$, etc.,[13] exhibit a single strong absorption around 1600 cm.$^{-1}$ Thus, a carbonyl group bonded to one carbon atom and one transition-metal atom occurs at a lower frequency that a carbon group bonded to two carbon atoms such as in organic ketones.

In olefin complexes, an uncomplexed carbon-carbon double bond exhibits a medium intensity sharp band around 1620 cm.$^{-1}$ if the substituents are not unusual ones such as fluorine. Complexing a double bond to a transition metal by π-bonding weakens the infrared absorption and lowers its frequency. Characteristic of π-cyclopentadienyl derivatives is a strong absorption around 800 cm.$^{-1}$ and a weak to medium absorption around 1000 cm.$^{-1}$

When a tertiary phosphine or similar Lewis base bonds to a transition metal, the spectrum of the complexed ligand is very similar to that of the free ligand. A transition-metal-hydrogen bond exhibits weak to medium absorptions in the 2200–1500-cm.$^{-1}$ range. Preparation of the corresponding deuterium derivative is frequently helpful in locating this frequency.

3. Nuclear Magnetic Resonance Spectroscopy

Like infrared spectroscopy, n.m.r. (nuclear magnetic resonance) spectroscopy is extremely useful in establishing structures of a wide variety of transition-metal organometallic compounds. This type of spectroscopy permits the determination of the number and, more important, the various types of hydrogen or fluorine atoms in a given compound. Infrared and n.m.r. spectroscopy are thus complementary, probing

[11] See J. Chatt, P. L. Pauson, and L. M. Venanzi, *In* "Organometallic Chemistry" (H. H. Zeiss, ed.), p. 477. Reinhold, New York, 1960 (and references cited therein).
[12] See, for example, R. B. King and M. B. Bisnette, *Inorg. Chem.* **3**, 791 (1964).
[13] E. Pitcher and F. G. A. Stone, *Spectrochim. Acta.* **18**, 585 (1962).

different structural features of the same molecule. Generally, the n.m.r. spectra of transition-metal organometallic compounds may be interpreted in greater detail than their infrared spectra.

Most n.m.r. spectral studies of transition-metal organometallic compounds, as with most other classes of compounds, are concerned with proton spectra. Proton n.m.r. spectra may be run on a spectrometer (e.g., Varian Associates A-60) with a self-contained standard (water) and the spectra will be recorded on a precalibrated chart. Although the region of 2 to 10 τ is normally routinely investigated with this type of spectrometer, resonances between -15 and $+18$ τ may be studied in special cases. Thus, the only type of *proton* spectral studies that cannot be investigated with an A-60 spectrometer are those of certain transition-metal hydrides with more extreme chemical shifts[14] and certain paramagnetic compounds also with extreme chemical shifts (e.g., nickel(II) troponeiminate derivatives[15]). Recently developed accessories (available from NMR Specialties, Inc., New Kensington, Pennsylvania) even permit spin-spin decoupling experiments with the A-60 spectrometer.

The biggest advantage of the A-60 spectrometer is the ability to obtain readily chemical shifts directly from the spectrum as a result of the precalibrated chart. Rather tedious side-banding techniques are therefore unnecessary for chemical shift measurements. The actual process of obtaining proton n.m.r. spectra on an A-60 spectrometer is no more complicated or time consuming than obtaining an infrared spectrum, although the servicing and maintenance of the A-60 n.m.r. spectrometer are significantly more difficult, expensive, and critical. The biggest disadvantage of the A-60 spectrometer is the inability to obtain spectra other than those of protons.[16] In other cases, the poorer signal-to-noise ratio obtained with the A-60 spectrometer operating at 60 mc.[17] as compared with the HR-100 spectrometer operating at 100 mc.[18] is detrimental.

---

[14] M. L. H. Green, *Angew. Chem.* **72**, 719 (1960).

[15] D. R. Eaton, A. D. Josey, R. E. Benson, W. D. Phillips, and T. L. Cairns, *J. Am. Chem. Soc.* **84**, 4100 (1962).

[16] Recently, a spectrometer has become available from Varian Associates (the A56.4/60) which can obtain spectra on precalibrated charts of fluorine as well as protons. However, many laboratories studying transition-metal organometallic chemistry are not likely to have sufficient research in fluorine chemistry in progress to justify the purchase of such a specialized spectrometer.

[17] For a given sample size, the signal-to-noise ratio increases approximately as the square of the frequency.

[18] An n.m.r. spectrometer using a ~50,000 gauss superconducting magnet permitting observation of proton spectra at ~200 mc. should soon be available. This should improve the signal-to-noise ratio of proton spectra by about a factor of four as compared with even the HR-100.

As of January 1964, no precalibrated instrument comparable to the A-60 was available for F^{19} spectra rather than proton spectra. Therefore, for F^{19} spectra a more conventional spectrometer such as the Varian DP-60 generally operated at 56.4 mc. must be used. The lack of a precalibrated spectrum from this spectrometer makes necessary the determination of chemical shift by superimposing a sideband of known frequency from the standard onto the resonance of interest.

Proton and fluorine n.m.r. spectra are run in solution[19] in spinning 5-mm. (outside diameter) sample tubes. After charging the sample tube with 30 to 200 mg. of the compound to be investigated,[20] the solvent containing 3 to 20% of an appropriate internal standard (see following) and saturated with nitrogen[21] is added to a depth of at least 3 cm. The tube then is either cooled to $-196°$ and sealed in vacuum or flushed with nitrogen and capped. The latter more convenient and economical procedure, although less rigorous in removing oxygen, is adequate for most compounds. The sample tube is then inserted into the probe of the spectrometer and the spectrum taken. If the spectrometer is equipped with an integrator, relative peak areas may then be estimated by integration. The resulting integrals are most reliable and accurate with strong spectra and resonances of similar widths.

A problem almost unique to the n.m.r. spectroscopy of transition-metal compounds is the presence of paramagnetic impurities that broaden the spectrum destroying fine structure and in extreme cases the spectrum itself. In many cases, this appears to arise from a paramagnetic metal oxide either present as an impurity in the original sample or formed by oxidation of some of the solution. Since most metal oxides are insoluble in organic solvents, this effect can often be alleviated by spinning the sample tube in the spectrometer several minutes before taking the spec-

---

[19] Spectra of sufficiently abundant liquid compounds can be taken as pure liquids without the addition of a solvent. The chemical shifts of some such spectra may be appreciably different from those obtained from a solution of the same liquid in one of the usual organic n.m.r. solvents.

[20] The amount of compound required for the spectrum will depend on the percentage of hydrogen or fluorine, the number of different kinds of hydrogen and fluorine atoms, and finally the amount of spin-spin splitting of each resonance. The largest samples will be required with compounds containing a small amount of hydrogen or fluorine, many different types of the element under investigation, and much spin-spin splitting.

[21] Saturating the n.m.r. solvent with nitrogen minimizes the possibility of oxidation of less stable samples to give paramagnetic oxides. For extremely stable compounds such as ferrocene this precaution is probably relatively unimportant. The paramagnetic oxygen present in air does not exhibit a noticeable broadening effect on n.m.r. spectra.

trum. The insoluble paramagnetic particles are "centrifuged" to the edges of the tube away from the "active" region of the sample. Iron compounds are more prone than molybdenum compounds to give these paramagnetic impurities. If paramagnetic impurities are present, it may be necessary to decrease the radiofrequency power and increase the filtering and spectrum amplitude to obtain a usable spectrum.

In proton n.m.r. spectroscopy, it is desirable to use a solvent that does not contain any hydrogen atoms so that the entire spectrum except for the standard (see following) is clearly attributable to the compound and none of the regions of the spectrum are blocked out by strong solvent resonances. Sufficiently powerful solvents that do not contain hydrogen atoms are relatively rare. The only such common solvent generally established as useful in the n.m.r. spectroscopy of transition-metal organometallic compounds is *carbon disulfide*. Other fairly inexpensive proton-free solvents that have been used in n.m.r. spectroscopy of transition-metal organometallic compounds are hexachloroacetone[22] and liquid sulfur dioxide.[23] Carbon tetrachloride is often too reactive with transition-metal organometallic compounds to be generally useful as an n.m.r. solvent. Tetrachloroethylene does not appear to be a more powerful solvent than carbon disulfide for transition-metal organometallic compounds.

Frequently, no hydrogen-free solvent is available for a given transition-metal organometallic compound that sufficiently dissolves it without reaction to permit taking an n.m.r. spectrum. It is then necessary to use a solvent containing either protons or deuterium. Proton-containing solvents are obviously much less expensive than their deuterated analogs. Chloroform exhibits only a single proton resonance at 2.73 τ[24] and may be used at $>3.5\ \tau$ and $<2\ \tau$ without difficulty. Benzene also exhibits only a single proton resonance in a similar region (2.63 τ). However, the higher percentage of hydrogen in benzene (7.7%) as compared with chloroform (0.84%) makes the benzene resonance much stronger, destroying a slightly wider region of the spectrum. Benzene also appears to exhibit an appreciable solvent effect changing many chemical shifts

---

[22] D. J. Bertelli, Ph.D. Thesis, University of Washington, 1961 (H. Dauben, Research Adviser) pp. 52–53, discusses using hexachloroacetone as solvent for the n.m.r. of $C_7H_9Fe(CO)_2I$.

[23] J. K. P. Ariyaratne and M. L. H. Green, *J. Chem. Soc.* 2976 (1963); 1 (1964).

[24] Commercial chloroform contains ∼0.5% ethanol to remove phosgene formed in its slow oxidation. This ethanol may be removed by treatment of the chloroform with Linde molecular sieves or chromatography-grade alumina. Ethanol in chloroform may be detected by resonances at 6.30 τ (quartet, J = ∼7 cps), 7.42 τ (singlet) and 8.78 τ (triplet, J = ∼7 cps). In 60 mc., spectra taken in chloroform solution a singlet at ∼4.5 τ may be observed as the C^{13} satellite of the strong chloroform resonance at 2.73 τ.

including π-C_5H_5 resonances by 0.5 τ or even more. Chemical shifts determined in benzene solution are not always directly comparable with those obtained in chloroform or carbon disulfide solution.

Chloroform and benzene may block out certain resonances due to aromatic and olefinic protons (see following) but permit observation of resonances due to π-cyclopentadienyl and aliphatic protons among others. If the aromatic and olefinic proton region around 3 τ is of primary interest and no hydrogen-free solvent is available, the spectrum may be run in any of several solvents especially acetone and dimethylsulfoxide whose only protons arise from methyl groups and appear at 7 to 9 τ. A complete n.m.r. spectrum of a compound requiring hydrogen-containing solvents may be obtained without using expensive deuterated solvents by investigating the region above about 4 τ in chloroform solution and the region below this in acetone solution.

When hydrogen-free solvents such as carbon disulfide give unsatisfactory results and proton-containing solvents such as chloroform or acetone obscure important regions, it is necessary to resort to deuterated solvents. Although the prices of a few deuterated solvents notably D_2O (\$20/100 g.) and $CDCl_3$ (\$150/100 g.) are fairly reasonable and within the range of most budgets, most other deuterated solvents such as hexadeuteroacetone (\$800/100 g.) and hexadeuterobenzene (\$1200/100 g.) are so expensive that several dollars' worth of solvent are consumed with each spectrum. All deuterated solvents contain appreciable quantities of the proton analog and possibly other impurities; therefore, a blank n.m.r. spectrum should be run on the pure solvent and the resulting spectrum subtracted from the spectrum of the solution. In most cases, these impurity resonances of deuterated solvents are weaker than the strongest resonances of the solute.

Solvent selection for F^{19} n.m.r. spectroscopy is much less difficult than that for proton n.m.r. spectroscopy since most organic solvents contain no fluorine. Two excellent solvents for F^{19} n.m.r. spectroscopy are dichloromethane and tetrahydrofuran. If carbon disulfide or chloroform is used as a solvent and appropriate internal standards are added, the same sample tube can be used for both hydrogen and fluorine n.m.r. spectra of a compound containing these two elements. Another solvent useful in F^{19} n.m.r. spectroscopy is trichlorofluoromethane (Freon-11) which provides its own internal standard.

All n.m.r. chemical shifts are measured in cps or, more commonly, ppm displacement from the resonance of a *standard* substance. Either an *internal* standard that is present in the solution under study or, less conveniently and commonly, an *external* standard in a sealed capillary that is immersed in the solution under study may be used. Proton chemical shifts are often reported on the τ scale[25] where the chemical shift of tetramethylsilane is assigned the value 10.00 τ and a change of 1 τ correspond to 1 ppm. Similarly, fluorine chemical shifts are often reported on the ϕ scale[26] which is identical to ppm upfield from the resonance of trichlorofluoromethane.

The most commonly used standard in proton n.m.r. spectroscopy is internal tetramethylsilane (10.00 τ). For transition-metal organometallic compounds internal hexamethyldisiloxane (9.95 τ) is equally satisfactory and more convenient to use since it boils at 100° as compared with the rather low boiling point of 26.5° for tetramethylsilane. In special cases especially where the compound may exhibit a resonance near 10 τ, chloroform (2.73 τ), benzene (2.63 τ), or cyclohexane (8.57 τ) may be used as internal standards. For aqueous solutions (H_2O or D_2O) either water itself (4.97 τ) or the methyl resonance of t-butanol (8.78 τ) may be used as internal standards.

There appears to be less agreement in the use of standards for F^{19} n.m.r. spectroscopy. Internal trichlorofluoromethane (b.p. 24°, 0.0 ϕ) is frequently used. Less frequently used, but more convenient, is internal 1,1,2,2,-tetrachloro-1,2-difluoroethane (b.p. 92°, 67.8 ϕ). Also used are benzotrifluoride (63.9 ϕ) and external[27] trifluoroacetic acid (78.4 ϕ).

A detailed discussion of the interpretation of n.m.r. spectra is far beyond the scope of this book.[28] Only brief mention of the principles most pertinent to the crude interpretation of the proton[29] n.m.r. spectra of transition-metal organometallic compounds can be given here.

An outline of the chemical shifts for the types of protons most frequently encountered in transition-metal organometallic compounds is given in Table II. The relative areas under the resonances are propor-

---

[25] G. V. D. Tiers, *J. Phys. Chem.* **62,** 1151 (1958).

[26] G. Filipovich and G. V. D. Tiers, *J. Phys. Chem.* **63,** 761 (1959).

[27] Trifluoroacetic acid is a strong acid (K_a ~0.59). It is, therefore, too reactive to use as an *internal* standard in most cases.

[28] For more detailed discussions on n.m.r. spectra see especially the following books: W. D. Phillips, *In* "Determination of Organic Structures by Physical Methods," (W. D. Phillips and F. C. Nachod, eds.), pp. 401–463, Academic Press, New York, 1962; H. S. Gutowsky, *In* "Physical Methods of Organic Chemistry" (A. Weissberger, ed.), pp. 2663–2799, Wiley (Interscience), New York, 1960; J. A. Pople, W. G. Schneider, and H. J. Bernstein, "High Resolution Nuclear Magnetic Resonance," McGraw-Hill, New York, 1959; J. D. Roberts, "Nuclear Magnetic Resonance," McGraw-Hill, New York, 1959; and L. M. Jackman, "Applications of Nuclear Magnetic Resonance Spectroscopy in Organic Chemistry," Macmillan (Pergamon), New York, 1959.

[29] For a discussion of the F^{19} n.m.r. spectra of fluorocarbon-transition metal derivatives see E. Pitcher, A. D. Buckingham and F. G. A. Stone, *J. Chem. Phys.* **36,** 124 (1962).

tional to the number of protons they represent; thus, in the compound $C_5H_5Fe(CO)_2CH_3$, the relative intensities of the cyclopentadienyl and methyl resonances are 5:3.

A complicating but often useful phenomenon in many n.m.r. spectra is spin-spin splitting generally by atoms of spin $\frac{1}{2}$ (e.g., hydrogen, fluorine,

TABLE II

N.M.R. Chemical Shifts of Protons Frequently Encountered in
Transition-Metal Organometallic Chemistry

Type of proton		Chemical shift range, τ
Phenyl	⬡—H	1 to 3[a]
Uncomplexed olefinic	C=C⟨^{H}	3 to 5
Complexed olefinic	C=C⟨^{H} ↓ M	1 to 10[b]
π-Cyclopentadienyl	(ring) M	3 to 7[c]
Aliphatic	C\C/H C/ \H or C\C/H C/ \C	6 to 9.5
Methyl	CH_3	6 to 11[d]
Transition metal hydride	M—H	16 to 32

[a] Most frequently this value is 2.5 to 3.0 τ.

[b] Most frequently this value is 3.5 to 6.0 τ.

[c] Generally, this value is 4 to 6 τ in cyclopentadienyl metal carbonyl derivatives and 5 to 6.5 τ in "sandwich" complexes with *only* two π-bonded hydrocarbon ligands.

[d] This value depends on the electronegativity of the group to which the methyl group is bonded; decreasing electronegativity gives increased chemical shifts. Thus, this accounts for the chemical shift increase in the series $CH_3N < CH_3C < CH_3Si$, CH_3Fe, etc.

phosphorus, platinum, or rhodium) located two or three bonds away from the nucleus under investigation. Spin-spin splitting causes the resonance in question to be split into $N + 1$ equidistant lines of relative intensities corresponding to the coefficients of $(a + 1)^N$ where N represents the number of spin $\frac{1}{2}$ nuclei located in equivalent positions relative to the nucleus in question. The separation between these lines is known as the *coupling constant* J, and, unlike the chemical shift, is independent of the frequency at which the spectrum is taken. It is therefore generally measured in cps. In a simple example of spin-spin splitting, the resonance of the methyl protons in tris(dimethylamino)-phosphine, $[(CH_3)_2N]_3P$, is split into a doublet with peaks of equal intensity due to the spin ½ phosphorus atom three bonds away. Coupling constants caused by a nucleus two or three bonds away from the nucleus in question generally range from the minimum detectable ∼1 cps to about 15 cps[30] although sometimes when a nucleus besides hydrogen such as phosphorus or fluorine is involved, the coupling can be considerably larger (e.g., $J_{H-F}{}^{\beta}$ of $HCF_2CF_2Mn(CO)_5$ of 58 cps). If several nonequivalent spin ½ nuclei are located sufficiently close to the nucleus in question, their spin-spin splitting effects are superimposed, and, in many cases, the resulting complex pattern defies interpretation. The effects of spin-spin splitting may often be eliminated by *decoupling* ("double resonance") in which the nucleus causing the splitting is irradiated strongly at its resonance frequency while scanning the spectrum through the resonance of the nucleus in question. Commercial equipment is now available from several firms[31] for homonuclear (involving nuclei of the same type) and heteronuclear (involving nuclei of different types) decoupling experiments.[32]

4. Elemental Analysis and Molecular Weight Determinations

Although one of the oldest characterization techniques, elemental analyses still play an indispensable role in the characterization of transition-metal organometallic compounds. Even with all of the powerful spectroscopic techniques now available, most new compounds are still not considered adequately characterized until satisfactory elemental analyses have been obtained.

Modern microanalytical techniques in general use permit determinations of practically all elements in a given compound[33] on samples ranging in size from 3 to 50 mg. for each determination. The amount required for a given determination depends on the determination in question and the amount of the element to be determined present in the sample. These microanalytical techniques often require special skills and most preparative organometallic chemists resort to professional microanalysts either

---

[30] Much larger coupling constants are found when the interacting nuclei are separated by only one bond (e.g., $J_{W^{183}-H}$ in $C_5H_5W(CO)_3H = 36$ cps).

[31] E.g., NMR Specialties, Inc., New Kensington, Pennsylvania.

[32] The types of instrumentation required for homonuclear and for heteronuclear spin-spin decoupling are rather different.

[33] The author has never encountered any successful oxygen analyses in the presence of fluorine in organometallic compounds.

within their own institutions or in commercial microanalytical laboratories[34] for at least some of their analytical work. For an active preparative organometallic research program, microanalytical costs are often extremely high. Samples for analysis in small vials or sealed tubes packed in sturdy boxes may be sent anywhere in the world in a few days with little risk of breakage and at a cost that is small compared with that of the analyses.

Since most of the users of this book will employ professional analysts for their microanalytical work, a detailed discussion of the microanalytical techniques will not be given.[35] In general, these techniques as used for transition-metal organometallic compounds differ little from those used for more conventional organic compounds. Carbon and hydrogen are determined simultaneously by the usual combustion technique involving burning to carbon dioxide and water, respectively. A modified Unterzaucher method[36] may be used for the direct oxygen determination provided fluorine is not present. Basically, in this type of direct oxygen determination, the sample is decomposed at a high temperature ($\sim 1100°$) in the presence of excess carbon either from the compound or from an added organic substance such as indulin. Carbon monoxide is formed which is determined either iodometrically or by oxidation to carbon dioxide. Nitrogen may be determined by the standard Dumas method and phosphorus by a standard method such as precipitation of ammonium phosphomolybdate. In the determination of sulfur, the com-

---

[34] Commercial microanalytical laboratories which have successfully carried out elemental analyses on transition-metal organometallic compounds include the following:

(a) Pascher Mikroanalytisches Laboratorium, Buschstrasse 54, Bonn, Germany.

(b) Dr. A. Bernhardt, Mikroanalytisches Laboratorium, Max-Planck Institut für Kohlenforschung, Höhenweg 17, Mülheim (Ruhr), Germany.

(c) Dr. G. Weiler and Dr. F. B. Strauss, Microanalytical Laboratory, 164 Banbury Road, Oxford, England.

(d) Schwarzkopf Microanalytical Laboratory, 56–19 37th Avenue, Woodside 77, New York.

(e) Microanalysis, Inc., P. O. Box 5097, Wilmington 8, Delaware.

(f) Galbraith Laboratories, Inc., P. O. Box 4187, Knoxville 21, Tennessee.

(g) Huffman Microanalytical Laboratories, 3830 High Court, P. O. Box 350, Wheatridge, Colorado.

[35] For more detailed discussions on elemental organic microanalysis see the following books: F. Pregl and J. Grant, "Quantitative Organic Microanalysis," McGraw-Hill (Blakiston), New York 1951; S. J. Clark, "Quantitative Methods of Organic Microanalysis," Butterworth, London and Washington, D.C. 1956; and G. Ingram, "Methods of Organic Elemental Microanalysis," Reinhold, New York, 1962.

[36] The method described by F. H. Oliver, *Analyst* **80**, 593 (1955), has been used in the presence of metals.

pound may either be oxidized and the sulfur determined as sulfate in the usual manner or the compound may be burned in a stream of hydrogen[37] and the hydrogen sulfide determined iodometrically.

An analytical problem more specific to transition-metal organometallic chemistry is the determination of the percentage of metal in the compound. Sometimes, the metal determination may simply be carried out by weighing the ash from the combustion of the carbon-hydrogen determination. In the absence of other elements that form nonvolatile oxides, iron, chromium, and molybdenum, for example, can be estimated from this residue as Fe_2O_3, Cr_2O_3, and MoO_3, respectively. However, the application of this relatively simple technique for estimation of the metal content is rather limited not only because of the difficulty of obtaining a definite metal oxide by this technique of combustion but also because of the physical nature of many of these ashes making handling without mechancial losses very difficult. Therefore, it is more desirable to determine the metal independently from the carbon-hydrogen determination. In these separate metal determinations, the sample is first decomposed by heating with concentrated nitric acid or another strong oxidizing acid taking care to avoid losses of any volatile compounds. In some cases, the resulting residue may be ignited to the metal oxide.[38] In other cases, the residue may be dissolved in water and the solution titrated with sodium ethylenediaminetetraacetate (EDTA) in the presence of a suitable indicator.[39] In other cases, especially those in which two different metals are present, more specific metal determinations may be indicated.

In many areas of organic chemistry, analytical data are not considered satisfactory unless they are within 0.3 to 0.4% of the theoretical value. With stable and readily purified solid organometallic transition-metal compounds, this degree of accuracy is also often readily obtainable. However, with unstable compounds purified with more difficulty and containing a greater variety of especially complicating elements such as fluorine, this degree of accuracy often cannot be honestly at-

---

[37] W. Zimmermann, *Mikrochemie Ver. Mikrochim. Acta* **31**, 13 (1943).

[38] The following metals may be determined by ignition to oxides or by other gravimetric methods: titanium, zirconium, hafnium, vanadium, niobium, tantalum, chromium, molybdenum, tungsten, nickel, and the alkali metals.

[39] The following metals may be determined either directly or indirectly by EDTA titrations: aluminum, barium, bismuth, cadmium, calcium, chromium, cobalt, copper, gold, iron, lead, magnesium, manganese, mercury, nickel, rhodium, sodium, strontium, thallium, tin, zinc, and the lanthanides. For a general discussion of this analytical technique see H. A. Flaschka, "EDTA Titrations," Macmillan (Pergamon), New York, 1959; G. Schwarzenbach, "Complexometric Titrations." Methuen, London, 1957; and F. J. Welcher, "The Analytical Uses of Ethylenediaminetetraacetic Acid." Van Nostrand, Princeton, New Jersey, 1958.

tained, and determined values deviate as much as 1% (or even 2% in some cases) from the theoretical values for one or more of the elements in samples indicated to be pure by physical techniques. Also even the best analysts occasionally make mistakes. Therefore, in crucial cases, it is best to check the analyses on another sample preferably from an independent preparation.

Molecular weight determinations in general are less satisfactory than elemental analyses although the rather recent introduction of the Mechrolab "vapor pressure osmometer"[40] has greatly improved the reliability of molecular weight determinations.

The operation of the Mechrolab osmometer is based on the temperature differential caused by differing rates of evaporation of a solution of the sample of known concentration and the pure solvent. This measurement is made in isolated chambers using thermistors. The apparatus is calibrated against solutions of known compounds in the various solvents to be used. Molecular weight determinations of transition-metal organometallic compounds by the osmometer are most frequently carried out in benzene solution.

Prior to the introduction of the Mechrolab osmometer, most molecular weight determinations of transition-metal organometallic compounds were carried out either cryoscopically in benzene solution or isopiestically in chloroform, benzene, or trichlorofluoromethane solutions. In general, these methods are either less convenient or less reliable than the Mechrolab osmometer.

5. Ultraviolet and Visible Spectroscopy

It is more difficult to obtain specific structural information on transition-metal organometallic compounds by ultraviolet and visible spectroscopy than by infrared and n.m.r. spectroscopy. Moreover, solutions used for ultraviolet and visible spectroscopy are much more dilute than for these other techniques. Therefore, exclusion of oxygen is much more crucial to ultraviolet and visible spectroscopy since the same amount of oxidation represents destruction of a much larger percentage of the sample and more drastically affects the results. For these reasons, ultraviolet spectroscopy is relatively infrequently used in transition-metal organometallic chemistry.

The technique for ultraviolet and visible spectroscopy of organometallic compounds is relatively similar to that of organic compounds provided that ~0.1% solutions of the compound under investigation

---

[40] The vapor pressure osmometer may be purchased from Mechrolab, Inc., 1062 Linda Vista Ave., Mountain View, California.

may be handled in air for at least 5 minutes without appreciable oxidation. Cyclohexane[41] rather than 95% ethanol is preferred as a solvent when solubility permits since solutions are more stable in this nonpolar hydrocarbon. For less soluble compounds, peroxide-free dioxane may be used as a solvent. For very air-sensitive compounds, special techniques are required for ultraviolet and visible spectral investigations. A detailed description of such techniques successfully used for some of the most air-sensitive known transition-metal complexes has been recently given[42] and will not be repeated here.

Characteristic of the ultraviolet spectra of metal carbonyl derivatives is a maximum in the range 275–400 mμ.[43,44] The extinction coefficient of this maximum ("MC-band"[43]) increases roughly in proportion to the number of metal carbonyl groups present, but some compounds with no carbonyl groups, particularly ferrocene and its organic substitution products, exhibit a similar but much weaker maximum. Acyl derivatives of transition metals (e.g., $CF_3COFe(CO)_2C_5H_5$) also exhibit a stronger maximum at 240 to 280 mμ which apparently arises from the acyl carbonyl group.

6. Less Frequently Used Techniques

Conductivity measurements on transition-metal organometallic compounds are useful in distinguishing possible ionic from nonionic formulations for a given compound. Such measurements may be carried out in acetone solution[45] using a standard conductivity bridge.[46] Precise measurements are not necessary to distinguish between ionic and nonionic formulations since generally the molar conductance of an ionic compound in acetone solution is about fifty times that of a similar nonionic compound. Ionic organometallic transition-metal compounds, such as hexafluorophosphate, tetrafluoroborate, and tetracarbonylcobaltate salts of complex cations, generally exhibit molar conductances of 100–200 ohm^{-1} cm^2 mole^{-1} in $\sim$0.001 M solution.

Magnetic susceptibility measurements are relativity unimportant in transition-metal *organometallic* chemistry in comparison to other types

[41] The cyclohexane must be free from benzene. A spectral grade of solvent is recommended and a blank should be run even on this solvent.
[42] E. König, H. L. Schläfer, and S. Herzog, *Z. Chem.* 4, 95 (1964).
[43] R. T. Lundquist and M. Cais, *J. Org. Chem.* 27, 1167 (1962).
[44] R. B. King and M. B. Bisnette, *J. Organometal. Chem.* 2, 15 (1964).
[45] Reagent grade acetone stored over Linde molecular sieves may be used for conductivity determinations.
[46] For a more detailed discussion on conductivity measurements see T. Shedlovsky, *In* "Physical Methods of Organic Chemistry" (A. Weissberger, ed.), pp. 3011–3048. Wiley (Interscience), New York, 1960.

of transition-metal chemistry. Most transition-metal organometallic derivatives contain many strong-field ligands, and, therefore, have a very large tendency to attain the diamagnetic "inert gas" configuration; magnetically interesting paramagnetic organometallic derivatives are therefore very rare in comparison with paramagnetic oxides, sulfides, halides, ammines, etc. Magnetic susceptibilities have been measured by the Gouy or Faraday methods[47]; the latter is more suitable since it requires much less sample. More recently, a method based on the change in n.m.r. chemical shifts by a paramagnetic material has been developed for measurements in solution[48] and applied to several transition-metal organometallic compounds.[49]

Since many transition-metal organometallic compounds are appreciably volatile, *mass spectrometry*[50] should be a very useful technique for more exact molecular weight determination and should aid in structure elucidation from the fragmentation pattern. However, very little use of mass spectrometry has been made in this area of chemistry. Mass spectral studies of biscyclopentadienylmetal derivatives,[51] certain hydrocarbon-metal carbonyl derivatives,[52] and fluorocarbon-metal carbonyl derivatives[53] have been made, but the data thus obtained, although valuable for specific problems, are still too limited to assess clearly the usefulness and limitation of this technique in the study of transition-metal organometallic compounds. Very recently the mass spectra of $Fe(CO)_5$ and $Ni(CO)_4$ were studied in detail.[54]

A promising new technique for the study of organo*iron* compounds is *Mössbauer resonance spectroscopy*.[55] Equipment suitable for other Möss-

---

[47] For a general discussion of the experimental techniques of magnetochemistry see P. W. Selwood, "Magnetochemistry." Wiley (Interscience), New York, 1956.

[48] D. F. Evans, *J. Chem. Soc.* 2003 (1959).

[49] H. P. Fritz and K. E. Schwarzhans, *J. Organometal. Chem.* 1, 208 (1964).

[50] For a general discussion of chemical applications of mass spectrometry see F. W. McLafferty, *In* "Determination of Organic Structures by Physical Methods" (F. C. Nachod and W. D. Phillips, eds.), pp. 93–179. Academic Press, New York, 1962; C. A. McDowell, Ed., "Mass Spectrometry," McGraw-Hill, New York, 1963; and K. Biemann, "Mass Spectrometry: Organic Chemical Applications," McGraw-Hill, New York, 1962.

[51] L. Friedman, A. P. Irsa, and G. Wilkinson, *J. Am. Chem. Soc.* 77, 3689 (1955).

[52] D. J. Bertelli, Ph.D. Thesis, University of Washington, 1961 (H. J. Dauben, Research Adviser).

[53] H. H. Hoehn, L. Pratt, K. F. Watterson, and G. Wilkinson, *J. Chem. Soc.* 2738 (1961)

[54] R. E. Winters and R. W. Kiser, *Inorg. Chem.* 3, 699 (1964).

[55] For a general discussion of Mössbauer resonance spectroscopy see H. Frauenfelder, "The Mössbauer Effect," Benjamin, New York, 1962; G. K. Wertheim, *Science* 144, 253 (1964).

bauer studies may be used for organoiron compounds, although the measurements must be made in the solid state at liquid nitrogen temperature (−196°). The most obvious quantity obtained from the Mössbauer spectrum of an iron compound is the *isomer shift*, i.e., the displacement on the velocity scale of the centroid of the sample resonance from that of a reference substance such as a certain stainless steel or sodium nitroprusside. In an iron complex with the inert gas configuration and without π-bonding ligands, the measured isomer shift is the sum of approximately constant partial isomer shifts (ζ values) of each ligand.[56] The analogous ζ values for π-bonding ligands are not constant, but the ζ value for the π-cyclopentadienyl group in a given compound may be estimated readily from the n.m.r. chemical shift of the π-cyclopentadienyl protons in the compound in question.[56]

Many Mössbauer spectra of compounds containing only one type of iron atom exhibit two peaks. The separation between these peaks (*quadrupole splitting*) corresponds to the deviation of the symmetry of the field gradient around the iron atoms from cubic symmetry. In compounds with octahedral and tetrahedral coordination of the iron atom with different ligands,[57] the quadrupole splitting ranges from 0.0 to 0.1 cm./sec. In compounds with one π-cyclopentadienyl ring or similar π-bonding ligand and three σ-bonding ligands, the quadrupole splitting ranges from 0.14 to 0.19 cm./sec. In ferrocene and similar compounds with two rings π-bonded to an iron atom, the quadrupole splitting ranges from 0.23 to 0.25 cm./sec. In trigonal bipyramidal compounds, the quadrupole splitting ranges from 0.22 to 0.25 cm./sec. Similar data on the deviation of the symmetry of the field gradient around a metal atom from cubic symmetry may be obtained on manganese and cobalt compounds by pure nuclear quadrupole resonance (n.q.r.) spectroscopy,[58] but very few compounds have been studied in this manner.

---

[56] R. H. Herber, R. B. King, and G. K. Wertheim, *Inorg. Chem.* 3, 101 (1964).

[57] In compounds with an octahedral or tetrahedrally coordinated iron atom with identical ligands a single resonance is observed; quadrupole splitting is absent.

[58] J. Voitländer, H. Klocke, R. Longino, and H. Thieme, *Naturwissenschaften* 49, 491 (1962).

D. Precautions

1. Precautions Against Oxidation

Most transition-metal organometallic compounds although somewhat air-sensitive oxidize sufficiently slowly in air so that ordinary chemical techniques that have been outlined are satisfactory as long as the reactions are run under nitrogen, the filtrates are collected under nitrogen, and nitrogen rather than air is admitted to evacuated vessels to break the vacuum. Using ordinary techniques and these added precautions, it is generally not necessary to expose compounds to air for more than a few minutes at a time unless a filtration operation is very slow.[1]

However, some transition-metal organometallic compounds, such as the neutral biscyclopentadienyl derivatives of vanadium and chromium, are destroyed upon exposure to air within a short time. It is necessary to handle such compounds without exposure to air. Two general types of techniques are available for this purpose conveniently designated as *glove-box* and *Schlenk-tube* techniques.

Ideally, the glove-box technique uses conventional equipment but it is enclosed in a large box[2] containing an oxygen-free atmosphere generally of pure nitrogen.[3] Long rubber gloves are inserted through airtight openings in one side of the box to permit manipulations. A smaller second chamber (the *air lock*) is then attached to the main large chamber so that items can be introduced into and removed from the main chamber without admitting any air to the atmosphere of the main chamber. A transparent front panel on the box permits observation of operations. The construction of the box should permit evacuation.

---

[1] Fast filtrations are desirable when working with potentially air-sensitive organometallic compounds to minimize decomposition.

[2] Much less expensive devices for working in an inert atmosphere may be constructed by replacing the box with a polyethylene bag. Air may be forced out of such an inert atmosphere bag by squeezing as tightly as possible. The bag is then blown up again with pure nitrogen. It is difficult to provide such bags with a second air-lock chamber but this is not as important as with the box since the bag is more easily filled with nitrogen.

[3] The purest available tank nitrogen is suitable for most purposes. If necessary, purer nitrogen may be obtained by passage through sodium benzophenone ketyl, triisobutylaluminum, active copper heated to 200°, or BTS-Katalysator.

After filling the glove box with all of the required apparatus and materials for the series of experiments to be carried out, the box is evacuated and refilled with pure nitrogen several times. The last traces of oxygen may then be removed by opening a container of a very oxygen-sensitive material such as liquid sodium-potassium alloy or triisobutyl-aluminum in the box. The desired manipulations can then be carried out. When it is necessary to remove items from the glove box, these items are transferred first from the main chamber to the second air-lock chamber from which the air has been previously replaced with pure nitrogen. The door between the main chamber and the air lock is then closed tightly. The door between the air lock and the outside is then opened and the items removed.

In practice, glove boxes have often proved to be unsatisfactory for very air-sensitive organometallic compounds with which such precautions are the most necessary. It is often very difficult to free the atmosphere from the last traces of oxygen. Air leaking into the box from the outside can also be an annoying problem. Finally, manipulations with the rubber gloves are often rather awkward. It is for these reasons that most workers with extremely air-sensitive compounds prefer to use the Schlenk-tube technique.

A Schlenk tube[4] (Fig. 2) is a simple two-necked vessel designed to permit passage of a nitrogen stream through the narrow neck with the stopcock while using the wider neck without a stopcock for operations such as inserting a spatula for scraping or removal of material, additions from a pressure-equalized dropping funnel or a spatula, and connection to a "Fritte" for filtration. If agitation is required, a magnetic stirring bar may be inserted through the wider opening and turned in the usual manner by a rotating magnet located below the Schlenk tube.

Air-sensitive compounds may be stored in Schlenk tubes by capping the open joint and closing the stopcock. Filtration is carried out by connecting a Schlenk tube containing the solution to be filtered to a "Fritte" (Fig. 21) containing a sintered glass disk of the correct porosity or a perforated disk to accommodate a small disk of filter paper. An empty Schlenk tube is connected to the other end of the Fritte to accommodate the filtrate. After filling the entire system with nitrogen, it is inverted and the solution is allowed to run through the filter with the aid of nitrogen pressure.

Other special types of apparatus have been developed for use in conjunction with Schlenk tubes for such operations with the rigorous exclu-

---

[4] The Schlenk tube is named after Wilhelm Schlenk, 1879–1943, a pioneering worker in the chemistry of alkali-metal organometallic derivatives.

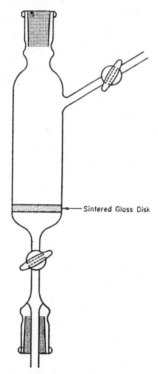

Sintered Glass Disk

FIG. 21. Diagram of a Fritte.

sion of air as sample tube filling, extraction, etc. For a detailed description of these more specialized items, the reader is referred to the recent article by Herzog and Dehnert.[5]

2. Precautions Against Toxic Materials

Unfortunately, many materials encountered in transition-metal organometallic chemistry have undesirable effects on the human body when ingested, inhaled, or spilled on the skin. The obvious precautions of never eating in the laboratory and washing hands before eating eliminate these hazards. Careful laboratory technique and use of rubber gloves with dangerous materials minimize hazards from spillage. The major toxicity hazard in the organometallic laboratory arises from inhalation of noxious vapors. Thus, the greatest dangers stem from toxic volatile compounds.

By far the most dangerous metal carbonyl is nickel tetracarbonyl, a highly volatile material (b.p. ~43°) more toxic than hydrogen cyanide.

[5] S. Herzog and J. Dehnert, Z. Chem. 4, 1 (1964).

Other volatile nickel compounds, notably cyclopentadienylnickel nitrosyl, are also extremely toxic although not as hazardous as nickel tetracarbonyl. Iron pentacarbonyl is also dangerously toxic although its toxicity is much less than that of nickel tetracarbonyl. Dicobalt octacarbonyl and diamanganese decacarbonyl are also very toxic but create a lesser hazard since they are less volatile and generally much rarer than iron or nickel carbonyls. The hexacarbonyls of chromium, molybdenum, and tungsten do not present a significant hazard from inhalation.[6]

In view of its extreme toxicity, nickel tetracarbonyl should be handled in an excellent hood in containers closed as much as possible to the atmosphere. Iron pentacarbonyl and other transition-metal compounds with a vapor pressure of 0.1 mm. or more at room temperature should also regularly be handled in an excellent hood. Reactions of other transition-metal organometallic compounds should be carried out in a hood when more than 0.1 mole is used.

Most free ligands used in transition-metal organometallic chemistry are also toxic. Carbon monoxide, a colorless, odorless, but highly toxic gas, is frequently used in autoclaves under high pressure in great excess for the preparation of various metal carbonyl derivatives. Such experiments should be carried out in a location where the excess carbon monoxide is removed into a well-ventilated area. Volatile phosphines, arsines, stibines, and isocyanides are not only malodorous but highly toxic. Volatile divalent sulfur compounds are often even more malodorous but aside from several important exceptions[7] are not particularly dangerously toxic.

Many solvents encountered in transition-metal organometallic chemistry, although not as toxic as the metal carbonyl derivatives and free ligands, are more dangerous and obnoxious since they are used in much larger quantities. Especially bad in this respect is benzene which is often used in large quantities and which is often not readily replaceable by less toxic solvents.

Finally, corrosive gases such as nitrogen dioxide, hydrogen halides, acid halides, and free halogens are encountered occasionally in organometallic chemistry as in other areas of chemistry. Especially obnoxious are the brown nitrogen dioxide fumes often formed when concentrated nitric acid is used to clean apparatus. Other cleaning agents including chromic acid-sulfuric acid cleaning solution should be substituted for

---

[6] The carbon monoxide produced from the thermal decomposition of these hexacarbonyls is potentially hazardous in large quantities.
[7] 2,5-Dithiahexane, $CH_3SCH_2CH_2SCH_3$, may cause headaches when inhaled in small quantities. 2-Chloroethyl sulfides such as "mustard gas," $(ClCH_2CH_2)_2S$, are, of course, extremely toxic and often powerful vesicants.

concentrated nitric acid when practicable. When concentrated nitric acid is used, the cleaning should be carried out in a good hood. Eye protection in the form of safety glasses, although always desirable in the laboratory, is particularly important when handling such corrosive materials.

3. Precautions Against Fire and Explosion

Many flammable materials are encountered in transition-metal organometallic chemistry. Frequently used flammable solvents include pentane, hexane, benzene, ether, acetone, and tetrahydrofuran. Since one or more of these solvents are almost constantly used in an organometallic laboratory, smoking or other operations using free flames in such a laboratory should be prohibited. It is also advisable to use explosion-proof electric motors when stirring reactions with such flammable solvents.

More characteristic of transition-metal organometallic chemistry are pyrophoric, black, metallic residues frequently obtained as by-products in thermal reactions of various metal carbonyls especially $Fe_3(CO)_{12}$. These residues suspected to be pyrophoric are best discarded in open metal cans in a hood and allowed to burn. Residues from sodium cyclopentadienide reactions can also be pyrophoric.

Also frequently encountered in transition-metal organometallic chemistry are materials such as the alkali metals or lithium aluminum hydride which exothermically evolve hydrogen on treatment with water causing fires and/or explosions.[8] It is dangerous to cool large-scale reactions of such materials in an ice bath since breakage of the reaction flask could cause a serious accident. The use of water-cooled condensers in reactions of sodium and other such materials also presents a potential hazard. However, the chance of breakage of such a condenser is very slight. The risk involved in so using a water-cooled condenser appears to be a much lesser evil than attempts to condense the vapors from such reactions without a water-cooled condenser. Such experiments, however, are best carried out behind a shield.

Ethers used in organometallic chemistry, especially tetrahydrofuran and diisopropyl ether, have a tendency to form explosive peroxides on exposure to air. Therefore, these materials should never be distilled to dryness. Distillations of these ethers are best carried out behind a shield. However, no major hazard appears to be present upon evaporating these ethers under reduced pressure from organometallic reaction mixtures.

---

[8] Explosions may also be caused by heating alkali-metals with halogenated hydrocarbons. Several serious accidents have resulted from explosions during the attempted purification of carbon tetrachloride by distillation over sodium. Therefore, solvents containing halogen atoms should *never* be distilled over sodium.

A final hazard in transition-metal organometallic chemistry is the isolation of organometallic transition-metal cations as the often very explosive perchlorate salts. The nonexplosive tetrafluoroborates and hexafluorophosphates[9] crystallize at least as well as the corresponding perchlorates and are recommended as safe substitutes.

---

[9] Tetrafluoroborate and hexafluorophosphate salts of silver and the alkali-metals and the corresponding free acids may be purchased at reasonable prices from Ozark-Mahoning Co., Tulsa, Oklahoma. In Great Britain, some of these salts may be obtained from Hopkin and Williams, Freshwater Road, Chadwell Heath, Essex and from R. N. Emanuel Ltd., 3/4 Leather Market, London, S.E. 1.

PART II

Preparations of Specific Transition-
Metal Organometallic Compounds

Introduction

In the pages that follow specific details for the preparations of about 60 specific transition-metal organometallic derivatives are given. These illustrate many of the general techniques discussed in Part I of this book and indicate the most efficient methods known to the author for obtaining important organometallic compounds. In a few cases (e.g. ferrocene and dibenzenechromium), excellent procedures have already been described in *Inorganic Syntheses* or *Organic Syntheses* obviating description in this book of the experimental details. In these cases, pertinent references are given. In other cases (e.g., triiron dodecacarbonyl, dicobalt octacarbonyl, and cyclopentadienylvanadium tetracarbonyl), procedures previously described in *Inorganic Syntheses* have subsequently been improved with respect to yield, convenience, and/or larger scale. These improved procedures are described in this book.

Although only one of the procedures in the following section (cyclopentadienylcycloheptatrienylvanadium) in its original form was discovered by the author, approximately two-thirds of the preparations have been run at least once either by the author or under his close supervision either at Harvard, du Pont, or the Mellon Institute. Preparations not checked by the author have been carried out in two or more laboratories although not necessarily in an identical manner. For these reasons little difficulty should be experienced in repeating the preparations in this book.

A. Biscyclopentadienylmetal Derivatives

1. Biscyclopentadienylvanadium

Biscyclopentadienylvanadium $(C_5H_5)_2V$ has been prepared by the action of sodium cyclopentadienide or cyclopentadienylmagnesium bromide on vanadium trichloride or vanadium tetrachloride in various solvents, such as tetrahydrofuran, dioxane, or ether-benzene,[1,2] or by lithium aluminum hydride reduction of $(C_5H_5)_2VCl_2$.[3] Probably the most convenient and efficient method is the action of sodium cyclopentadienide on vanadium trichloride in tetrahydrofuran solution.

Procedure:

$$VCl_3 + 3NaC_5H_5 \rightarrow (C_5H_5)_2V + 3NaCl + \{C_5H_5\}$$

The reaction is carried out under nitrogen in a 1-liter three-necked flask fitted with a motor stirrer, reflux condenser, nitrogen inlet, and pressure-equalized dropping funnel. After filling the system with nitrogen either by passing a rapid stream of nitrogen through the apparatus for several minutes or preferably by evacuating the apparatus and refilling with nitrogen, the flask is charged with 23 g. (1 mole) of sodium metal and ~300 ml. of dry toluene or xylene. This mixture is heated to the boiling point and the sodium is dispersed into fine sand-like granules by vigorous stirring at the boiling point.[4] After cooling to room temperature,

---

[1] E. O. Fischer and S. Vigoureux, *Chem. Ber.* **91**, 2205 (1958).

[2] G. Wilkinson, F. A. Cotton, and J. M. Birmingham, *J. Inorg. Nucl. Chem.* **2**, 95 (1956).

[3] G. Wilkinson, *Naturwissenschaften* **42**, 96 (1955).

[4] A commercial sodium dispersion in xylene may be used. Sodium dispersions in mineral oil are also available. The use of such sodium dispersions in mineral oil however results in a less pure product in cases in which the product is isolated by direct vacuum sublimation from the residue (as in the $(C_5H_5)_2V$ preparation) because of the tendency for the mineral oil to volatilize and contaminate the product during its sublimation.

the xylene is siphoned off and 500 ml. of tetrahydrofuran[5] is added. The suspension of sodium in tetrahydrofuran is treated dropwise with sufficient cyclopentadiene (freshly prepared by thermal dedimerization of commercial dicyclopentadiene) to dissolve all of the sodium forming a pink to dark-red-violet[6] solution of sodium cyclopentadienide. Generally, 98 to 123 ml. (79 to 99 g., 1.2 to 1.5 moles) of cyclopentadiene is necessary.

This resulting sodium cyclopentadienide solution is then treated with 47.2 g. (0.3 mole) of vanadium trichloride[7] at such a rate that the exothermic reaction does not become so vigorous that mechanical losses occur. The reaction mixture becomes dark purple. After the reaction has subsided, the reaction mixture is boiled under reflux for ~2 hr. to insure complete reaction.

After cooling to room temperature, the stirrer is removed from the flask while maintaining a stream of nitrogen and it is immediately replaced with a stopper. After checking all of the joints for tightness and regreasing any if necessary, the solvent is removed from the reaction mixture in a water-aspirator vacuum (~10–50 mm.) through an adapter equipped with a stopcock. If the residue is still sticky after all of the

---

[5] Tetrahydrofuran and 1,2-dimethoxyethane used for the preparation of sodium cyclopentadienide and similar reactive derivatives must be free of water and peroxides. The author purifies tetrahydrofuran and 1,2-dimethoxyethane by redistillation over lithium aluminum hydride (available from Metal Hydrides, Beverly, Massachusetts) immediately before use. Tetrahydrofuran may also be purified by distillation over sodium metal preferably in the presence of benzophenone to form the ketyl or by passage through a column of molecular sieves (Linde Air Products, Morristown, New Jersey).

[6] Sodium cyclopentadienide, a white extremely air-sensitive compound, gives colorless solutions in tetrahydrofuran in the absence of every trace of impurity including oxygen. However, it reacts with oxygen and other possible impurities extremely readily to form highly colored violet and brown materials. Therefore, colorless solutions of sodium cyclopentadienide are almost never obtained except when very dilute with even the most stringent protection against oxidation generally taken in preparative organometallic chemistry. Under the best conditions generally used, pink solutions of sodium cyclopentadienide are obtained; often solutions of sodium cyclopentadienide prepared carefully under nitrogen may be red-orange, red, or even red-violet. In practice, the yields of cyclopentadienyl derivatives prepared from sodium cyclopentadienide appear to be essentially the same whether the sodium cyclopentadienide solution is pink, dark red-violet, or any of the intermediate shades of red. A solution of sodium cyclopentadienide that has oxidized too extensively to give reliable results will be dark brown.

[7] Vanadium trichloride may be obtained commercially in the United States (e.g., Anderson Chemical Company, Weston, Michigan). It may be prepared by boiling vanadium pentoxide with disulfur dichloride (S_2Cl_2) [G. Brauer, In "Handbuch der Präparativen Anorganischen Chemie" (G. Brauer, ed.), p. 1099. Ferdinand Enke Verlag, Stuttgart, 1962].

solvent has been removed in the water-aspirator vacuum, the flask is closed off with the stopcock; the evacuated flask is transferred to an oil pump vacuum, and the remaining volatile materials such as xylene and dicyclopentadiene (formed by dimerization of some of the cyclopentadiene) are removed at 1.0–0.1 mm.

When the residue is dry, nitrogen is admitted to the evacuated flask, and the very air-sensitive residue is transferred under nitrogen to a sublimation apparatus.[8] Since the final product, biscyclopentadienylvanadium, is rather air-sensitive, provision must be made for removal of the product without exposure to air. This may be done by having a gloved box or polyethylene bag available (page 55) which may be filled with pure oxygen-free nitrogen and which can accommodate the sublimer after the sublimation is complete. Alternatively, a sublimer designed to permit removal of the sublimate into a Schlenk tube completely under nitrogen (page 26) may be used. The residue is sublimed at temperatures up to 200° at ~0.1 mm. to give purple air-sensitive crystals of $(C_5H_5)_2V$ in ~50% yield. The sublimate is removed into a nitrogen-filled Schlenk tube or other suitable air-free container for storage.

Biscyclopentadienylvanadium forms purple crystals that are soluble in organic solvents and that oxidize rapidly in air occasionally with deflagration. Under nitrogen, it melts at 167–168°. It reacts with carbon monoxide under pressure to form $C_5H_5V(CO)_4$[9] and with vanadium hexacarbonyl and carbon monoxide at atmospheric pressure to form the salt $[(C_5H_5)_2V(CO)_2][V(CO)_6]$.[10]

2. Biscyclopentadienylchromium

Like the vanadium derivative that has been discussed, biscyclopentadienylchromium, $(C_5H_5)_2Cr$, has been prepared by the action of sodium cyclopentadienide or cyclopentadienylmagnesium bromide on anhydrous chromium(III) chloride in tetrahydrofuran or ether-benzene, respectively.[2,11] It is also obtained in smaller quantities from the thermal decomposition of $[Cr(NH_3)_6](C_5H_5)_3$[12] or by the action of cyclopentadiene on chromium hexacarbonyl at 280–350°.[13] Again, the preferred prepara-

[8] If a sufficiently large sublimation apparatus is not available, the sublimation may be carried out in several portions in a smaller sublimer avoiding, of course, exposure of either the crude residue or the sublimate to air.

[9] E. O. Fischer and S. Vigoureux, *Chem. Ber.* **91**, 2205 (1958).

[10] F. Calderazzo and S. Bacciarelli, *Inorg. Chem.* **2**, 721 (1963).

[11] E. O. Fischer, W. Hafner, and H. O. Stahl, *Z. Anorg. Allgem. Chem.*, **282**, 47 (1955).

[12] E. O. Fischer and W. Hafner, *Z. Naturforsch.*, **8b**, 444 (1953).

[13] G. Wilkinson, *J. Am. Chem. Soc.* **76**, 209 (1954).

tion of $(C_5H_5)_2Cr$ is the reaction between sodium cyclopentadienide and chromium(III) chloride in tetrahydrofuran.

Procedure:

$$CrCl_3 + 3NaC_5H_5 \rightarrow (C_5H_5)_2Cr + 3NaCl + \{C_5H_5\}$$

The procedure for preparing $(C_5H_5)_2V$ from vanadium(III) chloride and sodium cyclopentadienide in tetrahydrofuran may be adapted for the preparation of $(C_5H_5)_2Cr$ by substituting an equivalent quantity of *anhydrous* chromium(III) chloride for the vanadium(III) chloride. Even the purification of the product by sublimation may be carried out analogously. Biscyclopentadienylchromium(II) is at least as air-sensitive as biscyclopentadienylvanadium(II) which necessitates the same precautions against destruction of the product by oxidation.

Biscyclopentadienylchromium forms dark-red crystals that also oxidize rapidly in air, occasionally with ignition. Under nitrogen, it melts at 173°. On treatment with a mixture of carbon monoxide and hydrogen under pressure, it forms $C_5H_5Cr(CO)_3H$, $C_5H_5Cr(CO)_2C_5H_7$ and/or $Cr(CO)_6$ depending upon the reaction conditions.[11,14] With carbon monoxide alone under pressure at various temperatures, $[(C_5H_5)_2Cr]$ $[C_5H_5Cr(CO)_3]$ and $[C_5H_5Cr(CO)_3]_2$ have been obtained.[11] Allyl iodide oxidizes $(C_5H_5)_2Cr$ to the very air-sensitive ionic derivative $[(C_5H_5)_2Cr]I$.[15] A limited quantity of oxygen reacts with $(C_5H_5)_2Cr$ to form the air-sensitive tetrameric oxide $[C_5H_5CrO]_4$.[16]

3. Manganese(II) Cyclopentadienide

Manganese(II) cyclopentadienide has been prepared by the reaction between sodium cyclopentadienide and various anhydrous manganese halides in tetrahydrofuran or 1,2-dimethoxyethane.[2] One of the best methods uses the reaction between sodium cyclopentadienide and an especially reactive manganese(II) bromide prepared *in situ* from manganese metal and bromine in 1,2-dimethoxyethane.[2]

Procedure:

$$MnCl_2 + 2NaC_5H_5 \rightarrow (C_5H_5)_2Mn + 2NaCl$$

The manganese bromide is prepared under nitrogen in a 2-liter three-necked flask fitted with a motor stirrer, reflux condenser, nitrogen inlet, and pressure-equalized dropping funnel. After filling the system with

[14] E. O. Fischer and K. Ulm, *Chem. Ber.* 94, 2413 (1961).
[15] E. O. Fischer and K. Ulm, *Chem. Ber.* 95, 692 (1962).
[16] E. O. Fischer, K. Ulm, and H. P. Fritz, *Chem. Ber.* 93, 2167 (1960).

nitrogen, the flask is charged with 500 ml. of 1,2-dimethoxyethane[17] and 27.5 g. (0.5 mole) of manganese powder. From the dropping funnel, 27.3 ml. (80.0 g., 0.5 mole as Br_2) of undiluted liquid bromine is added dropwise to form a white pasty suspension of manganese(II) bromide (or possibly an etherate) in the 1,2-dimethoxyethane.

A separate 1-liter three-necked flask fitted with a motor stirrer, reflux condenser, nitrogen inlet, and pressure-equalized dropping funnel is used for the preparation of a solution of 1 mole of sodium cyclopentadienide in 500 ml. of 1,2-dimethoxyethane or tetrahydrofuran. The technique and precautions for preparing this sodium cyclopentadienide solution or suspension[18] are completely analogous to those described in the preparation of $(C_5H_5)_2V$.

After the sodium cyclopentadienide and the manganese(II) bromide have both been prepared, the sodium cyclopentadienide solution or suspension is added to the manganese(II) bromide suspension. Since sodium cyclopentadienide solutions are very air-sensitive (they turn brown rapidly), it is advisable to have a rapid stream of nitrogen passing through both flasks while adding the sodium cyclopentadienide to the manganese(II) bromide. After the addition of the sodium cyclopentadienide is complete, the tan reaction mixture is boiled under reflux for at least 3 hr. to insure complete reaction. The reaction mixture is then allowed to cool to room temperature and the stirrer is replaced with a stopper. After making sure all of the joints are tight, the solvent is removed in a water-aspirator vacuum (~10–50 mm.). If necessary, the residue is dried further in an oil-pump vacuum (~0.1–1 mm.). Finally, nitrogen is admitted to the evacuated flask and the very air-sensitive residue is transferred under nitrogen into a large sublimation apparatus.[8] The produce is driven out of the residue by sublimation at 100–150°/0.1 mm. When sublimation is complete, the sublimer is cooled, nitrogen is admitted, and the sublimate is removed into a nitrogen-filled Schlenk tube or other suitable air-free container for storage. The brown crystals of manganese(II) cyclopentadienide are thus obtained in yields up to 70%.

Manganese(II) cyclopentadienide forms dark brown crystals not only very sensitive to air but also hydrolyzed instantly by water with a characteristic crackling sound. On heating to 158° under nitrogen, the

---

[17] Tetrahydrofuran cannot be used as a solvent for bromination reactions since it reacts vigorously with bromine.

[18] Sodium cyclopentadienide, although very soluble in tetrahydrofuran, possesses only a limited solubility in 1,2-dimethoxyethane. Thus, when sodium cyclopentadienide is prepared in 1,2-dimethoxyethane solution, a suspension of white crystals is obtained unless the sodium cyclopentadienide solution is very dilute.

originally brown solid becomes pale pink and melts on further heating to 173°. Unlike the covalent neutral biscyclopentadienyl derivatives of neighboring transition elements such as vanadium, chromium, iron, cobalt, and nickel, manganese(II) cyclopentadienide clearly has an ionic structure. Thus, it gives moderately conducting solutions in polar solvents and is less soluble in nonpolar organic solvents such as various hydrocarbons than the covalent biscyclopentadienyl derivatives of the other metals. It appears to undergo many of the reactions of other ionic cyclopentadienides such as those of sodium and magnesium. Its unusual magnetic properties have been of some interest.[2] It reacts with carbon monoxide to form the very stable cyclopentadienylmanganese tricarbonyl.[19]

4. Biscyclopentadienyliron (Ferrocene)

A variety of satisfactory procedures for the preparation of ferrocene $(C_5H_5)_2Fe$, are now known. These include the following methods: (a) reactions of sodium cyclopentadienide or cyclopentadienylmagnesium bromide with ferrous or ferric chloride[2,20]; (b) reactions of cyclopentadiene with iron pentacarbonyl,[21] iron(II) oxalate,[22] iron(II) oxide,[23] or even appropriately prepared iron metal[24] at elevated temperatures; (c) treatment of cyclopentadiene with mercuric chloride followed by treatment of the resulting mercury derivative with iron metal[25]; and (d) treatment of a specially prepared iron(II) chloride with cyclopentadiene and diethylamine.[26] In the United States, ferrocene is available commercially at sufficiently low prices so that most laboratory workers will prefer to purchase it rather than prepare it themselves.

Recently, detailed directions have been published for the preparation of ferrocene by either the reaction between iron(II) chloride and sodium cyclopentadienide or by the reaction between iron(II) chloride, diethylamine, and cyclopentadiene.[26] Therefore, detailed directions for the preparation of ferrocene are not included in this book.

Ferrocene forms volatile, extremely stable, orange crystals, m.p. 173–174°, that are soluble in organic solvents but insoluble in water. It has

---

[19] E. O. Fischer and R. Jira, Z. Naturforsch. **9b**, 618 (1954); T. S. Piper, F. A. Cotton, and G. Wilkinson, J. Inorg. Nucl. Chem. **1**, 165 (1955).

[20] T. J. Kealy and P. L. Pauson, Nature **168**, 1039 (1951).

[21] G. Wilkinson, P. L. Pauson, and F. A. Cotton, J. Am. Chem. Soc. **76**, 1970 (1954).

[22] R. Riemschneider and D. Helm, Z. Naturforsch. **14b**, 811 (1959).

[23] British Patents 737,780, 744,450, 764,058, and 767,298 and U. S. Patent 2,804,468.

[24] S. A. Miller, J. A. Tebboth, and J. F. Tremaine, J. Chem. Soc. 632 (1952).

[25] K. Issleib and A. Brack, Z. Naturforsch. **11b**, 420 (1956).

[26] G. Wilkinson, Org. Syn. **36**, 31 (1956).

been used as a starting material in the preparation of hundreds of substituted ferrocene derivatives.

5. Biscyclopentadienylruthenium (Ruthenocene)

Ruthenocene, $(C_5H_5)_2Ru$, has been prepared by the reaction of sodium cyclopentadienide with anhydrous ruthenium chlorides. Since a satisfactory procedure has recently been given in detail for the preparation of ruthenocene from sodium cyclopentadienide and a specially prepared anhydrous ruthenium(II) chloride,[27] further details on the preparation of ruthenocene will not be given here.

6. Biscyclopentadienylcobalt (Cobaltocene)

Cobaltocene, $(C_5H_5)_2Co$, has been prepared by reaction between sodium cyclopentadienide and cobalt(II) chloride or hexammine cobalt(II) chloride in tetrahydrofuran,[2,28] by reaction between alkali-metal cyclopentadienides and cobalt(II) thiocyanate in liquid ammonia,[29] and by lithium aluminum hydride reduction of the cation $[(C_5H_5)_2Co]^+$.[30] A benzene solution of cobaltocene is available commercially in the United States (Arapahoe Chemicals, Inc., Boulder, Colorado). The preparation of cobaltocene from anhydrous cobalt(II) chloride and sodium cyclopentadienide in tetrahydrofuran follows.

Procedure:

$$CoCl_2 + 2NaC_5H_5 \rightarrow (C_5H_5)_2Co + 2NaCl$$

A solution of 1 mole of sodium cyclopentadienide in ~500 ml. of tetrahydrofuran[5] is prepared using the same procedure, quantities, and precautions that were given for the preparation of $(C_5H_5)_2V$. This sodium cyclopentadienide solution is treated with 65 g. (0.5 mole) of anhydrous cobalt(II) chloride[31]; the reaction mixture becomes dark purple in an exothermic reaction. After boiling under reflux for at least 2 hr. to insure complete reaction, the reaction mixture is allowed to cool to room temperature. After checking all of the joints for tightness and replacing the stirrer with a stopper, the solvent is removed from the reac-

---

[27] D. E. Bublitz, W. E. McEwen, and J. Kleinberg, *Org. Syn.* **41**, 96 (1961).

[28] J. F. Cordes, *Chem. Ber.* **95**, 3084 (1962).

[29] E. O. Fischer and R. Jira, *Z. Naturforsch.* **8b**, 327 (1953).

[30] G. Wilkinson, *Naturwissenschaften* **42**, 96 (1955).

[31] Anhydrous cobalt(II) chloride may be obtained by heating hydrated cobalt(II) chloride at ~160°/0.1 mm. until no more water is lost. The cobalt(II) chloride used for this reaction should be pure blue. A pinkish tinge signifies that the cobalt(II) chloride is not completely anhydrous indicating the need for further heating to remove remaining water.

tion mixture in a water-aspirator vacuum ($\sim$10–50 mm.) through an adapter equipped with a stopcock. If the residue is still sticky after all of the solvent has been removed in the water-aspirator vacuum, the flask is closed off with the stopcock, the evacuated flask is transferred to an oil-pump vacuum, and any remaining volatile materials such as xylene and dicyclopentadiene are removed at 1.0–0.1 mm. When the residue is dry, nitrogen is admitted to the evacuated flask, and the air-sensitive residue is transferred under nitrogen to a large sublimation apparatus.[8] The cobaltocene is driven from the residue as dark-violet crystals by sublimation at 60–200°/0.1 mm. After sublimation is complete, the sublimer is allowed to cool to room temperature and nitrogen is admitted. The sublimate is then removed to give purple crystals of cobaltocene in yields up to $\sim$90%. Cobaltocene is normally very air-sensitive and is best handled in the absence of air. However, material obtained in relatively large crystals such as by the sublimation procedure suggested previously is reported to be stable for brief periods in air.[28]

If the commercial benzene solution of cobaltocene is available, pure solid cobaltocene may be obtained from it by removal of the benzene in a water-aspirator vacuum and sublimation of the residue at $\sim$0.1 mm.

Cobaltocene forms purple-black air-sensitive crystals. It is readily oxidized to the very stable $[(C_5H_5)_2Co]^+$ cation. It reacts with carbon monoxide to form $C_5H_5Co(CO)_2$.[32]

7. Biscyclopentadienylnickel (Nickelocene)

Nickelocene, $(C_5H_5)_2Ni$, may be obtained from an alkali-metal cyclopentadienide and $[Ni(NH_3)_6](SCN)_2$ in liquid ammonia[33] or t-butanol[34] or from cyclopentadienylmagnesium bromide and nickel(II) acetylacetonate in a mixture of diethyl ether and benzene.[35] It is not obtained in appreciable quantities by the reaction between sodium cyclopentadienide and anhydrous nickel(II) chloride in tetrahydrofuran, but it may be obtained if hexamminenickel(II) chloride[28] or a specially prepared nickel(II) bromide (from nickel powder and bromine in 1,2-dimethoxyethane) is substituted for the anhydrous nickel(II) chloride. The following method involving the reaction between a specially prepared nickel(II) bromide, diethylamine, and cyclopentadiene is an illustration of the "amine" method of making biscyclopentadienylmetal derivatives.

[32] E. O. Fischer and R. Jira, Z. Naturforsch. **10b**, 355 (1955).
[33] E. O. Fischer and R. Jira, Z. Naturforsch. **8b**, 217 (1953).
[34] E. O. Fischer and H. Grubert, Z. Anorg. Allgem. Chem. **286**, 237 (1956).
[35] G. Wilkinson, P. L. Pauson, J. M. Birmingham, and F. A. Cotton, J. Am. Chem. Soc. **75**, 1011 (1953).

Procedure:

(1) $Ni + Br_2 \rightarrow NiBr_2$

(2) $NiBr_2 + 2(C_2H_5)_2NH + 2C_5H_6 \rightarrow (C_5H_5)_2Ni + 2[(C_2H_5)_2NH_2]Br$

The reaction is carried out in a 1-liter three-necked flask fitted with a motor stirrer, reflux condenser, nitrogen inlet, and pressure-equalized dropping funnel. After filling the system with nitrogen, the flask is charged with 500 ml. of 1,2-dimethoxyethane[17] and 29.4 g. (0.5 mole) of nickel powder. From the dropping funnel, 27.3 ml. (80.0 g., 0.5 mole as Br₂) of undiluted liquid bromine is added dropwise to form a yellow etherate of nickel(II) bromide[36] in an exothermic reaction. After the formation of nickel(II) bromide is complete[37] and the reaction mixture has cooled back to room temperature, the solvent is removed in a water-aspirator vacuum leaving a yellow solid residue. Nitrogen is admitted to this residue, and 400 ml. of diethylamine is added. A blue solution is obtained with slight heat evolution. The reaction mixture is then treated dropwise with 98 ml. (79 g., 1.2 mole) of freshly prepared cyclopentadiene; the reaction mixture becomes somewhat more greenish. After stirring overnight at room temperature, the solvent is removed from the reaction mixture in a water-aspirator vacuum leaving a greenish solid residue of a mixture of diethylammonium chloride and nickelocene. Nitrogen is admitted, and the solid residue is transferred to a thimble of a large Soxhlet extraction apparatus. A continuous extraction with boiling hexane is carried out under a blanket of nitrogen until all of the green material is extracted from the residue. By this time, large, dark-green crystals of nickelocene will have begun to separate from the dark-green hexane extract. When the extraction is completed, the hexane extract is allowed to cool to room temperature. Additional quantities of nickelocene crystallize. These large crystals of nickelocene are removed by filtration and dried briefly on the filter.[38] Although this material is sufficiently pure

---

[36] This yellow compound apparently $NiBr_2 \cdot 2C_2H_4(OCH_3)_2$ is a useful reactive form of nickel bromide for a variety of reactions. The coordinated molecules of 1,2-dimethoxyethane are readily replaced by other ligands including water. Anhydrous nickel halides obtained from the corresponding hydrated nickel halides by heating in a vacuum or by treatment with thionyl chloride are too inert and too insoluble in organic solvents for satisfactory results in the preparation of nickelocene.

[37] When the formation of nickel(II) bromide is complete, the reaction mixture should be a pure yellow with no red color caused by unchanged bromine. Sometimes, the yellow solid product will precipitate from the solution at this stage.

[38] Additional less pure nickelocene may be precipitated by evaporating the filtrate in a water-aspirator vacuum and cooling the filtrate in a −78° bath. Solutions of nickelocene are rather air-sensitive and this filtrate should therefore be kept under nitrogen if additional nickelocene is later to be isolated from it.

for many purposes, a purer material may be obtained by sublimation of this material at 100°/0.1 mm. Yields of up to 80% have been obtained in this reaction.

Nickelocene forms dark-green crystals, m.p. 173–174°. In the solid state, it oxidizes slowly in air over a period of days. It can thus be handled in air, but it must be stored for longer periods in the absence of air. Solutions are more air-sensitive and must therefore be handled in an inert atmosphere. Nickelocene may be oxidized to the rather unstable yellow-orange cation $[(C_5H_5)_2Ni]^+$. Reduction of nickelocene with sodium amalgam in methanol gives the red volatile complex C_5H_5-NiC_5H_7.[39] Of particular value is the reaction between nickelocene and nickel tetracarbonyl in hydrocarbon solvents which gives the cyclopentadienylnickel carbonyl derivatives $[C_5H_5NiCO]_2$ or $(C_5H_5)_3Ni_3(CO)_2$ depending upon the reaction conditions; this is, at present, the most convenient synthesis of these compounds.[40]

8. Bisindenyliron (*sym*-Dibenzoferrocene)

Bisindenyliron, $(C_9H_7)_2Fe$, has been prepared by the treatment of iron(III) or iron(II) chloride with indenylmagnesium halides or an alkali-metal indenide.[41] Perhaps the most convenient and efficient method is the following reaction between iron(II) chloride and sodium indenide in tetrahydrofuran.

Procedure:

$$(1) \quad 2FeCl_3 + Fe \rightarrow 3FeCl_2$$
$$(2) \quad 2C_9H_8 + 2Na \rightarrow 2C_9H_7Na + H_2\uparrow$$
$$(3) \quad FeCl_2 + 2C_9H_7Na \rightarrow (C_9H_7)_2Fe + 2NaCl$$

A suspension of iron(II) chloride in tetrahydrofuran is prepared under nitrogen in a 1-liter three-necked flask fitted with a nitrogen inlet, reflux condenser, and motor stirrer. After filling with nitrogen, the flask is charged with 300 ml. of tetrahydrofuran,[5] 10.85 g. (0.067 mole) of commercial anhydrous iron(III) chloride,[42] and 1.85 g. (0.033 mole) of iron

---

[39] A. H. Filbey, J. C. Wollensak, and K. A. Keblys, *Abstr. 138th Meeting Am. Chem. Soc., New York* p. 54-P (1960).

[40] E. O. Fischer and C. Palm, *Chem. Ber.* **91**, 1725 (1958).

[41] E. O. Fischer and D. Seus, *Z. Naturforsch.* **8b**, 694 (1953); P. L. Pauson and G. Wilkinson, *J. Am. Chem. Soc.* **76**, 2024 (1954).

[42] Anhydrous iron(III) chloride is a *black* crystalline solid. Material which is brown has become hydrated and possibly partially hydrolyzed, and, therefore, is not satisfactory for this preparation. Suitable anhydrous iron(III) chloride is readily and inexpensively obtained from most general distributors of laboratory chemicals.

powder. The reaction mixture is refluxed with stirring for at least 4 hours to form a grayish suspension of iron(II) chloride.

Meanwhile, a solution of sodium indenide is prepared in a second 1-liter three-necked flask fitted with a nitrogen inlet, reflux condenser, motor stirrer, and pressure-equalized dropping funnel. After filling with nitrogen, the flask is charged with 6.2 g. (0.27 mole) of finely divided sodium metal and 300 ml. of redistilled tetrahydrofuran.[5] The sodium may be added in the form of a dispersion in mineral oil or an aromatic hydrocarbon such as toluene or xylene.[43] Alternatively, pieces of sodium metal may be suspended in xylene and finally dispersed by rapid stirring at the boiling point of the xylene. In this case, as much of the xylene as possible is removed after dispersing the sodium before adding the tetrahydrofuran and proceeding further with the preparation.

This suspension of sodium in tetrahydrofuran is treated with 31.0 g. (0.267 mole) of indene[44] from the dropping funnel. The reaction is not particularly vigorous, and the indene can therefore be added relatively rapidly. After all of the indene has been added, the reaction mixture is boiled under reflux with stirring until all the sodium has disappeared to form a yellow solution of sodium indenide.[45,46]

After formation is complete, the sodium indenide solution is cooled to room temperature and then poured under nitrogen[46] into a large pressure-equalized dropping funnel. It is then added from this dropping funnel to the iron(II) chloride suspension in a thin stream, the reaction mixture turning black. To insure complete reaction, the reaction mixture is boiled under reflux for 16 hr.

After the reaction period is over, the reaction mixture is allowed to cool to room temperature, and the solvent is removed from the reaction mixture in a water-aspirator vacuum (10–50 mm.). Nitrogen is then admitted, and the residue is transferred to the thimble of a large Soxhlet extraction apparatus.[47] The product is extracted continuously with pen-

---

[43] The sodium dispersion may be commercially available.

[44] When pure, indene is a colorless liquid. However, on standing indene gradually darkens due to oxidation and/or polymerization. If the history of the indene used for this experiment is known and if its color is no deeper than yellow, redistillation prior to use is unnecessary. However, if the history of the indene is unknown and especially if it has become brown, redistillation of the indene in a water-aspirator vacuum (b.p. 62°/10 mm.) is recommended prior to conversion into sodium indenide.

[45] Crystals may sometimes separate from the sodium indenide solution.

[46] The yellow solution of sodium indenide is very air-sensitive and rapidly becomes black on exposure to air. When pouring solutions of sodium indenide from one flask to another, a rapid stream of nitrogen should pass through both containers.

[47] If an insufficiently large Soxhlet apparatus is available, the extraction may be

tane.[48] The pentane vapors protect the compound sufficiently from oxidation so that a nitrogen atmosphere is not needed. In order to prevent overheating, the pentane is heated by means of an oil or water bath at the minimum temperature necessary for reflux of the pentane at a reasonable rate.

The extraction of the bisindenyliron from the crude reaction product is allowed to proceed in this manner until the fresh extracts are no longer colored (~40 hr.). At this stage, the pentane extract of the product is black. The product is caused to precipitate from the extract by cooling in a −78° bath until crystallization appears to be complete. The black crystals of crude bisindenyliron are then filtered and dried in a vacuum to give 7.5 g. (26.5% yield) of crude bisindenyliron.

In order to obtain a purer sample of bisindenyliron, the crude material may be sublimed at 130°/0.25 mm. An 80% recovery of glistening black crystalline $(C_9H_7)_2Fe$ is obtained.

Bisindenyliron forms black volatile crystals, m.p. 184–185°, that are soluble in organic solvents and give violet-black solutions that are gradually oxidized by air to give brown iron(III) oxide. Its proton n.m.r. spectrum (CS_2 solution) exhibits resonances at 3.20 τ (singlet), 5.54 τ (doublet, J = 2.5 cps), and 6.08 τ (triplet, J = 2.5 cps) of relative intensities 4:2:1.[49] Bisindenyliron may be readily hydrogenated to give the orange liquid bis(tetrahydroindenyl)iron $(C_9H_{11})_2Fe$.[50]

9. Biscyclopentadienylmetal Dichlorides

The four compounds $(C_5H_5)_2MCl_2$ (M = Ti, V, Zr, Hf) have been obtained by the action of sodium cyclopentadienide or cyclopentadienylmagnesium *chloride* (from butylmagnesium chloride and cyclopentadiene) on the metal tetrahalide[51–53] in various solvents. The procedure

---

carried out in several portions, storing the air-sensitive residue under nitrogen until after it has been extracted.

[48] Attempts to isolate bisindenyliron by direct sublimation out of the residue as in the preparation of the $(C_5H_5)M$ compounds that have been described were much less satisfactory than pentane extraction. Volatile liquid materials, apparently mainly indene, were obtained which contaminated the sublimate and made the sublimation relatively difficult.

[49] R. B. King and M. B. Bisnette, *Inorg. Chem.* 3, 796 (1964).
[50] E. O. Fischer and D. Seus, *Z. Naturforsch*, 9b, 386 (1954).
[51] G. Wilkinson and J. M. Birmingham, *J. Amer. Chem. Soc.* 76, 4281 (1954); G. Wilkinson, P. L. Pauson, J. M. Birmingham and F. A. Cotton, *J. Amer. Chem. Soc.* 75, 1011 (1953).
[52] L. Summers, R. H. Uloth, and A. Holmes, *J. Am. Chem. Soc.* 77, 3604 (1955).
[53] M. A. Lynch, Jr., and J. C. Brantley, British Patent 785,760.

given here is generally applicable for the preparation of all four compounds with only very minor modifications.

Procedure:

$$MCl_4 + 2NaC_5H_5 \rightarrow (C_5H_5)_2MCl_2 + 2NaCl \quad (M = Ti, Zr, Hf, V)$$

A solution of sodium cyclopentadienide in 1,2-dimethoxyethane[54] is prepared under nitrogen in a 2-liter three-necked flask fitted with a motor stirrer, reflux condenser, nitrogen inlet, and pressure-equalized dropping funnel. After filling with nitrogen, the flask is charged with 23 g. (1 mole) of finely divided sodium metal (see $(C_9H_7)_2Fe$ preparation), 1000 ml. of 1,2-dimethoxyethane, and 98 to 123 ml. (79 to 99 g., 1.2 to 1.5 mole) of freshly prepared cyclopentadiene added dropwise to convert the grayish sodium to a pink to dark-red-violet[6] solution of sodium cyclopentadienide containing suspended white crystals.

A second 2-liter three-necked flask is likewise fitted with a motor stirrer, reflux condenser, nitrogen inlet, and a large pressure-equalized dropping funnel. After filling with nitrogen, this flask is charged with 200 ml. of dry benzene[55] and 0.5 mole of the anhydrous tetrachloride of titanium, vanadium, zirconium, or hafnium.[56] The large dropping funnel is charged under nitrogen with the sodium cyclopentadienide suspension which is then added gradually with stirring to the metal tetrachloride solution or suspension.[57] A very exothermic reaction occurs which can become too vigorous if the sodium cyclopentadienide is added too rapidly. When all of the sodium cyclopentadienide has been added, the reaction mixture, which becomes approximately the color of the $(C_5H_5)_2MCl_2$ derivative, is then stirred for at least 1 hr. after it cools back to room temperature to insure complete reaction. The solvent is then removed from the reaction mixture in a water-aspirator vacuum (10–50 mm.).

After admitting nitrogen to the evacuated flask, the residue is transferred to the thimble of a large Soxhlet extraction apparatus. The residue is extracted continuously with boiling chloroform ($\sim$500 ml.) until no

---

[54] 1,2-Dimethoxyethane is more resistant than tetrahydrofuran to cleavage by the rather reactive metal tetrahalides.

[55] Reagent grade benzene may be used. It may be treated with Linde "molecular sieves" to insure dryness.

[56] These halides may either be purchased commercially or prepared either by treatment of the metal with chlorine at elevated temperatures or chlorination of the oxide with a chlorocarbon such as carbon tetrachloride.

[57] This "inverse" order of addition is especially important in the preparation of the titanium or vanadium derivatives. Reduction to $(C_5H_5)_3Ti$ or $(C_5H_5)_2V$ by the excess of sodium cyclopentadienide present will occur if the "normal" addition of the metal tetrachloride to the sodium cyclopentadienide is used.

further product is extracted.[58] In the case of the red $(C_5H_5)_2TiCl_2$ and the green $(C_5H_5)_2VCl_2$, the color of the extracts clearly indicate this point. Generally, by the time the extraction is complete, crystals of the $(C_5H_5)_2MCl_2$ will have formed in abundant quantity in the chloroform solution in the flask.

Upon cooling the chloroform extract to room temperature and allowing it to stand at room temperature for several hours, most of the $(C_5H_5)_2MCl_2$ derivative present will crystallize out and may be removed by filtration and washed with pentane or diethyl ether. Additional, less pure product may be obtained by evaporating the chloroform filtrate in a water-aspirator vacuum. The yields in these preparations should be greater than 50%.

Small, very pure samples of the titanium, zirconium, and hafnium derivatives may be obtained by sublimation at 160°/0.1 mm.

Biscyclopentadienyltitanium dichloride is a red solid, m.p. 289–291°, sparingly but noticeably soluble in nonpolar organic solvents, but somewhat more soluble in polar organic solvents. Its proton n.m.r. spectrum exhibits a single sharp resonance at 3.45 τ due to the ten equivalent cyclopentadienyl protons. It has been used as a starting material for the preparation of some alkyl and aryl derivatives of general formula $(C_5H_5)_2TiR_2$,[52,59] for the preparation of $(C_5H_5)_3Ti$,[60] for the preparation of the only known carbonyl derivative of titanium $(C_5H_5)_2Ti(CO)_2$,[61] and for the preparation of $C_5H_5TiCl_3$.[62a,b] It has been of interest as a component in certain Ziegler-Natta catalyst systems. It has been offered commercially by several companies in the United States.

The white zirconium and hafnium analogs $(C_5H_5)_2ZrCl_2$ and $(C_5H_5)_2HfCl_2$ have been investigated in much less detail.

Biscyclopentadienylvanadium dichloride is a green solid similar in most other properties to the titanium derivative. Strong reducing agents convert it to derivatives of trivalent vanadium and finally to $(C_5H_5)_2V$.

---

[58] It has been suggested[51] that this chloroform extraction be carried out in a hydrogen chloride atmosphere to minimize hydrolysis of the products. The author's experience indicates that this precaution is unnecessary for the preparations of the $(C_5H_5)_2MCl_2$ compounds described in this book. However, it would appear desirable to use the precaution of a hydrogen chloride atmosphere during the preparation of $(C_5H_5)_2NbCl_3$ which is more sensitive to hydrolysis.[51] In the cases of the preparation of the $(C_5H_5)_2MCl_2$ compounds described in this book, the use of a nitrogen atmosphere is not necessary during the chloroform extraction step.

[59] T. S. Piper and G. Wilkinson, *J. Inorg. Nucl. Chem.* **3**, 104 (1956).

[60] E. O. Fischer and A. Löchner, *Z. Naturforsch.* **15b**, 266 (1960).

[61] J. G. Murray, *J. Am. Chem. Soc.* **83**, 1287 (1961).

[62a] C. L. Sloan and W. A. Barber, *J. Am. Chem. Soc.* **81**, 1364 (1959).

[62b] R. D. Gorsich, *J. Am. Chem. Soc.* **82**, 4211 (1960).

A black phenyl derivative $(C_5H_5)_2VC_6H_5$ has been obtained by treatment of $(C_5H_5)_2VCl_2$ with phenyllithium.[63]

10. Cyclopentadienyltitanium Trichloride

Cyclopentadienyltitanium trichloride has been obtained by the reaction between titanium tetrachloride and biscyclopentadienyltitanium dichloride,[62b] by the cleavage of one of the cyclopentadienyl rings of biscyclopentadienyltitanium chloride with chlorine,[62b] and by the reaction between titanium tetrachloride and biscyclopentadienylmagnesium.[62a] The most convenient and efficient method for preparing cyclopentadienyltitanium trichloride appears to be the reaction between titanium tetrachloride and biscyclopentadienyltitanium dichloride in xylene solution.[62b]

Procedure:

$$(C_5H_5)_2TiCl_2 + TiCl_4 \xrightarrow{\Delta} 2C_5H_5TiCl_3$$

A mixture of 12.0 g. (0.048 mole) of biscyclopentadienyltitanium dichloride, 25.1 g. (0.136 mole) of titanium tetrachloride, and 90 ml. of dry xylene is heated at the boiling point ($\sim140°$) for 2½ hr. The reaction mixture is then cooled to room temperature, and yellow crystals of the product separate. These are filtered under dry nitrogen,[64] washed with dry hexane, and dried briefly under nitrogen.

The crude product is purified by recrystallization from benzene. For this, it is dissolved in a minimum of boiling benzene.[64] Charcoal is added to the solution which is then filtered while hot. The filtrate is then concentrated at the boiling point in a dry atmosphere[64] until crystals of the product begin to deposit. The solution is then allowed to cool slowly to room temperature and is finally placed in an ice bath. The product is filtered in a dry atmosphere[64] and dried in a vacuum to give 12.6 g. (60% yield) of cyclopentadienyltitanium trichloride, m.p. 208–211°. Additional crops of less pure product (~1.7 g.) may be obtained by concentrating the filtrate.

Cyclopentadienyltitanium trichloride forms yellow crystals which are very sensitive to hydrolysis. It reacts with methyllithium to form the rather unstable pyrophoric trimethyl derivative $C_5H_5Ti(CH_3)_3$.[65]

---

[63] H. J. de L. Meijer, M. J. Janssen, and G. J. M. van der Kerk, *Chem. Ind.* (*London*) 119 (1960).

[64] Cyclopentadienyltitanium trichloride, although very stable to oxidation, is sensitive to hydrolysis. Therefore, all solvents used in this preparation must be dry and the product must be handled in a dry atmosphere.

[65] U. Giannini and S. Cesca, *Tetrahedron Letters* No. 14, 19 (1960).

11. Biscyclopentadienylmetal Dihydrides

The hydrides $(C_5H_5)_2MH_2$ (M = Mo and W) are obtained by treatment of the halides $MoCl_5$ or WCl_6 with excess sodium cyclopentadienide in tetrahydrofuran or 1,2-dimethoxyethane solution[66,67] preferably in the presence of sodium borohydride as a source of hydride.[66]

Procedure:

(A) $WCl_6 + 4NaC_5H_5 + 2NaBH_4 \rightarrow (C_5H_5)_2WH_2 + 6NaCl + 2\{C_5H_5\cdot\} + B_2H_6$

(B) $MoCl_5 + 3NaC_5H_5 + 2NaBH_4 \rightarrow (C_5H_5)_2MoH_2 + 5NaCl + \{C_5H_5\cdot\} + B_2H_6$

A solution of 0.6 mole of sodium cyclopentadienide in 250 ml. of tetrahydrofuran[5] is prepared by a procedure completely analogous to the procedure that was given for the preparation of biscyclopentadienyl-vanadium. After adding 10 g. (0.263 mole) of sodium borohydride,[68] the reaction mixture is cooled to ~0°, and then treated with 40 g. (0.1 mole) of tungsten hexachloride[69] or 27 g. (0.1 mole) of molybdenum pentachloride.[69] The resulting reaction mixture is boiled under reflux with stirring for ~4 hr. to insure complete reaction.

After cooling the reaction mixture to room temperature, the stirrer is replaced with a stopper, and the solvent is then removed in a water-aspirator vacuum (~10–50 mm.) taking the same precautions as in the preparation of biscyclopentadienylvanadium. If the residue is still sticky after all of the solvent has been removed in the water-aspirator vacuum, the remaining volatile materials are removed at 25°/1.0–0.1 mm. (oil-pump vacuum).

When the residue is dry, nitrogen is admitted to the evacuated flask, and the very air-sensitive residue is transferred under nitrogen to a large sublimation apparatus.[8] The product is sublimed out of the residue at 120°/0.01 mm. After removal of the product under nitrogen, it may be purified further by a second sublimation at 80°/0.01 mm. A yield up to 50% of yellow crystals is obtained.

Instead of sublimation, the $(C_5H_5)_2MH_2$ derivatives may be extracted from the crude residue with dilute (~2N) hydrochloric acid. The hydrochloric acid solution of $[(C_5H_5)_2MH_3]^+$ is filtered under nitrogen, and

───────────────

[66] M. L. H. Green, J. A. McCleverty, L. Pratt, and G. Wilkinson, *J. Chem. Soc.* 4854 (1961)

[67] E. O. Fischer and Y. Hristidu, *Z. Naturforsch.* **15b**, 135 (1960).

[68] Available from Metal Hydrides, Inc., Beverly, Massachusetts.

[69] These halides may be purchased commercially (e.g., Climax Molybdenum Company, New York, New York) or prepared by chlorination of the metal at elevated temperatures.

the filtrate is made basic under nitrogen with $2N$ aqueous sodium hydroxide. The hydrides $(C_5H_5)_2MH_2$ precipitate from the basic solution. They may be removed by filtration under nitrogen or by extraction under nitrogen with nitrogen-saturated diethyl ether. The product is purified finally by sublimation.

The hydrides $(C_5H_5)_2MH_2$ ($M = Mo$ and W) are yellow solids soluble in organic solvents but insoluble in pure water. They possess basic character dissolving in aqueous acids to form solutions of the cations $[(C_5H_5)_2MH_3]^+$. Recently, the tungsten derivative has been observed to form a 1:1 boron trifluoride adduct, $(C_5H_5)_2WH_2 \cdot BF_3$.[70] The hydrides $(C_5H_5)_2MH_2$ are air-sensitive, especially the molybdenum derivative and especially in solution. Nevertheless, the tungsten derivative can be handled in air for very brief periods without extensive decomposition although handling in the absence of air is preferable.

12. Biscyclopentadienylrhenium Hydride

Biscyclopentadienylrhenium hydride has been prepared by the reaction between sodium cyclopentadienide and rhenium pentachloride in tetrahydrofuran solution preferably in the presence of excess sodium borohydride.[71]

Procedure:

$$2ReCl_5 + 8NaC_5H_5 + 2NaBH_4 \rightarrow 2(C_5H_5)_2ReH + 4\{C_5H_5 \cdot\} + 10NaCl + B_2H_6$$

A solution of 0.2 mole of sodium cyclopentadienide in 150 ml. of tetrahydrofuran[5] is prepared under nitrogen by a procedure analogous to that for the preparation of biscyclopentadienylvanadium(II) but using only 4.6 g. of sodium metal and ~22 ml. (17.7 g.) of cyclopentadiene. This solution is cooled to ~0° and treated with 10.9 g. (0.03 mole) of rhenium pentachloride.[72] After stirring for 5 hr. at 50°, the reaction mixture is treated with 3.0 g. (0.08 mole) of sodium borohydride.[68] After stirring for ~5 hr. at the boiling point, the biscyclopentadienyl rhenium hydride is isolated from the reaction mixture by removal of solvent and sublimation of the air-sensitive residue in the same manner as for the preparations of the dihydrides $(C_5H_5)_2MH_2$. Extraction of the residue with dilute hydrochloric acid and precipitation of the $(C_5H_5)_2ReH$ from the $[(C_5H_5)_2ReH_2]^+$ solution with dilute sodium hydroxide may also be used.

---

[70] D. F. Shriver, *J. Am. Chem. Soc.* **85**, 3509 (1963).
[71] M. L. H. Green, L. Pratt, and G. Wilkinson, *J. Chem. Soc.* 3916 (1958).
[72] Prepared by chlorination of rhenium metal at 600°.

Biscyclopentadienylrhenium hydride forms yellow crystals, m.p. 161–162°, that are soluble in organic solvents, insoluble in water, and volatile at $\sim$80°/0.01 mm. It dissolves in dilute aqueous acids to form solutions of the cation $[(C_5H_5)_2ReH_2]^+$. Treatment with carbon monoxide under pressure gives the olefin complex $C_5H_5Re(CO)_2C_5H_6$.[73]

[73] M. L. H. Green and G. Wilkinson, *J. Chem. Soc.* 4314 (1958).

B. Metal Carbonyls Without Other Ligands

1. Bisdiglymesodium Hexacarbonylvanadate(−I) and Vanadium Hexacarbonyl

Bisdiglymesodium hexacarbonylvanadate(−I) may be obtained by reduction of vanadium trichloride with sodium metal in diglyme[1] solution in the presence of carbon monoxide under pressure.[2]

Procedure:

(1) $VCl_3 + 4Na + 2C_6H_{14}O_3 + 6CO \rightarrow [Na(C_6H_{14}O_3)_2][V(CO)_6] + 3NaCl$

(2) $2[Na(C_6H_{14}O_3)_2][V(CO)_6] + 2HCl \rightarrow 2V(CO)_6 + H_2\uparrow + 4C_6H_{14}O_3 + 2NaCl$

The reaction is carried out in a rocking autoclave of 1-liter internal capacity that is capable of withstanding pressures of at least 330 atmospheres.[3] This autoclave is charged in a nitrogen stream with 31.5 g. (0.2 mole) of anhydrous vanadium trichloride,[4] 27.5 g. (1.2 mole) of sodium metal preferably dispersed in mineral oil,[5] 400 ml. of pure

---

[1] For brevity, the abbreviation "diglyme" will be used for *di*ethylene *gly*col dimethyl ether, $CH_3OCH_2CH_2OCH_2CH_2OCH_3$, as done by most workers in this field.

[2] R. P. M. Werner and H. E. Podall, *Chem. Ind. (London)* 144 (1961).

[3] A smaller or larger autoclave may be used with a corresponding change in the quantities of reactants. If the maximum pressure rating of the system is less than 330 atmospheres, a lower pressure of carbon monoxide is required in order that the pressure not exceed the maximum rating at some stage of the reaction. If a lower pressure of carbon monoxide is used, the yield and/or reaction rate may be appreciably lower; these effects have not been explored in detail for many of the reactions in this chapter.

[4] Vanadium trichloride is commercially available from Anderson Chemical Company, Weston, Michigan. It may be prepared by boiling vanadium pentoxide with disulfur dichloride (S_2Cl_2). [G. Brauer, "Handbuch der Präparativen Anorganischen Chemie" (G. Brauer, ed.), p. 1099. Ferdinand Enke Verlag, Stuttgart, 1962.] Vanadium trichloride, a purple solid, is hygroscopic and should be exposed to air only during the brief period of weighing.

[5] A commercially available 40% or 50% sodium dispersion in mineral oil may be used with good results.

diglyme,[6] and 2 ml. of iron pentacarbonyl.[7] The autoclave is then closed and connected to a source of carbon monoxide under pressure.[8] First, the autoclave is flushed once with at least 50 atmospheres of carbon monoxide.[9] After releasing this carbon monoxide, the autoclave is then pressurized with 200 atmospheres of carbon monoxide, and then heated with rocking to 160° for ~48 hr. During this reaction period, a decrease in pressure of ~47 atmospheres occurs. After cooling the autoclave to room temperature, the carbon monoxide is released, and the autoclave is opened. The black reaction mixture is then filtered, and a yellow filtrate is obtained. The residue is washed with two 100-ml. portions of diglyme. The combined filtrate and washings are shaken with ~1 liter of hexane or petroleum ether. A lower liquid layer is obtained which contains the product. This is removed in a separatory funnel and treated with a mixture of 200 ml. of anhydrous diethyl ether and 200 ml. of pentane, hexane, or petroleum ether. Yellow solid [Na(diglyme)₂][V(CO)₆] precipitates. This is removed by filtration, washed with several portions of pentane, and dried finally in a vacuum to give approximately 56.0 g. (55% yield) of yellow solid [Na(diglyme)₂][V(CO)₆].

Bisdiglymesodium hexacarbonylvanadate(−I) is a yellow solid that is moderately stable to air (unusual for a carbonyl anion), but it darkens on exposure to light. It is insoluble in nonpolar organic solvents such as pentane or benzene, but is somewhat soluble in various polar organic solvents such as tetrahydrofuran. It dissolves in water forming a yellow solution. Treatment of this solution with strong acids ultimately leads to the production of vanadium hexacarbonyl via the unstable intermediate HV(CO)₆ or possibly the hydronium salt [H₃O][V(CO)₆].

In order to obtain pure vanadium hexacarbonyl from [Na(diglyme)₂][V(CO)₆],[10] an aqueous solution of [Na(diglyme)₂][V(CO)₆] is treated with 4N hydrochloric acid in the presence of diethyl ether until the pH of the solution is about 1. The diethyl ether layer becomes yellow-orange.

---

[6] The diglyme (b.p. 161°) may be dried by distillation over lithium aluminum hydride or by standing over sodium-lead alloy; the former method is preferred.

[7] The iron pentacarbonyl acts as a catalyst to speed up the reaction. Anhydrous ferric chloride may be substituted or the addition of iron compounds completely omitted with satisfactory results.

[8] Since the maximum pressure available in commercial tanks of carbon monoxide is 70 to 100 atmospheres, a compressor is required to attain the necessary pressures for the reaction.

[9] If the carbon monoxide tank contains less than 50 atmospheres, more than one flushing with less than 50 atmospheres of carbon monoxide instead of one flushing with 50 atmospheres of carbon monoxide may be used. Nitrogen or hydrogen may also be used as the flushing gas.

[10] F. Calderazzo and R. Ercoli, *Chim. Ind. (Milan)* **44**, 990 (1962).

It is removed, and the aqueous layer is extracted with diethyl ether until the diethyl ether solution is no longer colored (about two extractions should suffice). The ether extracts are dried over anhydrous magnesium sulfate for several minutes. The extracts are then filtered from the drying agent, and the solvent is removed from the diethyl ether solution in a water-aspirator vacuum (~10–50 mm.). Toward the end of this evaporation, gas is vigorously evolved. After this gas evolution is complete, this residue is transferred under nitrogen[11] to a sublimer, and the vanadium hexacarbonyl is sublimed out at 50°/15 mm. in a closed system. The sublimate is treated with excess phosphorus pentoxide to remove chemically any water, and then it is sublimed a second time to give blue-green air-sensitive crystals of vanadium hexacarbonyl.

Vanadium hexacarbonyl reacts with cycloheptatriene to give the nonionic derivative $C_7H_7V(CO)_3$ and the ionic derivative $[C_7H_7VC_7H_8]$ $[V(CO)_6]$.[12] Treatment of vanadium hexacarbonyl with $(C_5H_5)_2V$ in the presence of carbon monoxide at atmospheric pressure gives the salt $[(C_5H_5)_2V(CO)_2][V(CO)_6]$.[13] Vanadium hexacarbonyl reacts with a variety of Lewis bases to give a variety of derivatives of the $[V(CO)_6]^-$ anion.[14] Bisdiglymesodium hexacarbonylvanadate($-$I) besides being an intermediate in the preparation of vanadium hexacarbonyl is also an intermediate in a convenient preparation of cyclopentadienylvanadium tetracarbonyl (page 107).[15]

2. Chromium Hexacarbonyl

Chromium hexacarbonyl has been prepared by (a) the reduction of chromium(III) chloride with a Grignard reagent in the presence of carbon monoxide,[16] (b) treatment of $(C_5H_5)_2Cr$ with carbon monoxide and hydrogen under pressure,[17] (c) reduction of a suitable chromium(III)

---

[11] The very air-sensitive vanadium hexacarbonyl must be protected from the air. It is recommended that this transfer be made with vigorous streams of nitrogen running through both the flask containing the crude vanadium hexacarbonyl and the bottom portion of the sublimation vessel.

[12] F. Calderazzo and P. L. Calvi, *Chim. Ind. (Milan)* **44**, 1217 (1962).

[13] F. Calderazzo and S. Bacciarelli, *Inorg. Chem.* **2**, 721 (1963).

[14] W. Hieber, J. Peterhans, and E. Winter, *Chem. Ber.* **94**, 2572 (1961); W. Hieber, E. Winter, and E. Schubert, *Chem. Ber.* **95**, 3070 (1962).

[15] R. P. M. Werner, A. H. Filbey, and S. A. Manastyrskyj, *Inorg. Chem.* **3**, 298 (1964).

[16] A. Job and A. Cassal, *Compt. Rend.* **183**, 392 (1926); A. Job and J. Rouvillois, *Bull. Soc. Chim. (France)* **41**, 1041 (1927); W. Hieber and E. Romberg, *Z. Anorg. Allgem. Chem.* **221**, 321 (1935); B. B. Owen, J. English, Jr., H. G. Cassidy, and C. V. Dundon, *J. Am. Chem. Soc.* **69**, 1723 (1947).

[17] E. O. Fischer and W. Hafner, *Z. Naturforsch.* **10b**, 140 (1955).

compound such as the acetylacetonate with magnesium or zinc in pyridine in the presence of carbon monoxide under pressure,[18] (d) reduction of chromium(III) chloride with lithium aluminum hydride[19] or alkylaluminum compounds[20] in the presence of carbon monoxide under pressure, (e) reduction of chromium(III) chloride with sodium benzophenone ketyl in tetrahydrofuran solution in the presence of carbon monoxide under pressure,[21] (f) reduction of chromium(III) chloride with aluminum metal in the presence of aluminum chloride, benzene, and carbon monoxide under pressure,[22] and (g) reduction of chromium(III) chloride with magnesium in diethyl ether solution in the presence of iodine and hydrogen.[23]

The two most convenient of these methods appear to be the reduction of chromium(III) acetylacetonate with magnesium in the presence of carbon monoxide and pyridine (Ercoli-Calderazzo method) and the reaction between chromium(III) chloride, aluminum powder, aluminum chloride, benzene, and carbon monoxide (Fischer-Hafner-Öfele method). Both of these methods will be described.

Procedure A:

$$CrCl_3 + Al + 6CO \xrightarrow[C_6H_6]{AlCl_3} Cr(CO)_6 + AlCl_3$$

The reaction is carried out in a rocking autoclave of 1-liter internal capacity capable of withstanding pressures of at least 330 atmospheres.[3] This autoclave is charged with 46.3 g. (0.292 mole) of chromium(III) chloride,[24] 46.3 g. (1.72 mole) of aluminum powder, 370 ml. of dry

[18] G. Natta, R. Ercoli, F. Calderazzo, and A. Rabizzoni, *J. Am. Chem. Soc.* 79, 3611 (1957); R. Ercoli, F. Calderazzo, and G. Bernardi, *Gazz. Chim. Ital.* 89, 809 (1959).
[19] A. N. Nesmeyanov, K. N. Anisimov, V. L. Volkov, A. E. Fridenberg, E. P. Mikheev, and A. V. Medvedeva, *Z. Neorgan. Khim.* 4, 1827 (1959); *Chem. Abstr.* 54, 11795 g (1960).
[20] H. E. Podall, J. H. Dunn, and H. Shapiro, *J. Am. Chem. Soc.* 82, 1325 (1960); L. I. Zakharkin, V. V. Gavrilenko, and O. Yu. Okhlobystin, *Izvest. Akad. Nauk. SSSR Otdel Khim. Nauk.* 100 (1958).
[21] R. D. Closson, L. R. Buzbee, and G. C. Ecke, *J. Am. Chem. Soc.* 80, 6167 (1958).
[22] E. O. Fischer, W. Hafner, and K. Öfele, *Chem. Ber.* 92, 3050 (1959).
[23] I. Wender, U. S. Patent 3,012,858 (Diamond Alkali).
[24] Anhydrous chromium(III) chloride is readily available commercially in the United States from companies such as Diamond Alkali Corp., Painesville, Ohio. It may also be obtained by treatment of the commercially available hydrated chromium(III) chloride with thionyl chloride [A. R. Pray, *Inorg. Syn.* 5, 153 (1957)]. Fischer, Hafner, and Öfele[22] recommend grinding the chromium(III) chloride with about three times its weight of methanol or benzene and then removing the organic liquid prior to use in their synthesis.

thiophene-free benzene, and finally 40 g. (0.3 mole) of pure anhydrous aluminum chloride.[25] The autoclave is then closed and connected to a source of carbon monoxide under pressure.[8] After flushing once with at least 50 atmospheres of carbon monoxide,[9] the autoclave is pressurized with 150–200 atmospheres of carbon monoxide and heated to 140° with shaking. At this temperature, the pressure of carbon monoxide is increased to the limit of the system (300–350 atmospheres). The autoclave is shaken at ~140° until no further absorption of carbon monoxide takes place (24–30 hr.). From time to time, additional carbon monoxide is introduced to replace the absorbed carbon monoxide. When the reaction period is over, the autoclave is cooled to room temperature, and the carbon monoxide is then vented. The autoclave is then opened and several pieces of ice are added to decompose the aluminum chloride.[26] The contents of the autoclave are then transferred to a large three-necked

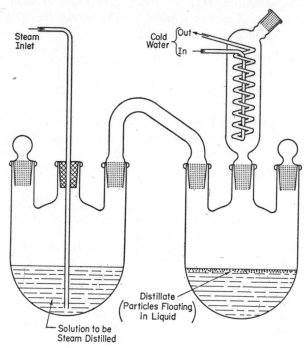

FIG. 22. Illustration of the apparatus for steam distillation of solid metal carbonyls such as $Cr(CO)_6$ and $Mn_2(CO)_{10}$.

[25] A good quality of commercial anhydrous aluminum chloride may be used.

[26] Initially a vigorous reaction will occur upon introduction of the ice. When introduction of additional pieces of ice causes no further change, the decomposition is complete and the steam distillation may then be begun.

flask equipped for steam distillation of solid carbonyls (Fig. 22).[27] Steam is then passed through the reaction mixture[28] at such a rate that it is all condensed into the receiver.[29] Chromium hexacarbonyl will appear in the receiver as white crystals.[30] The steam distillation is continued until no more chromium hexacarbonyl is obtained. After the distillate has cooled to room temperature, the chromium hexacarbonyl is filtered, washed with several portions of methanol, and sucked dry.[30] If further purification is desired, the chromium hexacarbonyl may be sublimed at 50–80°/15 mm. onto a water-cooled probe.[31] A yield of 56.3 g. (88%) of chromium hexacarbonyl has been obtained from this reaction.

Procedure B:

$$2Cr(C_5H_7O_2)_3 + 3Mg + 12CO \xrightarrow[I_2, Co_2(CO)_8]{C_4H_8O, C_5H_5N} 2Cr(CO)_6 + 3Mg(C_5H_7O_2)_2$$

The reaction is carried out in a rocking autoclave of 1-liter internal capacity capable of withstanding pressures of at least 300 atmospheres.[3] This autoclave is charged with 50 g. (0.143 mole) of chromium(III) acetylacetonate,[32] 2 g. of iodine, 20 g. (0.834 mole) of magnesium turnings,[33] 102 ml. (100 g.) of pyridine, 200 ml. of pure dry tetrahydrofuran, and 4 g. of dicobalt octacarbonyl.[34] The autoclave is then closed and connected to a source of carbon monoxide under pressure. After flushing once with at least 50 atmospheres of carbon monoxide,[9] the autoclave is

---

[27] The special steam distillation apparatus illustrated in Fig. 22 has the advantage over a more usual steam distillation apparatus that the solid chromium hexacarbonyl or dimanganese decacarbonyl does not clog it up as readily.

[28] The steam may be taken directly from a steam line. If a steam line is not available ~2 liters of water may be added to the reaction mixture and then distilled. The distillation of the water is continued until no more chromium hexacarbonyl or dimanganese decacarbonyl codistills.

[29] If the steam is not completely condensed, some of the chromium hexacarbonyl or dimanganese decacarbonyl will be lost.

[30] Chromium hexacarbonyl is rather volatile, and, thus, should not be sucked dry for long periods of time lest some be lost by volatilization.

[31] In this manner, large colorless and odorless crystals of chromium hexacarbonyl are obtained. Sublimation is the best way to free completely chromium hexacarbonyl from traces of water and methanol.

[32] Chromium(III) acetylacetonate may be purchased commercially or prepared from hydrated chromium(III) chloride, acetylacetone, and urea in warm aqueous solution [W. C. Fernelius and J. E. Blanch, *Inorg. Syn.* 5, 130 (1957)].

[33] The grade of magnesium turnings suitable for Grignard reactions may be used.

[34] If not readily available, the dicobalt octacarbonyl may be omitted from the reaction mixture. In this case, it will be necessary to increase the reaction time to 6 or more hours. When the carbon monoxide pressure no longer decreases the reaction, it can be considered finished.

pressurized with 180 atmospheres of carbon monoxide and heated to 135–152° over 2 hr.[34] with shaking. The pressure which originally is ~270 atmospheres when the reaction temperature is reached gradually decreases to 230 atmospheres as the reaction proceeds. When the reaction period is over, the autoclave is cooled to room temperature, and the excess carbon monoxide is vented. The autoclave is then opened, and the chromium hexacarbonyl is subjected to steam distillation, filtration, methanol washing, and then vacuum sublimation as was described for the Fischer-Hafner-Öfele method. A yield of ~27.2 g. (86%) of chromium hexacarbonyl has been obtained from this reaction.

Chromium hexacarbonyl is a white odorless solid, m.p. 152–153°, which is air-stable but very volatile. It is insoluble in water and soluble only to a limited extent in organic solvents. Characteristic of its infrared spectrum is a single strong band at 2000 cm.[-1] due to the six metal carbonyl groups. Of particular importance are the reactions of chromium hexacarbonyl with a wide variety of benzenoid aromatic compounds (e.g. benzene, hexamethylbenzene, phenol, aniline, chlorobenzene, naphthalene) at 120–220° to give arene-chromium tricarbonyl derivatives.[35] Certain related nonbenzenoid aromatic derivatives such as thiophene[36] and cyclopentadienide ion[37] react with chromium hexacarbonyl at elevated temperatures to form similar chromium tricarbonyl derivatives.

3. Molybdenum and Tungsten Hexacarbonyls

Molybdenum and tungsten hexacarbonyls have been obtained by treatment of molybdenum pentachloride and tungsten hexachloride, respectively, with various reducing agents in the presence of carbon monoxide under pressure. Suitable reducing agents include aluminum,[38] zinc,[39] aluminum alkyls,[20] or "Grignard reagents"[15] in diethyl ether; sodium metal in diglyme solution[40]; or iron pentacarbonyl.[41]

[35] E. O. Fischer, K. Öfele, H. Essler, W. Fröhlich, J. P. Mortensen, and W. Semmlinger, Z. Naturforsch. 13b, 458 (1958); Chem. Ber. 91, 2763 (1958); B. Nicholls and M. C. Whiting, J. Chem. Soc. 551 (1959); G. Natta, R. Ercoli, F. Calderazzo, and S. Santambrogio, Chim. Ind. (Milan) 40, 1003 (1958).

[36] E. O. Fischer and K. Öfele, Chem. Ber. 91, 2395 (1958).

[37] E. O. Fischer, W. Hafner, and H. O. Stahl, Z. Anorg. Allgem. Chem. 282, 47 (1955).

[38] D. T. Hurd, Inorg. Syn. 5, 135 (1957).

[39] K. A. Kocheskov, A. N. Nesmeyanov, M. M. Nadj, I. M. Rossinskaya, Compt. Rend. Acad. Sci. U.R.S.S. 26, 54 (1940).

[40] H. E. Podall, H. B. Prestridge, and H. Shapiro, J. Am. Chem. Soc. 83, 2057 (1961).

[41] A. N. Nesmeyanov, E. P. Mikheev, K. N. Anisimov, V. L. Volkov, and Z. P. Valueva, Zh. Neorgan. Khim. 4, 503, 249 (1959); Chem. Abstr. 53, 21327h, 12907c (1959).

For the last few years, a reliable commercial source for these two carbonyls has been Climax Molybdenum Company, 1270 Avenue of the Americas, New York, New York. As of January 1, 1963, prices of these two carbonyls in ¼- to 1-lb. lots were $17 per pound [Mo(CO)$_6$] and $95 per pound [W(CO)$_6$]. In view of the ready commercial availability, detailed directions for the preparations of molybdenum and tungsten hexacarbonyls have not been included in this book.

4. Dimanganese Decacarbonyl

Dimanganese decacarbonyl has been obtained by reduction of a specially prepared manganese(II) iodide with magnesium in diethyl ether in the presence of carbon monoxide under pressure ($\sim$1% yield)[42]; by reduction of manganese(II) chloride with phenylmagnesium bromide in diethyl ether in the presence of carbon monoxide under pressure (8–10% yield)[43]; by reduction of manganese(II) chloride with sodium benzophenone ketyl in tetrahydrofuran in the presence of carbon monoxide under pressure ($\sim$32% yield)[44]; by reduction of manganese(II) acetate with trialkylaluminum compounds in various solvents in the presence of carbon monoxide under pressure (yield greatly dependent on solvent and mole ratios of reactants)[45]; by reduction of methylcyclopentadienylmanganese tricarbonyl with sodium in diglyme[1] solution in the presence of carbon monoxide under pressure[46]; and by reduction of manganese(II) chloride with magnesium in dimethylformamide solution in the presence of carbon monoxide under pressure (11% yield reported).[47]

None of these published preparative methods for dimanganese decacarbonyl is very satisfactory. All suffer from one or more of the following disadvantages: (a) low yield, (b) large volume of reaction mixture required in order to obtain a relatively small amount of dimanganese decacarbonyl, (c) large quantities of dangerous pyrophoric trialkylaluminum compounds required in order to obtain a relatively small amount of dimanganese decacarbonyl, (d) exotic manganese compound required as a starting material, (e) poor reproducibility in the author's laboratory, and (f) highly obnoxious reaction mixture.

As an aid to readers who may desire to prepare small amounts of

[42] E. O. Brimm, M. A. Lynch, Jr., and W. J. Sesny, *J. Am. Chem. Soc.* **76**, 3831 (1954).

[43] V. Hnizda, U. S. Patent 2,822,247 (1958).

[44] R. D. Closson, L. R. Buzbee, and G. C. Ecke, *J. Am. Chem. Soc.* **80**, 6167 (1958).

[45] H. E. Podall, J. H. Dunn, and H. Shapiro, *J. Am. Chem. Soc.* **82**, 1325 (1960).

[46] H. E. Podall and A. P. Giraitis, *J. Org. Chem.* **26**, 2587 (1961).

[47] J. F. Cordes and D. Neubauer, *Z. Naturforsch.* **17b**, 791 (1962).

dimanganese decacarbonyl, the following preparation from anhydrous manganese(II) chloride, sodium benzophenone ketyl, and carbon monoxide is provided.

Procedure:

$$2MnCl_2 + 4(C_6H_5)_2CONa + 10CO \xrightarrow[\Delta]{C_4H_8O} Mn_2(CO)_{10} + 4NaCl + 4(C_6H_5)_2CO$$

The first part of this preparation is carried out under nitrogen in a 1-liter three-necked flask fitted with a motor stirrer, reflux condenser, and nitrogen inlet. After filling the system with nitrogen either by passing a rapid stream of nitrogen through the apparatus for several minutes or preferably by evacuating the apparatus and refilling with nitrogen, the flask is charged with 9.5 g. (0.43 mole) of sodium metal and ~300 ml. of dry toluene or xylene. This mixture is heated to the boiling point, and the sodium is dispersed into fine sand-like granules by vigorous stirring at the boiling point.[48] After cooling to room temperature, the xylene is siphoned off and 450 ml. of tetrahydrofuran is added. This suspension of sodium in tetrahydrofuran is treated with 80 g. (0.44 mole) of benzophenone in portions to form the deep-blue sodium benzophenone ketyl.[49] After all of the sodium has reacted and the reaction mixture has cooled to room temperature, the sodium benzophenone ketyl is treated with 27.5 g. (0.218 mole) of anhydrous manganese(II) chloride,[50] and the mixture is refluxed with stirring for 2 hr. The reaction mixture becomes yellow and more viscous upon addition of the manganese(II) chloride but returns to its previous dark-blue color during the heating. After cooling to room temperature, the blue manganese(II) ketyl solution is then poured under nitrogen[51] into a rocking autoclave of 1-liter internal capacity capable of withstanding pressures of at least 330 atmospheres.[3] The autoclave is then connected to a source of carbon monoxide under pressure. After flushing once with at least 50 atmospheres of carbon

---

[48] A commercial 40% to 50% sodium dispersion in mineral oil or xylene may be used if available.

[49] The formation of sodium benzophenone ketyl is rather exothermic. It is therefore necessary to add the benzophenone gradually to the sodium dispersion to prevent the reaction from becoming too vigorous.

[50] Anhydrous manganese(II) chloride may be obtained from hydrated manganese(II) chloride either by heating to 400°/0.1 mm. until no more water is evolved or by treatment with thionyl chloride [A. R. Pray, *Inorg. Syn.* **5**, 153 (1957)]. Some commercial samples of anhydrous manganese(II) chloride may be suitable for this reaction.

[51] The blue solutions of sodium and manganese benzophenone ketyls are very air-sensitive and must always be kept under nitrogen.

monoxide,[9] the autoclave is then pressurized with 200 atmospheres of carbon monoxide and then heated with rocking to 200° for at least 3 hr. After the reaction period is over, the autoclave is cooled to room temperature, and the carbon monoxide is then vented. The autoclave is then opened and the contents are transferred to a large three-necked flask equipped for steam distillation of solid metal carbonyls (Fig. 22).[26] The reaction mixture is then decomposed with ~200 ml. of water. Steam is then passed through the reaction mixture[27] at such a rate that it is all condensed into the receiver.[29,52] Dimanganese decarbonyl will appear in the receiver as golden-yellow crystals. After no more dimanganese decacarbonyl is being collected in the receiver, the steam distillation is continued while adding dropwise 250 ml. of 10% aqueous sulfuric acid to the distilling flask over a period of 1 hr.[53] After all of the aqueous sulfuric acid has been added and no more dimanganese decacarbonyl is distilling over, the steam distillation is discontinued and the distillate is allowed to cool to room temperature. The yellow dimanganese decacarbonyl is removed by filtration, sucked dry, and finally dried at 25°/ 0.1 mm.

The crude product as thus obtained may be contaminated with appreciable quantities of benzophenone, which is also volatile with steam. In order to remove this, the crude product is dissolved in a minimum of toluene at room temperature (~3.5 ml. of toluene/1 g. $Mn_2(CO)_{10}$) and the yellow toluene solution cooled to ~ −15° (ice-salt bath or freezing compartment of a refrigerator) to precipitate yellow crystals of $Mn_2(CO)_{10}$ which are filtered and sucked dry. If a still purer product is desired, the recrystallized material may be sublimed at 50–70°/ ~0.5 mm.

The maximum yield in this reaction obtainable with the best quality of reagents is ~35%. If the manganese(II) chloride is not completely anhydrous or if the reaction is attempted in more concentrated solutions in order to permit a larger-scale preparation in an autoclave of given size, the yield drops appreciably (often to ~10%).

Dimanganese decacarbonyl is a yellow crystalline solid, m.p. 153–154°. It is insoluble in water but soluble in organic solvents. Solid dimanganese decacarbonyl oxidizes in air only very slowly over a period of weeks whereas its yellow solutions begin to deposit appreciable amounts of a brown precipitate in air during several hours. It is ap-

---

[52] Dimanganese decacarbonyl appears to be very toxic. The hazard of exposure to its toxic vapors is especially great during the steam-distillation step which, therefore, should be done in an efficient hood.

[53] Sometimes additional dimanganese decacarbonyl is obtained after acidification of the reaction mixture.

parently very toxic although no details are given in the literature. The manganese-manganese bond in $Mn_2(CO)_{10}$ is cleaved by halogens to form the halides $Mn(CO)_5X$ (X=Cl, Br, and I)[54] and by sodium amalgam in tetrahydrofuran or similar solvent to give the sodium salt $Na[Mn(CO)_5]$.[55] The halides and the anion are both useful intermediates for the preparation of a variety of interesting organomanganese compounds.

5. Dirhenium Decacarbonyl

Dirhenium decacarbonyl has been obtained by the treatment of rhenium(VII) oxide or other halogen-free rhenium compounds with carbon monoxide at elevated pressures and temperatures[56] or by treatment of rhenium pentachloride with sodium in diglyme[1] in the presence of carbon monoxide under pressure.[57] The preparation from rhenium(VII) oxide is more convenient than the preparation from rhenium pentachloride and it will be given. The preparation of appreciable quantities of dirhenium decacarbonyl is less difficult at the present time than the preparation of appreciable quantities of the analogous dimanganese decacarbonyl.

Procedure:

$$Re_2O_7 + 17CO \xrightarrow{\Delta} Re_2(CO)_{10} + 7CO_2 \uparrow$$

The reaction is carried out in a rocking autoclave of 1-liter internal capacity capable of withstanding pressures of at least 330 atmospheres.[2] This autoclave is charged in a nitrogen stream with 50 g. (0.103 mole) of rhenium(VII) oxide.[58] The autoclave is then closed and connected to a source of carbon monoxide under pressure.[8] After flushing once with at least 50 atmospheres of carbon monoxide, the autoclave is pressurized with 180 atmospheres of carbon monoxide and heated with rocking to 250° for 16 hr. The autoclave is then cooled to room temperature, and the carbon monoxide is released. The autoclave is opened, and the grayish solid residues washed on a filter with 50-ml. portions of water until the water washings are neutral in order to remove any unchanged Re_2O_7.

[54] E. W. Abel and G. Wilkinson, *J. Chem. Soc.* 1501 (1959).
[55] R. D. Closson, J. Kozikowski, and T. H. Coffield, *J. Org. Chem.* 22, 598 (1957).
[56] W. Hieber and H. Fuchs, *Z. Anorg. Allgem. Chem.* 248, 256 (1941).
[57] A. Davison, J. A. McCleverty, and G. Wilkinson, *J. Chem. Soc.* 1133 (1963).
[58] Rhenium(VII) oxide may be purchased from the Department of Chemistry, University of Tennessee, Knoxville, Tennessee, or other sources. Rhenium(VII) oxide like phosphorus pentoxide is very hygroscopic and should be kept away from moist air. If rhenium(VII) oxide is unavailable, potassium perrhenate may be substituted with some sacrifice in yield if the reaction temperature is increased to at least 270°.

The residue remaining from the water washings is sublimed at 70°/ 0.1 mm. to give white crystalline dirhenium decacarbonyl. A nearly quantitative yield has been reported for this reaction, but in the author's experience the yields are much lower (10–60%). If the yield obtained is appreciably less than quantitative, the rhenium not converted to the carbonyl may be recovered from the residue remaining after the sublimation.

Dirhenium decacarbonyl is a white air-stable crystalline solid, m.p. 177°. It is insoluble in water and sparingly soluble in organic solvents. The chemistry of dirhenium decacarbonyl resembles that of dimanganese decacarbonyl in most respects but has been investigated in less detail.

6. Iron Pentacarbonyl

Iron pentacarbonyl is so inexpensive and readily available commercially throughout the world that there is no reason to attempt its laboratory synthesis.[59] Because of its ready availability, many reactions of iron pentacarbonyl are carried out on a large scale. In such experiments, it is necessary to remember the toxicity of iron pentacarbonyl and work in a well-ventilated area. Quantities up to 500 g. of iron pentacarbonyl have been handled in the author's laboratory without ill effect; the experiments were carried out in an efficiently working hood. However, if the hood were not working properly or if the iron pentacarbonyl vapors were allowed to escape into the open laboratory, dangerous concentrations were built up creating discomfort and requiring evacuation of the room. Nevertheless, iron pentacarbonyl is much less dangerous than nickel tetracarbonyl.

7. Diiron Enneacarbonyl

Diiron enneacarbonyl, $Fe_2(CO)_9$ has been obtained by irradiating iron pentacarbonyl either alone or in solution.[60] The author has found that close attention to detail is essential for success in this preparation. The procedure that is described here has given satisfactory results in his laboratory.

Procedure:

$$2Fe(CO)_5 \xrightarrow{\text{uv}} Fe_2(CO)_9 + CO \uparrow$$

A mixture of 30 ml. (43.8 g., 0.223 moles) of commercial iron pentacarbonyl and 220 ml. of glacial acetic acid is charged into a $\sim 5 \times 25$ cm.

---

[59] For laboratory syntheses of iron pentacarbonyl see F. Seel *In* "Handbuch der Präparativen Anorganische Chemie" (G. Brauer, ed.), Second Edition, p. 1509. Ferdinand Enke Verlag, Stuttgart, 1962.

[60] J. Dewar and H. O. Jones, *Proc. Roy. Soc. (London) Ser. B.* **76**, 564 (1905); E. Speyer and H. Wolf, *Chem. Ber.* **60**, 1424 (1927).

cylindrical quartz vessel. It is irradiated several hours 40–50 cm. from a tubular mercury ultraviolet lamp of ~1000 watts input power equipped with a reflector confining the irradiation to a 90–120° segment. As the irradiation proceeds, yellow fluffy crystals of $Fe_2(CO)_9$ separate from the reaction mixture. After ~12 hr., these may be removed by filtration. The filtrate may be irradiated further to give additional quantities of $Fe_2(CO)_9$; eventually a nearly quantitative (>90%) yield may be obtained. However, as the iron pentacarbonyl is consumed, the formation of $Fe_2(CO)_9$ becomes slower. In view of the low cost of iron pentacarbonyl relative to the cost of the electricity supplying the lamp and to the value of the experimenter's time, it is seldom worthwhile to attempt to obtain more than a 50–70% yield of $Fe_2(CO)_9$ from each batch of iron pentacarbonyl and glacial acetic acid.

The yellow crystals of $Fe_2(CO)_9$ are washed with 50-ml. portions of water to remove glacial acetic acid. Finally, it is washed with two 50-ml. portions of 95% ethanol, and two 50-ml. portions of pentane to remove the water. After sucking dry briefly, the product may then be transferred to a bottle for storage.

This preparation of $Fe_2(CO)_9$ may fail in several ways: (a) The yellow glacial acetic acid solution of iron pentacarbonyl will fail to precipitate any crystals of $Fe_2(CO)_9$ or change in appearance in any other way. This indicates that insufficient radiation is reaching the reaction mixture. Using a quartz vessel and a moderate to large ultraviolet lamp rather than glass vessels and weak sunlight should eliminate this problem. This observation may also mean that the ultraviolet lamp is burned out or that the reaction vessel has acquired a nearly invisible film opaque to ultraviolet irradiation. (b) A deep-green reaction mixture possibly containing a black precipitate is produced. The deep-green color is due to $Fe_3(CO)_{12}$ in solution and the black precipitate to solid $Fe_3(CO)_{12}$ and/or metallic iron (may be pyrophoric). This is a sign that the reaction mixture has been overheated by the energy from the lamp. Diiron enneacarbonyl is known to decompose as follows on heating[61]:

$$3Fe_2(CO)_9 \xrightarrow{\Delta} 3Fe(CO)_5 + Fe_3(CO)_{12}$$

$$Fe_3(CO)_{12} \xrightarrow{\Delta} 3Fe + 12CO$$

If this occurs in the preparation of $Fe_2(CO)_9$, it is necessary to repeat the preparation with the vessel further from the source of radiation to minimize overheating or to change to a different ultraviolet source that

---

[61] H. G. Cutforth and P. W. Selwood, *J. Am. Chem. Soc.* 65, 2414 (1943).

produces less heating without sacrificing ultraviolet output. (*c*) A white amorphous water-soluble precipitate rather than the yellow crystalline precipitate of $Fe_2(CO)_9$ is produced. This white precipitate, probably iron(II) acetate, apparently arises from a side reaction of glacial acetic acid and iron pentacarbonyl. Its formation appears to be a consequence of too much heat from the lamp and too little ultraviolet irradiation. This white material can be removed from any $Fe_2(CO)_9$ also produced by washing it out with water.

Some of these difficulties in the preparation of $Fe_2(CO)_9$ may be minimized by carrying out the irradiation of the glacial acetic acid solution of iron pentacarbonyl in a three-necked flask cooled in an ice bath using a tubular ultraviolet lamp immersed in the solutions through one of the necks.[62]

Diiron enneacarbonyl, $Fe_2(CO)_9$, forms yellow-orange crystals insoluble in most solvents. It is fairly stable in air and oxidizes noticeably only over a period of several months. At $\sim 60°$ it decomposes in the presence of organic solvents to give iron pentacarbonyl and triiron dodecacarbonyl without loss of carbon monoxide.[61] A variety of interesting complexes of general formulas (fulvene)$Fe(CO)_3$, (fulvene)$Fe_2(CO)_8$, (fulvene)$Fe_2(CO)_6$, (fulvene)$Fe_2(CO)_5$, (fulvene)$_2Fe(CO)_2$, and (fulvene)$_2Fe_2(CO)_5$ have been obtained by treatment of $Fe_2(CO)_9$ with various fulvenes.[63] Treatment of $Fe_2(CO)_9$ with various olefins with negative substituents (cyanide, carboalkoxy, acid anhydride, etc.) gives stable olefin complexes of the type (olefin)$Fe(CO)_4$.[64]

8. Triiron Dodecacarbonyl

Triiron dodecacarbonyl, $Fe_3(CO)_{12}$, has been obtained by mild heating of $Fe_2(CO)_9$ in a variety of solvents,[61] by oxidation of solutions of the $HFe(CO)_4^-$ anion by certain oxidizing agents such as hydrogen peroxide, manganese(IV) oxide, and potassium permanganate[65] followed by acidification and by action of triethylamine on iron pentacarbonyl followed by acidification.[66] One of the best procedures considering yield, reliability, convenience, and cost of reagents appears to be the oxidation of a buffered solution of $HFe(CO)_4^-$ with a specially prepared active manganese dioxide followed by decomposition of the excess manganese

---

[62] Suitable ultraviolet sources for this purpose may be purchased from Nester/Faust Manufacturing Corporation, Newark, Delaware.
[63] E. Weiss and W. Hübel, *Chem. Ber.* **95**, 1186 (1962).
[64] E. Weiss, K. Stark, J. E. Lancaster, and H. D. Murdoch, *Helv. Chim. Acta* **46**, 288 (1963).
[65] W. Hieber, *Z. Anorg. Allgem. Chem.* **204**, 165 (1932).
[66] M. Heintzelor, German Patent 928,044 (1955).

dioxide with iron(II) sulfate and then acidification.[67] The procedure described here is a scaled-up version of this reaction.

Procedure:

$$(1) \quad Fe(CO)_5 + 2OH^- \rightarrow HFe(CO)_4^- + HCO_3^-$$
$$(2) \quad 3HFe(CO)_4^- + 3MnO_2 \rightarrow Fe_3(CO)_{12} + 3OH^- + 3MnO$$

The reaction is carried out in a well-ventilated hood in a 5-liter three-necked flask fitted with a motor stirrer, reflux condenser, nitrogen inlet, and pressure-equalized dropping funnel. After filling the system with nitrogen, the flask is charged with 105 ml. (153 g., 0.78 mole) of commercial iron pentacarbonyl and 400 ml. of technical methanol. A solution of 112 g. (2.8 moles) of sodium hydroxide in 300 ml. of water[68] is added to the iron pentacarbonyl-methanol solution and the reaction mixture is stirred at least 30 minutes to form a brownish solution of $HFe(CO)_4^-$. This solution of $HFe(CO)_4^-$ is then treated with 300 ml. of a saturated (at 20–30°) aqueous solution of ammonium chloride to act as a buffer.

During the preparation of $HFe(CO)_4^-$ it is convenient to prepare in a separate vessel the manganese dioxide later required for the oxidation. For this purpose, a 2-liter Erlenmeyer flask is charged with 170 g. (1.08 mole) of potassium permangante and 750 ml. of water.[69] After adding ~20 ml. of 95% ethanol, the mixture is allowed to stand or preferably is heated *cautiously* on a steam bath until the reduction of the potassium permanganate begins as indicated by the onset of an exothermic reaction with gas evolution and formation of brown, muddy manganese dioxide. When the reaction has begun and then subsided somewhat, ~230 ml. of 95% ethanol are added in several portions with shaking and the mixture is allowed to stand with occasional shaking until the purple color of the permanganate ion has been completely replaced by a brown, muddy suspension of manganese dioxide. The reduction of permanganate by ethanol in this manner is very vigorous and it is wise to keep the mouth of the flask pointed away from personnel and from anything which the brown manganese dioxide would stain or which the hot aqueous ethanol would damage. Since the amount of manganese dioxide prepared is somewhat in excess of that required for the oxidation of the $HFe(CO)_4^-$, minor mechanical losses during its preparation can be ig-

---

[67] R. B. King and F. G. A. Stone, *Inorg. Syn.* **7**, 193 (1963).

[68] The aqueous solutions of sodium hydroxide and sulfuric acid that become warm during their preparation should be cooled back to room temperature before being added to the reaction mixture.

[69] Most of the potassium permanganate will remain undissolved.

nored. Before addition to the $HFe(CO)_4^-$ solution, the manganese dioxide suspension should be cooled to room temperature using cold running water or an ice bath to hasten the process if necessary. It is, however, unnecessary to separate the manganese dioxide in a pure state from the potassium salts, the ethanol, or other products by filtration or any other technique since these impurities do not interfere in the $Fe_3(CO)_{12}$ preparation.

The manganese dioxide suspension is added to the $HFe(CO)_4^-$ solution. An exothermic reaction occurs and the reaction mixture becomes a deep red. To insure complete oxidation, the reaction mixture is stirred for at least 1 hr.

After the oxidation is complete, the excess manganese dioxide is decomposed by the dropwise addition of a solution of 100 g. (0.36 mole) of $FeSO_4 \cdot 7H_2O$ in 500 ml. of water containing $\sim$50 ml. of concentrated sulfuric acid.[70] After stirring for 15 minutes, a solution of 375 ml. of concentrated sulfuric acid in 375 ml. of water is added dropwise.[68,70] During the addition of the sulfuric acid, very malodorous red fumes (arising apparently from $H_2Fe(CO)_4$ and decomposition products) are generally observed. After all of the sulfuric acid has been added, the reaction mixture is stirred for at least 20 minutes. When the reaction mixture consists of black solid $Fe_3(CO)_{12}$ suspended in a weak pink or green solution, the product is filtered[71] and washed with at least two 150-ml. portions of hot $\sim$3N sulfuric acid, two 150-ml. portions of cold water, two 150-ml. portions of 95% ethanol, and finally two 150-ml. portions of hexane, pentane, or petroleum ether. After sucking dry for about 10 minutes, the product is bottled under nitrogen. The yields generally fall in the range of 79 g. to 92 g. (60–70%). Although these yields are generally somewhat inferior to those obtained in smaller-scale preparations,[65,67] the opportunity of obtaining much larger quantities of $Fe_3(CO)_{12}$ in only slightly more time makes the larger-scale preparation preferable when significant quantities of $Fe_3(CO)_{12}$ are required.

Triiron dodecacarbonyl is a black solid resembling charcoal in general appearance but dissolving, although only sparingly, in organic solvents to give intense dark-green solutions. Although it may be filtered and otherwise handled briefly without protection from air, triiron dodecacarbonyl should be stored under nitrogen since prolonged exposure to air may result in complete oxidation to brown iron(III) oxide (readily

---

[70] Concentrated sulfuric acid should always be added to water rather than water to the acid.

[71] It is advisable to use either a sintered glass filter funnel or two or more thicknesses of filter paper because of the strongly acid character of the reaction mixture.

recognized by its appearance). Sometimes prolonged storage under nitrogen will give a pyrophoric material (presumably metallic iron) with no change in general appearance. Caution is therefore indicated in handling samples of $Fe_3(CO)_{12}$ that have stood for some time.

When isolated from the reaction mixture by filtration and washed as described, triiron dodecacarbonyl is suitable for most preparative purposes such as reactions with various diolefins[72] and organosulfur compounds.[73] In certain cases, it may be desirable to dry the $Fe_3(CO)_{12}$ for several hours at 25°/0.1 mm. to insure the complete absence of traces of water or ethanol that would interfere with certain reactions such as with alkali metals to form $[Fe(CO)_4]^{2-}$ salts.[74] More thorough drying of $Fe_3(CO)_{12}$ appears to increase its susceptibility to air oxidation and is therefore recommended only when necessary. Very pure $Fe_3(CO)_{12}$ that might be required for various physical measurements may be obtained as green-black crystals by sublimation of the crude product at 70°/ 0.1 mm. onto a water-cooled probe. Unfortunately, the recovery of pure product by this method is only 10–20% of the crude material.

9. Dicobalt Octacarbonyl

Originally, dicobalt octacarbonyl was generally obtained by spontaneously decomposing the hydride $HCo(CO)_4$ that can be obtained by acidification of solutions of the anion $Co(CO)_4^-$ obtained from simple cobalt(II) salts and carbon monoxide at atmospheric pressure in the presence of cyanide ion or other reducing agents.[75] This preparation of $Co_2(CO)_8$, although not requiring the use of carbon monoxide under pressure, could not be carried out readily on a large scale. Later, when high pressure equipment became more generally available, several procedures were developed for obtaining dicobalt octacarbonyl from various cobalt compounds and a mixture of carbon monoxide and hydrogen under pressure in the presence of an inert organic solvent such as petroleum ether or aromatic hydrocarbon. A procedure of this type, the reaction of cobalt(II) carbonate suspended in petroleum ether with a mixture of carbon monoxide and hydrogen under pressure, has been described in *Inorganic Syntheses.*[76]

In general, such preparations furnish solutions of dicobalt octacar-

---

[72] R. B. King, T. A. Manuel, and F. G. A. Stone, *J. Inorg. Nucl. Chem.* **16**, 233 (1961).

[73] See R. B. King, *J. Am. Chem. Soc.* **85**, 1918 (1963) and references cited therein.

[74] R. B. King and F. G. A. Stone, *Inorg. Syn.* **7**, 196 (1963).

[75] For a typical such procedure see P. Gilmont and A. A. Blanchard, *Inorg. Syn.* **2**, 238 (1946).

[76] I. Wender, H. W. Sternberg, S. Metlin, and M. Orchin, *Inorg. Syn.* **5**, 190 (1957).

bonyl in a hydrocarbon solvent from which pure crystals, if required, must then be isolated by crystallization. Because of the instability of dicobalt octacarbonyl, this can present difficulties. For example, if dicobalt octacarbonyl is crystallized too rapidly, the resulting finely divided crystals are pyrophoric.[76]

These difficulties are circumvented by carrying out the preparation of dicobalt octacarbonyl from cobalt(II) acetate, carbon monoxide, and hydrogen in acetic acid solution. Under these conditions, crystalline dicobalt octacarbonyl may be isolated by simple filtration of the reaction mixture obtained after cooling the autoclave to room temperature and venting the excess gases. In practice, it is more convenient to use the commercially available cobalt(II) acetate *tetrahydrate* and enough acetic anhydride to convert all of the water of hydration to acetic acid. Details of such a procedure worked out by Szabó, Markó, and Bor[77] will be given.

Procedure:

$$2[Co(H_2O)_4][CH_3CO_2]_2 + 8(CH_3CO)_2O + 8CO + 2H_2 \xrightarrow{\Delta} Co_2(CO)_8 + 20CH_3COOH$$

The reaction is carried out in a rocking autoclave of 1-liter internal capacity that is capable of withstanding pressures of at least 330 atmospheres.[2] This autoclave is charged with 200 g. (0.8 mole) of cobalt(II) acetate tetrahydrate and 330 g. (3.25 mole) of acetic anhydride. The autoclave is then closed and connected to a source of carbon monoxide under pressure.[8] First, the autoclave is flushed once with at least 50 atmospheres of carbon monoxide or hydrogen.[9] After releasing this gas, the autoclave is pressurized with 40 atmospheres of hydrogen and then 160 atmospheres of carbon monoxide. It is then heated to 160–180°. After a short induction period, a rapid reaction occurs. The reaction is allowed to proceed for 2 hr.; additional carbon monoxide is introduced to replace that consumed in the reaction. After the reaction period is over, the autoclave is allowed to cool to room temperature, and the excess gases are vented. At this stage, the reaction mixture should contain orange crystals of dicobalt octacarbonyl. These are isolated by filtration under nitrogen[78] and washed at least three times with distilled water. After drying at room temperature in a vacuum desiccator, 82 g. (60% yield) of orange crystalline dicobalt octacarbonyl is obtained.

---

[77] P. Szabó, L. Markó, and G. Bor, *Chem. Tech. (Berlin)* **13,** 549 (1961).

[78] Dicobalt octacarbonyl is too air-sensitive to be filtered in air by the usual suction filtration procedure. A filtration with nitrogen pressure possibly with mild suction is recommended.

Dicobalt octacarbonyl forms orange crystals soluble in organic solvets and unstable to both thermal decomposition and air oxidation. Storage at 0° or preferably −78° is recommended since tetracobalt dodecacarbonyl and ultimately cobalt metal is produced by carbon monoxide loss, which occurs slowly at room temperature and rapidly at 50°. On exposure to air for several minutes, dicobalt octacarbonyl is oxidized completely to a purple cobalt(II) derivative presumably either the oxide or the carbonate. However, samples for preparative purposes in which small quantities of oxidized material are not detrimental may be weighed in air if the crystals are reasonably large and the weighing rapid. Very pure samples of dicobalt octacarbonyl can be obtained by careful sublimation at 25°/0.1 mm. Dicobalt octacarbonyl is very toxic but probably not as hazardous as the much more volatile iron and nickel carbonyls.

Besides its use as a catalyst in certain carbonylation reactions of organic compounds, sometimes carried out on an industrial scale, dicobalt octacarbonyl is a useful starting material for the preparation of a variety of other cobalt carbonyl derivatives. It thus reacts with acetylenes to form derivatives of the type $RC_2R \cdot Co_2(CO)_6$[79] and occasionally $(RC_2R)_3Co_2(CO)_4$[80]; with certain diolefins such as butadiene and bicycloheptadiene to give compounds of the type $(diolefin)_2Co_2$ $(CO)_4$[81]; with cyclopentadiene and cycloheptatriene under appropriate conditions to give the red liquid derivatives $C_5H_5Co(CO)_2$[82] and $C_7H_7Co(CO)_3$,[83] respectively; and with halides of the general formula YCX_3 (X = halogen, Y = H, CH_3, halogens, CF_3, etc.) to form trinuclear derivatives of the type $YCCo_3(CO)_9$.[84] Treatment with a variety of Lewis bases causes disproportionation into $[Co(base)_6]^{2+}$ and $Co(CO)_4^-$; the anion $Co(CO)_4^-$ may also be obtained by reduction of dicobalt octacarbonyl with alkali metals and from "simple" cobalt(II) salts by reduction in the presence of carbon monoxide at atmospheric pressure as illustrated in the synthesis of $Hg[Co(CO)_4]_2$ which follows. The $Co(CO)_4^-$ anion is also a useful intermediate in syntheses of π-allyl-

[79] H. Greenberg, H. W. Sternberg, R. A. Friedel, J. H. Wotiz, R. Markby, and I. Wender, *J. Am. Chem. Soc.* **78**, 120 (1956).

[80] U. Krüerke and W. Hübel, *Chem. Ber.* **94**, 2829 (1961).

[81] G. Winkhaus and G. Wilkinson, *J. Chem. Soc.* 602 (1961).

[82] T. S. Piper, F. A. Cotton, and G. Wilkinson, *J. Inorg. Nucl. Chem.* **1**, 165 (1955).

[83] R. B. King and M. B. Bisnette, *Inorg. Chem.* **3**, 785 (1964).

[84] W. T. Dent, L. A. Duncanson, R. G. Guy, H. W. B. Reed, and B. L. Shaw, *Proc. Chem. Soc.* 169 (1961); G. Bor, L. Markó, and B. Markó, *Chem. Ber.* **95**, 333 (1962); R. Ercoli, E. Santambrogio, and G. Tettamanti Casagrande, *Chim. Ind. (Milan)* **44**, 1344 (1962).

cobalt tricarbonyl and its substitution products,[85] in syntheses of the perfluoroalkylcobalt tetracarbonyls, $R_fCo(CO)_4$,[86] and in the synthesis of the nitrosyl $Co(CO)_3NO$.[87] Examples of some of these syntheses using dicobalt octacarbonyl are included in this book.

10. Bis(Cobalt Tetracarbonyl)mercury

Although not a "pure" metal carbonyl derivative, bis(cobalt tetracarbonyl)mercury, $Hg[Co(CO)_4]_2$, is included in this section since it is sometimes a useful intermediate in the preparation of other cobalt carbonyl derivatives. Unlike $Co_2(CO)_8$, $Hg[Co(CO)_4]_2$ is stable in air for prolonged periods (1 year or longer) and may be prepared in quantity by a process not requiring the use of high-pressure equipment.

Bis(cobalt tetracarbonyl)mercury may be obtained by treatment of the anion $Co(CO)_4^-$ with mercury derivatives,[88] by treatment of cobalt with carbon monoxide under pressure in the presence of mercury derivatives,[89] and by treatment of dicobalt octacarbonyl with sodium amalgam.[90] A procedure developed by Hieber, Fischer, and Böckly[88] for obtaining $Hg[Co(CO)_4]_2$ from the readily available cobalt(II) nitrate hexahydrate without using high-pressure equipment follows.

Procedure:

(1) $\quad 2[Co(H_2O)_6](NO_3)_2 + 8CO + 3Na_2S_2O_4 \xrightarrow[\text{NH}_3]{\text{H}_2\text{O}} 2NaCo(CO)_4 + 4NaNO_3$
$$+ 6SO_2 + 12H_2O$$

(2) $\quad 2NaCo(CO)_4 + Hg(CN)_2 \rightarrow Hg[Co(CO)_4]_2 + 2NaCN$

The reaction is conducted in a 2-liter three-necked flask fitted with an efficient motor stirrer, pressure equalized dropping funnel, reflux condenser, and carbon monoxide inlet. Since large quantities of carbon monoxide are used in this reaction especially if scaled up as indicated below, it is strongly recommended that the reaction be carried out in an efficient hood.

The reaction flask is charged with a mixture of 160 ml. of concen-

[85] R. F. Heck and D. S. Breslow, *J. Am. Chem. Soc.* 82, 750 (1960), 83, 1097 (1961); W. R. McClellan, H. H. Hoehn, H. N. Cripps, E. L. Muetterties, and B. W. Howk, *J. Am. Chem. Soc.* 83, 1601 (1961).

[86] W. R. McClellan, *J. Am. Chem. Soc.* 83, 1598 (1961); W. Hieber and E. Lindner, *Chem. Ber.* 95, 2042 (1962).

[87] F. Seel, *Z. Anorg. Allgem. Chem.* 269, 40 (1952); G. Bor and B. Mohai, *Acta. Chim. Acad. Sci. Hung.* 8, 335 (1956); *Chem. Abstr.* 50, 13643 (1956).

[88] W. Hieber, E. O. Fischer, and E. Böckly, *Z. Anorg. Allgem. Chem.* 269, 308 (1952).

[89] W. Hieber and U. Teller, *Z. Anorg. Allgem. Chem.* 249, 43 (1942).

[90] S. V. Dighe and M. Orchin, *Inorg. Chem.* 1, 965 (1962).

trated (~30%) aqueous ammonia and 240 ml. of water. A solution of
17.5 g. (0.06 mole) of cobalt(II) nitrate hexahydrate in 40 ml. of water
is added. The air in the flask is replaced by carbon monoxide by flushing
at a rapid rate for several minutes. After cooling to 10–15° by an ice
bath and slowing the flow of carbon monoxide to ~10 bubbles per min-
ute (mineral oil bubbler), the reaction mixture is treated dropwise
(1 drop/10–15 seconds) with a solution of 20 g. (0.092 moles) of 80%
sodium dithionite (Na$_2$S$_2$O$_4$)[91] in a mixture of 95 ml. of concentrated
(~30%) aqueous ammonia and 135 ml. of water maintaining rapid
stirring. After all of the sodium dithionite solution has been added, the
excess dithionite is removed by treatment with 1 ml. of commercial 35%
aqueous formaldehyde to form formaldehydesulfoxylate (Rongalite).[92]
After 5 minutes, a solution of 10 g. (0.0396 moles) of mercury(II)
cyanide in a mixture of 20 ml. of 30% aqueous ammonia and 30 ml. of
water is added. A grayish-yellow precipitate of Hg[Co(CO)$_4$]$_2$ forms.
This is removed by filtration and washed free of ammonia with pure
water (the pH of the washings may be checked).

After sucking somewhat dry, the crude product is dissolved in a
minimum of acetone. The solution is then filtered by gravity several
times until all of the gray free mercury is removed. The product is precipitated from the filtrate by addition of water and removal of the
acetone is a water-aspirator vacuum. The orange air-stable crystals are
finally dried in a vacuum disiccator. Under optimum conditions a yield
of ~90% may be obtained.

If larger quantities of Hg[Co(CO)$_4$]$_2$ are desired, the reaction may
be carried out with little sacrifice in yield in a 5-liter flask using three
times the quantities of reactants listed above or in a 12-liter flask using
6.5 times the quantities of reactants listed above. The less stable silver
derivative [AgCo(CO)$_4$]$_n$ may also be obtained by a similar procedure
but using silver nitrate instead of the mercury(II) cyanide.

Bis(cobalt tetracarbonyl)mercury is an orange solid, m.p. 81–82°,
that is stable in air for at least 1 year in contrast to the rather air-sensitive dicobalt octacarbonyl. On heating at 50°/0.1 mm., it sublimes
partially to give an orange crystalline sublimate and decomposes partially to give a deposit of cobalt amalgam which under certain conditions
may appear as a bright metallic mirror. Reaction with sodium sulfide
produces a black precipitate of mercury(II) sulfide and a solution of
Na[Co(CO)$_4$] useful for certain preparative purposes.[88]

---

[91] Commercially available and also known as sodium hydrosulfite or sodium hypo-
sulfite.
[92] If the excess sodium dithionite is not thus removed chemically, it will reduce some
of the mercury(II) cyanide to metallic mercury.

11. Tetracobalt Dodecacarbonyl

Tetracobalt dodecacarbonyl, $Co_4(CO)_{12}$, is readily formed by heating dicobalt octacarbonyl to $\sim50°$. However, it is inconvenient to separate large quantities of tetracobalt dodecacarbonyl in a pure condition from this reaction mixture. Therefore, an alternative preparation of Ercoli et al.[93] based on the reduction of an appropriate cobalt(II) derivative with hydrogen in the presence of dicobalt octacarbonyl that is given here is recommended for the preparation of larger quantities of tetracobalt dodecacarbonyl.

Procedure:

$$3Co_2(CO)_8 + 2Co(C_7H_{15}CO_2)_2 + 2H_2 \rightarrow 2Co_4(CO)_{12} + 4C_7H_{15}CO_2H$$

An autoclave or other pressure vessel of at least 150-ml. internal capacity and capable of withstanding at least 75 atmospheres[94] is charged with 9.66 g. (0.0282 moles) of dicobalt octacarbonyl, and 6.66 g. (0.0179 mole) of cobalt(II) 2-ethylhexanoate or an equivalent quantity of cobalt(II) acetylacetonate or other cobalt(II) derivative possessing appreciable solubility in saturated hydrocarbons. Finally, 50 ml. of n-heptane[95] is added. After stirring 2 hr. at 30°, hydrogen is introduced into the autoclave until the pressure is 59 atmospheres. After stirring an additional 8 hr. under pressure at 30°, the autoclave is cooled to room temperature, and the hydrogen is vented. The black crystals of tetracobalt dodecacarbonyl are removed by filtration under nitrogen[96] and washed with three 50-ml. portions of n-heptane[95] that has been previously cooled to $\sim-70°$ in a Dry Ice bath. After drying the crystals in a vacuum desiccator or under nitrogen, 9.89 g. (96.5% yield) of black tetracobalt dodecacarbonyl is obtained.

Tetracobalt dodecacarbonyl forms black crystals sparingly soluble in organic solvents to give brown solutions and subliming with some decomposition to pyrophoric cobalt at 90°/0.1 mm. Upon exposure to air, it oxidizes to the purple insoluble cobalt(II) oxide or carbonate

[93] R. Ercoli, P. Chini, and M. Massi-Mauri, *Chim. Ind. (Milan)* **41**, 132 (1959).

[94] If the 1-liter autoclave specified for the other experiments is also used for the preparation of tetracobalt dodecacarbonyl, the reaction may be scaled up by a factor of six or seven.

[95] Although Ercoli, Chini, and Massi-Mauri specify n-heptane for a solvent, there appears to be no reason why other saturated aliphatic hydrocarbons such as hexane, pentane, isohexane, or petroleum ether could not also be used.

[96] Like dicobalt octacarbonyl, tetracobalt dodecacarbonyl is too air-sensitive to be filtered by suction in the usual manner. A filtration using nitrogen pressure is therefore recommended.

but at an appreciably slower rate than $Co_2(CO)_8$. It may therefore be handled in the air for brief periods for purposes such as weighing but some care in this connection is recommended since it is not presently practical to recover tetracobalt dodecacarbonyl in the pure condition from partially oxidized samples; sublimation leads to appreciable losses from decomposition, and crystallization is impractical because of the large quantities of solvent required. Tetracobalt dodecacarbonyl reacts with acetylenes to form blue derivatives of the general formula $RC_2R \cdot Co_4(CO)_{10}$.[97]

12. Nickel Tetracarbonyl

Nickel tetracarbonyl, $Ni(CO)_4$, a colorless, very volatile (b.p. 43°), extremely toxic liquid, is readily available in steel cylinders in the United States and Great Britain and in glass bottles in West Germany. Because of its ready availability, its preparation is not included in this book. Two recommended methods for the preparation of nickel tetracarbonyl are the reaction of specially prepared metallic nickel with carbon monoxide at atmospheric pressure[98] and the reduction of nickel(II) salts with sodium dithionite in ammoniacal solution in the presence of carbon monoxide at atmospheric pressure.[88] The toxicity of nickel tetracarbonyl which is even greater than that of hydrogen cyanide makes its handling and especially its preparation very hazardous. A good hood is absolutely necessary for minimum risk with operations involving nickel tetracarbonyl.

[97] U. Krüerke and W. Hübel, *Chem. Ber.* **94,** 2829 (1961).
[98] W. L. Gilliland and A. A. Blanchard, *Inorg. Syn.* **2,** 234 (1946).

C. Cyclopentadienylmetal Carbonyls

1. Cyclopentadienylvanadium Tetracarbonyl

Until recently, the only known method for preparing $C_5H_5V(CO)_4$ was the reaction between $(C_5H_5)_2V$ and carbon monoxide under pressure first discovered by Fischer and Hafner.[1a,b] Although good yields (80 to 98% based on $(C_5H_5)_2V$ or 40–50% based on VCl_3) could be obtained by reacting pure solid $(C_5H_5)_2V$ with a mixture of carbon monoxide and hydrogen under pressure, the isolation of pure $(C_5H_5)_2V$ in quantity as previously described is inconvenient. This may be avoided by subjecting the crude solution obtained by treatment of sodium cyclopentadienide with vanadium(III) chloride to carbonylation; however, in this case, the yield of $C_5H_5V(CO)_4$ sinks to 15–25% based on vanadium(III) chloride. An example of such a procedure ("modified Fischer-Hafner method") for the preparation of $C_5H_5V(CO)_4$ will be given.

In view of the difficulties in obtaining large quantities of $C_5H_5V(CO)_4$ conveniently by reacting $(C_5H_5)_2V$ with carbon monoxide, the very recent discovery by Werner et al.[2] of an improved synthesis of $C_5H_5V(CO)_4$ by an entirely different reaction was a welcome development. Based on the reaction between the hexacarbonylvanadate(-I) anion, $V(CO)_6^-$, and cyclopentadienylmercuric chloride (prepared in situ from appropriate quantities of sodium cyclopentadienide and mercury(II) chloride), it not only provides a greatly improved $C_5H_5V(CO)_4$ synthesis but provides the first practical routes to the otherwise difficultly accessible $C_5H_5Nb(CO)_4$[3] and to the inaccessible $C_5H_5Ta(CO)_4$. Both the modified Fischer-Hafner and the Werner-Filbey-Manastyrskyj syntheses of $C_5H_5V(CO)_4$ are described.

Procedure A:

$$(C_5H_5)_2V + 4CO \xrightarrow{\Delta} C_5H_5V(CO)_4 + \{C_5H_5\cdot\}$$

The reaction is carried out in a 1-liter three-necked flask equipped with an efficient motor stirrer, nitrogen inlet, reflux condenser, and pres-

[1a] E. O. Fischer and W. Hafner, *Z. Naturforsch.* **9b**, 503 (1954).

[1b] E. O. Fischer and S. Vigoureux, *Chem. Ber.* **91**, 2205 (1958).

[2] R. P. M. Werner, A. H. Filbey, and S. A. Manastyrskyj, *Inorg. Chem.* **3**, 298 (1964).

[3] R. B. King, *Z. Naturforsch.* **18b**, 157 (1963).

sure-equalized dropping funnel. After filling with nitrogen, the flask is charged with 100 ml. of dry xylene, and 11.5 g. (0.5 mole) of sodium metal is added. The reaction mixture is heated to the boiling point, and the molten sodium is then stirred vigorously to form finely divided sodium sand. The stirring is discontinued, and the sodium is allowed to cool to room temperature. The xylene is removed with a syringe, and the sodium sand is washed once with 100 ml. of tetrahydrofuran.[4] After removing this tetrahydrofuran,[5] the sodium sand is treated with 150 ml. of additional tetrahydrofuran and then dropwise with 50 ml. (40 g., 0.607 mole) of cyclopentadiene freshly prepared by thermal dedimerization of commercial dicyclopentadiene. After all of the cyclopentadiene has been added, the mixture is stored until all of the sodium has dissolved to form a pink to dark-red-violet[6] solution of sodium cyclopentadienide.

This sodium cyclopentadienide solution is treated with 25 g. (0.0159 mole) of anhydrous vanadium trichloride.[7] An exothermic reaction occurs, and a deep-purple solution of biscyclopentadienylvanadium forms which is stirred for 2 hr.

The carbonylation of the biscyclopentadienylvanadium solution is carried out in an autoclave of 1-liter internal capacity that is capable of withstanding at least 100 atmospheres.[8] While passing a rapid stream of nitrogen both through the autoclave or its liner and through the flask containing the biscyclopentadienylvanadium solution, the $(C_5H_5)_2V$ solution is poured into the autoclave or its liner which is then assembled, closed, and connected to a source of carbon monoxide under pressure. The autoclave is flushed once with at least 50 atmospheres of carbon monoxide.[9] After releasing this carbon monoxide, the autoclave

---

[4] Tetrahydrofuran may be purified either by distillation over lithium aluminum hydride or sodium benzophenone ketyl or by passing through a column of molecular sieves.

[5] An appropriate quantity of a commercial sodium dispersion in xylene may be used in place of the sodium sand prepared as described. Use of commercial sodium dispersion in mineral oil may lead to contamination of the product cyclopentadienylvanadium tetracarbonyl with mineral oil because of similar volatilities of these two materials.

[6] The color of the sodium cyclopentadienide solution will depend on the amount of oxygen and other impurities present (see footnote 6, page 65).

[7] Vanadium trichloride may be obtained commercially in the United States (e.g., Anderson Chemical Company, Weston, Michigan). It may be prepared by boiling vanadium pentoxide with disulfur dichloride (S_2Cl_2). [G. Brauer, "Handbuch der Präparativen Anorganischen Chemie" (G. Brauer, ed.), p. 1099. Ferdinand Enke Verlag, Stuttgart, 1962.]

[8] A smaller or larger autoclave may be used with a corresponding change in the quantities of reactants.

[9] If the carbon monoxide tank contains less than 50 atmospheres, more than one

is then pressurized with at least 60 atmospheres of carbon monoxide and heated to $117 \pm 6°$ for 7 hr.

When the reaction period is over, the autoclave is cooled to room temperature, the carbon monoxide pressure is released, and the autoclave is then opened. The black reaction mixture is transferred to a flask, and tetrahydrofuran is removed in a water-aspirator vacuum (15 to 50 mm.). The residue (without admitting air) is then dried at ~1 mm. until it is no longer sticky and can readily be removed from the flask.

Nitrogen is then admitted to this flask, and the residue is then transferred to a large sublimation apparatus.[10] Sublimation at 80–110°/ 0.1 mm.[11] gives 8.2 g. (23% yield) of orange crystalline C$_5$H$_5$V(CO)$_4$.

Procedure B:

(1) $NaC_5H_5 + HgCl_2 \rightarrow C_5H_5HgCl + NaCl$

(2) $[Na(C_6H_{14}O_2)_2][V(CO)_6] + C_5H_5HgCl \rightarrow C_5H_5V(CO)_4 + 2CO \uparrow$
$+ Hg + 2C_6H_{14}O_3 + NaCl$

The reaction is carried out in a 2-liter three-necked flask equipped with a nitrogen inlet, reflux condenser, motor stirrer, and pressure-equalized dropping funnel. After filling the system with nitrogen, the flask is charged with 6.9 g. (0.3 mole) of sodium metal and 100 ml. of dry xylene. The sodium metal is converted to sodium sand as described in the preparation of C$_5$H$_5$V(CO)$_4$ by the modified Fischer-Hafner method.

This sodium sand or an equivalent quantity of commercial sodium dispersion in xylene or mineral oil is suspended in 600 ml. of tetrahydrofuran,[4] and 32 ml. (26.6 g., 0.39 mole) of freshly prepared cyclopentadiene is added to form a solution of sodium cyclopentadienide.

After all of the sodium has dissolved, the resulting solution of sodium cyclopentadienide is treated with 81.4 g. (0.3 mole) of mercury(II) chloride. The pale brown reaction mixture is stirred for 30 minutes. A solution of 102 g. (0.2 mole) of [Na(diglyme)$_2$][V(CO)$_6$] (page 82) in 500 ml. of tetrahydrofuran[4] is added to the cyclopentadienylmercuric chloride solution from the dropping funnel in a thin stream. Carbon

---

flushing with less than 50 atmospheres of carbon monoxide instead of one flushing with 50 atmospheres of carbon monoxide may be used. Nitrogen or hydrogen may also be used as the flushing gas.

[10] If a sufficiently large sublimation apparatus is not available, the sublimation may be carried out in several portions in a smaller sublimer.

[11] Cyclopentadienylvanadium tetracarbonyl is reported to lose carbon monoxide on heating in vacuum above 120°[1]; therefore, the sublimation should be conducted below 120°. The residues from the C$_5$H$_5$V(CO)$_4$ sublimation may be pyrophoric.

monoxide evolution occurs, and the reaction mixture becomes red-orange.

After stirring the reaction mixture overnight at room temperature, the solvent is removed in a water-aspirator vacuum (15 to 50 mm.). Nitrogen is admitted to the residue which is then treated with 200 ml. of water and filtered by suction. The gray-green residue is washed liberally (about five ~100-ml. portions) with water and sucked dry for about 10 minutes.[12]

The crude product is extracted with five 100-ml. portions of diethyl ether; the extracts are filtered by gravity, and the filtrate is collected under nitrogen. The free mercury produced in the reaction remains behind on the filter. The diethyl ether is removed from the filtrate in a water-aspirator vacuum leaving orange crystals. These are purified finally by sublimation at 80–110°/0.1 mm. to give 22.8 g. to 36.5 g. (50–80% yield) of $C_5H_5V(CO)_4$.

Cyclopentadienylvanadium tetracarbonyl forms orange crystals, m.p. 138°, that are insoluble in water but soluble in organic solvents and give yellow to orange solutions depending upon the concentration. The solid material blackens on exposure to air for a few days, and solutions oxidize appreciably in an hour or less. Storage under nitrogen preferably in a freezer or Dry Ice chest is recommended especially if the material is used for physical studies. Nevertheless, the blackening of decomposed samples is largely superficial at least if the crystals are of appreciable size. Thus, samples of $C_5H_5V(CO)_4$ that had turned jet-black on standing at room temperature in an imperfectly sealed bottle were still suitable for many preparative purposes.

The infrared spectrum (CS_2 solution) of $C_5H_5V(CO)_4$ exhibits strong metal carbonyl bands at 1890 and 1982 cm.$^{-1}$. Its proton n.m.r. spectrum (CS_2 solution) exhibits a single sharp resonance at 5.00 τ.

Cyclopentadienylvanadium tetracarbonyl is a useful precursor for the synthesis of many interesting cyclopentadienyl derivatives of vanadium. Treatment of $C_5H_5V(CO)_4$ with a mixture of dry hydrogen chloride and oxygen gives the oxychloride derivative $C_5H_5VOCl_2$.[13,14] Reduction of $C_5H_5V(CO)_4$ with alkali-metals in liquid ammonia gives the dianion $[C_5H_5V(CO)_3]^{2-}$.[1b] Treatment of $C_5H_5V(CO)_4$ with cyclo-

[12] If the cyclopentadienylvanadium tetracarbonyl is sublimed directly from this residue omitting the ether-extraction step, the product will be contaminated with mercury since it and $C_5H_5V(CO)_4$ are about equally volatile.

[13] E. O. Fischer and S. Vigoureux, *Chem. Ber.* **91**, 1342 (1958).

[14] E. O. Fischer and S. Vigoureux, *Chem. Ber.* **93**, 701 (1960).

heptatriene and with various dienes gives the complexes $C_5H_5VC_7H_7$[15] and $C_5H_5V(CO)_2(diene)$,[16] respectively. Treatment of $C_5H_5V(CO)_4$ with the organosulfur derivatives dimethyldisulfide[17] and bis(trifluoromethyl) dithietene[18] gives compounds of the general type $[C_5H_5V(SR)_2]_2$ believed to have structures with four sulfur bridges and to possess interesting magnetic properties.

2. Cyclopentadienylmolybdenum Tricarbonyl Dimer

Cyclopentadienylmolybdenum tricarbonyl dimer has been prepared by reaction between molybdenum hexacarbonyl and cyclopentadiene or its dimer[19,20] and by aerial oxidation of tetrahydrofuran solutions of the hydride $C_5H_5Mo(CO)_3H$.[21a,b] The most convenient route to $[C_5H_5Mo(CO)_3]_2$ is the thermal reaction between molybdenum hexacarbonyl and dicyclopentadiene.

Procedure:

$$2Mo(CO)_6 + C_{10}H_{12} \xrightarrow{\Delta} [C_5H_5Mo(CO)_3]_2 + 6CO \uparrow + H_2$$

The reaction is carried out under nitrogen in a 1-liter flask fitted with a nitrogen inlet, magnetic stirrer, straight reflux condenser,[22] and heating mantle. The flask is charged with 100 g. (0.379 mole) of molybdenum hexacarbonyl and 500 ml. of dicyclopentadiene.[23] The reaction mixture is heated gently (Variac setting on heating mantle 30 to 40 volts) at 135–145° (gentle reflux) until no more white molybdenum hexacarbonyl sublimes out of the reaction mixture.[24] From time to time,

---

[15] R. B. King and F. G. A. Stone, *J. Am. Chem. Soc.* 81, 5263 (1959).

[16] E. O. Fischer and H. P. Kögler, and P. Kuzel, *Chem. Ber.* 93, 3006 (1960).

[17] R. H. Holm, R. B. King, and F. G. A. Stone, *Inorg. Chem.* 2, 219 (1963).

[18] R. B. King, *J. Am. Chem. Soc.* 85, 1587 (1963).

[19] G. Wilkinson, *J. Am. Chem. Soc.* 76, 209 (1954).

[20] R. G. Hayter, *Inorg. Chem.* 2, 1031 (1963).

[21a] T. S. Piper and G. Wilkinson, *J. Inorg. Nucl. Chem.* 3, 104 (1956).

[21b] R. B. King and F. G. A. Stone, *Inorg. Syn.* 7, 107 (1963).

[22] A straight reflux condenser (either with or without bulbs) must be used in this reaction because of the necessity of periodically inserting a wire or rod into the condenser to return sublimed molybdenum hexacarbonyl to the reaction mixture.

[23] A good grade of dicyclopentadiene should be used. The material of 95% purity sold by Enjay Corp., 1024 South Avenue, Plainfield, New Jersey, is inexpensive and recommended for this reaction. Less pure dicyclopentadiene may lead either to less pure $[C_5H_5Mo(CO)_3]_2$ or to more ready solidification of the reaction mixture to an intractable mass.

[24] If the heating is continued beyond this point, the danger of resinification of the reaction mixture increases.

molybdenum hexacarbonyl that has sublimed into the reflux condenser is pushed back into the reaction mixture with a wire or rod.[25]

After the reaction period is over, the reaction mixture is cooled to room temperature. If the preparation has succeeded, red crystals of the product should separate. If the heating time has been too short or the temperature too low, the crystals which separate will be predominantly white molybdenum hexacarbonyl; in this case, heating the reaction mixture should be continued. If the reaction mixture settles to a brownish solid sticky mass of polymerized cyclopentadiene which cannot readily be removed from the flask, the reaction conditions have been too vigorous; in this case, the material should be discarded and a repeat preparation should be carried out using a lower reaction temperature and/or less reaction time. Unfortunately, the conditions for this preparation appear to be rather critical and not readily reproduced. The proper execution of this reaction is somewhat of an art.

The red-violet crystals of the product are filtered by suction and washed at least four times with hexane, pentane, or petroleum ether to remove excess dicyclopentadiene and other hydrocarbon impurities. The product is then heated at 50°/0.5 mm. for at least 12 hr. preferably in a sublimer to insure complete removal of any molybdenum hexacarbonyl. Molybdenum hexacarbonyl, if present, will condense on the cooler portions of the apparatus as large colorless crystals. The bright red-violet residue consists of $[C_5H_5Mo(CO)_3]_2$ of sufficient purity for most preparative purposes. The yield in this reaction is somewhat variable but may be as high as 80%.

If purer material is desired,[26] the crude product may be purified by dissolving in 1 liter of chloroform. The chloroform solution is filtered by gravity, and 200 ml. of hexane is added to the dark-red filtrate. The solvent is removed from this filtrate in a water-aspirator vacuum; the red-violet crystals of $[C_5H_5Mo(CO)_3]_2$ separate. When the volume reaches ~100 ml., the crystals are filtered and washed three times with pentane, hexane, or petroleum ether, and sucked dry.

Cyclopentadienylmolybdenum tricarbonyl dimer may also be purified by a slow vacuum sublimation at 160°/0.1 mm., but extensive decomposition occurs during this sublimation which makes the process inefficient.

---

[25] Any molybdenum hexacarbonyl remaining in the reflux condenser after the heating has stopped may be saved for a future $[C_5H_5Mo(CO)_3]_2$ preparation. Alternatively, the crystals of $Mo(CO)_6$ thus recovered after washing with methanol or pentane and resublimation may be used for other purposes.

[26] If the crude product is brownish rather than a pure red-violet, this purification procedure should be used.

Cyclopentadienylmolybdenum tricarbonyl dimer is a red-violet solid, m.p. 215–217°, that is almost insoluble in nonpolar organic solvents and soluble to only a limited extent in polar organic solvents. When pure, it is stable in air. Its infrared spectrum (KBr pellet) exhibits very strong metal carbonyl absorptions at 1957, 1926, 1904, and 1891 cm.$^{-1}$ It is reduced by sodium amalgam in tetrahydrofuran solution to give the sodium salt $Na[Mo(CO)_3C_5H_5]$,[20] a useful precursor to many interesting organomolybdenum compounds often of the type $C_5H_5Mo(CO)_3R$. Treatment of $[C_5H_5Mo(CO)_3]_2$ with iodine in chloroform solution gives the iodide $C_5H_5Mo(CO)_3I$.[27] Treatment of $[C_5H_5Mo(CO)_3]_2$ with dimethyldisulfide or bis(trifluoromethyl)dithietene at elevated temperatures gives derivatives of the general formula $[C_5H_5Mo(SR)_2]_2$ which appear to have structures with four sulfur bridges.[18]

3. Cyclopentadienylmanganese Tricarbonyl

Cyclopentadienylmanganese tricarbonyl was first obtained by the treatment of manganese(II) cyclopentadienide with carbon monoxide.[28a,b] Later, cyclopentadienylmanganese tricarbonyl and more particularly methylcyclopentadienylmanganese tricarbonyl became important as antiknocks for motor fuels which stimulated the search for improved preparative methods especially by the Ethyl Corporation. A variety of preparative methods for $C_5H_5Mn(CO)_3$ and $CH_3C_5H_4Mn(CO)_3$ are given in the patent literature.[29] Generally, these methods are based on the treatment of manganese salts with carbon monoxide in the presence of cyclopentadiene and a strong reducing agent.

Research quantities of $C_5H_5Mn(CO)_3$ are often available from the Ethyl Corporation. However, the continued commercial availability of this compound will probably be very dependent on the use of organomanganese compounds as antiknocks, a likely possibility only if automobiles in the future have high octane fuel requirements. Since $C_5H_5Mn(CO)_3$ may not be commercially available in the future, its

[27] E. W. Abel, A. Singh, and G. Wilkinson, *J. Chem. Soc.* 1321 (1960).

[28a] E. O. Fischer and R. Jira, *Z. Naturforsch.* 9b, 618 (1954).

[28b] T. S. Piper, F. A. Cotton, and G. Wilkinson, *J. Inorg. Nucl. Chem.* 1, 165 (1955).

[29] J. Kozikowski, U. S. Patent 3,015,668; T. H. Pearson and J. K. Presswood, U. S. Patent 3,028,404; Brit. 861,371; J. E. Brown, E. G. DeWitt, and H. Shapiro, U. S. Patents 2,868,699 and 2,868,700; H. E. Petree, U. S. Patent 2,868,816; J. Byron and A. F. Limper, U. S. Patent 2,868,697; H. J. Cragg, U. S. Patent 2,868,698, J. Kozikowski and M. L. Larson, U. S. Patent 2,870,180; Brit. 845,074; J. E. Brown, E. G. DeWitt, and H. Shapiro, U. S. Patent 2,960,514; L. L. Sims, U. S. Patent 2,987,529; T. H. Pearson and J. K. Presswood, U. S. Patent 2,987,530; J. E. Brown, E. G. DeWitt, and H. Shapiro, U. S. Patent 2,987,528, 2,987,531 and many other patents.

preparation is described by a relative new (1962) method of Cordes and Neubauer[30] of Badische Anilin- und Soda Fabrik in Germany.

Procedure:

$$2(C_5H_5N)_2MnCl_2 + Mg + 2C_5H_6 + 6CO \xrightarrow[\text{H}_2]{\text{(CH}_3)_2\text{NCOH}} 2C_5H_5Mn(CO)_3$$
$$+ 2[C_5H_5NH]Cl + MgCl_2 + 2C_5H_5N$$

The reaction is carried out in a rocking autoclave of 1 liter internal capacity capable of safely withstanding pressures of at least 300 atmospheres.[31] This autoclave is charged with 500 ml. of dimethylformamide,[32] 80 g. (1.212 mole) of freshly prepared cyclopentadiene (from dicyclopentadiene), 140 g. (0.493 mole) of dipyridinemanganese(II) chloride,[33] and 40 g. (1.667 mole) of magnesium turnings.[34] The autoclave is then closed and connected to a source of carbon monoxide and hydrogen under pressure.[35] First, the autoclave is flushed once with at least 50 atmospheres of nitrogen, hydrogen, or carbon monoxide.[9] After releasing this gas, the autoclave is then pressurized first with 50 atmospheres of hydrogen[36] followed by 80 atmospheres of carbon monoxide. The autoclave is then heated to 180° with rocking. At this temperature, the carbon monoxide pressure is increased to 300 atmospheres. The autoclave is then maintained at 180° for at least 12 hours. When the reaction period is over, the autoclave is then allowed to

---

[30] J. F. Cordes and D. Neubauer, Z. *Naturforsch.* **17b**, 791 (1962).

[31] A smaller or larger autoclave may be used with a corresponding change in the quantities of reactants. If the maximum pressure rating of the system is less than 300 atmospheres, a lower pressure of carbon monoxide must be used such that the pressure does not exceed the maximum rating at some stage of the reaction. If a lower pressure of carbon monoxide is used, the yield and/or reaction rate is appreciably lower but this effect has not been described in detail.

[32] Dimethylformamide may be purified by passing through a column of Linde molecular sieves or by distillation over phosphorus pentoxide.

[33] The following procedure of Cordes and Neubauer[30] is recommended for the preparation of dipyridine manganese(II) chloride: A solution of 300 g. (1.52 moles) of manganese(II) chloride 4-hydrate in 3 liters of ethanol is heated to the boiling point and treated dropwise with 250 ml. (245 g., 3.1 moles) of pyridine. After cooling to room temperature, the precipitate is filtered by suction, washed with diethyl ether and dried at 110°. A 90% yield (380 g.) of $(C_5H_5N)_2MnCl_2$ is thus obtained.

[34] The grade of magnesium turnings suitable for Grignard reactions is also suitable for this reaction.

[35] Since the maximum pressure available in commercial tanks of carbon monoxide is 70 to 100 atmospheres, a compressor is required to attain the pressures necessary for the reaction.

[36] The hydrogen can be omitted from the reaction mixture but with decreases in the yield and quality of the product.

cool to room temperature, the carbon monoxide and hydrogen are released, and the autoclave is opened. The contents are transferred to a large three-necked flask equipped for steam distillation of solid metal carbonyl derivatives (Fig. 22) (page 86). The reaction mixture is then decomposed with ~200 ml. of water. Steam is then passed through the reaction mixture[37] at such a rate that it is all condensed into the receiver.[38] Cyclopentadienylmanganese tricarbonyl distills into the receiver as a golden yellow oil solidifying on cooling. After no more C_5H_5Mn $(CO)_3$ distills over, the steam distillation is discontinued, and the distillate is cooled to room temperature and is finally placed in an ice bath to complete crystallization. The yellow $C_5H_5Mn(CO)_3$ is removed by filtration, sucked dry, and finally dried in a desiccator at 25°/0.1 mm.[39] If further purification is desired, the product is sublimed at 50°/0.1 mm. onto a water-cooled probe. A yield of 71 g. (70%) of $C_5H_5Mn(CO)_3$ has been reported from this reaction.

Cyclopentadienylmanganese tricarbonyl is a yellow, air-stable, crystalline solid, m.p. 77°, that is soluble in organic solvents and gives air-stable yellow solutions. Its infrared spectrum (KBr pellet) exhibits strong metal carbonyl bands at 2023 and 1939 cm.$^{-1}$. Its solution in carbon disulfide exhibits a single sharp resonance at 5.35 τ in the proton n.m.r. spectrum due to the five equivalent cyclopentadienyl protons.

Cyclopentadienylmanganese tricarbonyl reacts with dilute nitric acid or preferably nitrous acid to give the cation $[C_5H_5Mn(CO)_2NO]^+$.[28b] The cyclopentadienyl ring in $C_5H_5Mn(CO)_3$ may be acylated by acyl halides in the Friedel-Crafts reaction[40] and may be sulfonated by sulfuric acid in acetic anhydride.[41] On irradiation with a variety of ligands including both Lewis bases such as amines, phosphines, and sulfoxides,[42] and vari-

---

[37] The steam may be taken directly from a steam line. If a steam line is not available, ~2 liters of water may be added to the reaction mixture and then distilled. The distillation of the water is continued until no more cyclopentadienylmanganese tricarbonyl codistills.

[38] If the steam is not completely condensed, some of the cyclopentadienylmanganese tricarbonyl will be lost.

[39] This drying time should be held to a minimum to prevent significant losses of $C_5H_5Mn(CO)_3$ from its volatility.

[40] E. O. Fischer and K. Plesske, *Chem. Ber.* **91**, 2719 (1958); F. A. Cotton and J. R. Leto. *Chem. Ind.* (*London*) 1368 (1958); R. Riemschneider and H. G. Kassahn, *Z. Naturforsch.* **14b**, 348 (1959); K. Kozikowski, R. E. Maginn, and M. S. Klove, *J. Am. Chem. Soc.* **81**, 2995 (1959).

[41] M. Cais and J. Kozikowski, *J. Am. Chem. Soc.* **82**, 5667 (1960).

[42] W. Strohmeier and J. F. Guttenberger, *Z. Naturforsch.* **18b**, 667 (1963) and references cited therein; J. Lewis, R. S. Nyholm, A. G. Osborne, S. S. Sandhu, and M. H. B. Stiddard, *Chem. Ind.* (*London*) 1398 (1963).

ous olefins,[16,43] 1 mole of carbon monoxide is lost to form compounds of the general type $C_5H_5Mn(CO)_2L$; butadiene, however, forms the monocarbonyl $C_5H_5MnCOC_4H_6$.[16]

4. Cyclopentadienyliron Dicarbonyl Dimer

Cyclopentadienyliron dicarbonyl dimer has been prepared by heating iron pentacarbonyl either with dicyclopentadiene in an open flask[28b,44] or with cyclopentadiene in an autoclave.[45] The preparation from dicyclopentadiene is more convenient and is preferred when good quality dicyclopentadiene is available.

Alfa Inorganics, Inc., 8 Congress Street, Beverly, Massachusetts, is now selling $[C_5H_5Fe(CO)_2]_2$ in research quantities.

Procedure:

$$2Fe(CO)_5 + C_{10}H_{12} \rightarrow [C_5H_5Fe(CO)_2]_2 + 6CO \uparrow + H_2$$

The reaction is carried out in a well-ventilated hood in a flask of at least 4-liter capacity equipped with a nitrogen inlet, reflux condenser, and stirrer. After filling with nitrogen, the flask is charged with 2,000 g. (15.15 moles) of dicyclopentadiene[46] and 400 ml. (584 g., 2.975 moles) of iron pentacarbonyl.[47] This mixture is heated under gentle reflux[48] for about 16 hr.[49] The reaction mixture is then allowed to cool slowly to room temperature, and red-violet crystals of the product separate. These are filtered by suction, washed with at least four 200-ml. portions of pentane, hexane, or petroleum ether, and sucked dry[50] to give up to

[43] E. O. Fischer and H. P. Kögler, *Z. Naturforsch.* **16b**, 475 (1961).

[44] R. B. King and F. G. A. Stone, *Inorg. Syn.*, **7**, 110 (1963).

[45] B. F. Hallam and P. L. Pauson, *J. Chem. Soc.* 3030 (1956).

[46] A good quality of dicyclopentadiene is even more important for the preparation of $[C_5H_5Fe(CO)_2]_2$ than for the preparation of $[C_5H_5Mo(CO)_3]_2$[23] since use of inferior material may lead to a pyrophoric sample of $[C_5H_5Fe(CO)_2]_2$ apparently due to pyrophoric iron from decomposition. The material from Enjay Corporation[23] of 95% purity is recommended for this reaction.

[47] The use of this large quantity of iron pentacarbonyl presents a hazard from its toxicity. If a well-ventilated hood is not used, dangerous concentrations of iron pentacarbonyl vapor will be present in the laboratory atmosphere. The presence of iron pentacarbonyl vapors in the atmosphere may be recognized by its characteristic musty odor. Early symptoms of iron pentacarbonyl poisoning include headache and difficult breathing.

[48] The liquid temperature should be around 140°.

[49] When the reaction is over, no more yellow vapors of iron pentacarbonyl should be seen during the refluxing.

[50] If the dicyclopentadiene used for the reaction is of poor quality or if the reaction conditions are much more vigorous than those indicated, the product may be pyrophoric presenting a fire hazard if unexpected. No difficulties of this type have been experienced in carrying out the reaction with 95% cyclopentadiene and under the conditions described.

480 g. (91.5% yield) of [C$_5$H$_5$Fe(CO)$_2$]$_2$ that is sufficiently pure for most purposes.

If a purer sample of [C$_5$H$_5$Fe(CO)$_2$]$_2$ is desired, the crude product is dissolved in a minimum of dichloromethane or chloroform. After filtering the solution and collecting the filtrate under nitrogen, hexane is added, and the solvent is removed slowly in a water-aspirator vacuum. During this solvent removal process, the more volatile chloroform or dichloromethane is lost in preference to the less volatile hexane causing the [C$_5$H$_5$Fe(CO)$_2$]$_2$, which is almost insoluble in hexane, to crystallize out. The resulting crystals are filtered, washed with pentane, hexane, or petroleum ether, and sucked dry.

Cyclopentadienyliron dicarbonyl dimer forms dark-red-purple crystals, m.p. 194° (dec.), and is air-stable in the pure solid state. Although insoluble in water like the other cyclopentadienylmetal carbonyls, [C$_5$H$_5$Fe(CO)$_2$]$_2$ is sparingly soluble in nonpolar organic solvents and soluble in polar organic solvents to give deep-red solutions that oxidize gradually in air and precipitate brown iron(III) oxide. The infrared spectrum (KBr pellet) not only exhibits the characteristic strong terminal metal carbonyl bands at 1955 and 1940 cm.$^{-1}$ but also a strong band at 1756 cm.$^{-1}$ due to bridging metal carbonyl groups. The proton n.m.r. spectrum exhibits a single sharp resonance at 5.21 τ due to the equivalent cyclopentadienyl protons of the two rings. Not only because of its chemical properties but also because of its ready availability, cyclopentadienyliron dicarbonyl dimer is a very useful precursor to a variety of cyclopentadienyliron compounds. Thus, treatment with substituted cyclopentadienes produces unsymmetrical ferrocene derivatives.[45] The iron-iron bond is cleaved by halogens[28b,51] or sodium amalgam[21a,52] to form the derivatives C$_5$H$_5$Fe(CO)$_2$X (X = Cl, Br, or I) or Na[Fe(CO)$_2$C$_5$H$_5$], respectively; reactions of the latter with a great variety of both organic and inorganic halides give numerous compounds of the type C$_5$H$_5$Fe(CO)$_2$R. Dialkyldisulfides form compounds of the type [C$_5$H$_5$Fe-COSR]$_2$ when heated with [C$_5$H$_5$Fe(CO)$_2$]$_2$ to about 100°.[53]

5. Cyclopentadienylcobalt Dicarbonyl

Cyclopentadienylcobalt dicarbonyl may be obtained either from dicobalt octacarbonyl and cyclopentadiene[54,28b] or from cobaltocene and

[51] T. S. Piper and G. Wilkinson, *J. Inorg. Nucl. Chem.* **3**, 104 (1956).

[52] E. O. Fischer and R. Böttcher, *Z. Naturforsch.* **10b**, 600 (1955).

[53] R. B. King, P. M. Treichel, and F. G. A. Stone, *J. Am. Chem. Soc.* **83**, 3600 (1961); R. B. King, unpublished results (1962).

[54] A. Nakamura and N. Hagihara, *Nippon Kagaku Zasshi.* **82**, 1392 (1961); *Chem. Abs.* **59**, 2854 (1963).

carbon monoxide.[55-57] Several experimental modifications of these two basic methods are available. The decision to use a given method is relatively difficult and depends on the availability of materials and apparatus. Thus, if a liberal supply of dicobalt octacarbonyl either in the pure state or in solution is available, the preferred route to $C_5H_5Co(CO)_2$ is by treatment of $Co_2(CO)_8$ with cyclopentadiene.[54,28b] Availability of good high-pressure equipment makes the preparation of $C_5H_5Co(CO)_2$ from cobaltocene and carbon monoxide under pressure attractive.[55,56] If neither dicobalt octacarbonyl nor good high-pressure equipment are available, it is possible to prepare $C_5H_5Co(CO)_2$ from cobaltocene and carbon monoxide at atmospheric pressure but with some sacrifice in yield.[57] Further details of all of these methods are given.

Procedure A:

$$(C_5H_5)_2Co + 2CO \rightarrow C_5H_5Co(CO)_2 + \{C_5H_5\cdot\}$$

A solution of 1.0 mole of sodium cyclopentadienide in ~500 ml. of tetrahydrofuran[4] is prepared from sodium sand or dispersion and cyclopentadiene and treated with 0.5 mole of anhydrous cobalt(II) chloride as was described for the preparation of cobaltocene(biscyclopentadienylcobalt) (page 70).[58]

The carbonylation of the biscyclopentadienylcobalt solution is carried out in an autoclave of 1-liter internal capacity capable of withstanding at least 100 atmospheres.[8] The autoclave is charged under nitrogen with 500 ml. of a benzene or tetrahydrofuran solution of biscyclopentadienylcobalt. The autoclave is then assembled, closed, and connected to a source of carbon monoxide under pressure. The autoclave is flushed once with at least 50 atmospheres of carbon monoxide.[9] After releasing this carbon monoxide, the autoclave is pressurized with at least 60 atmospheres of carbon monoxide and heated to 130° for at least 10 hr.

When the reaction period is over, the autoclave is cooled to room temperature, the carbon monoxide pressure is released, and the autoclave

[55] E. O. Fischer and R. Jira, *Z. Naturforsch.* **10b**, 355 (1955).

[56] R. B. King, P. M. Treichel, and F. G. A. Stone, *J. Am. Chem. Soc.* **83**, 3600 (1961); R. B. King and F. G. A. Stone, *Inorg. Syn.* **7**, 112 (1963).

[57] R. B. King, *J. Am. Chem. Soc.* **84**, 4705 (1962).

[58] In order to be able to introduce a larger quantity of biscyclopentadienylcobalt into an autoclave of given size, the tetrahydrofuran is removed in a water-aspirator vacuum. Nitrogen is then admitted and the residue is dissolved in benzene. In this manner, the cobaltocene obtained from 1 mole of anhydrous cobalt(II) chloride may be carbonylated in a single charge in a 1-liter autoclave. A benzene solution of cobaltocene is commercially available (Arapahoe Chemicals, Inc., Boulder, Colorado) and may be charged directly into the autoclave for carbonylation with obvious savings of time.

is then opened. The reaction mixture is filtered and the residue is washed with benzene. The filtrate is transferred to a flask equipped for distillation. The tetrahydrofuran and/or benzene is removed first in a water-pump vacuum.[59] After transferring the dark-red liquid residue to a smaller flask, the $C_5H_5Co(CO)_2$ is distilled at 1 to 5 mm. Red liquid $C_5H_5Co(CO)_2$ is collected in ~25% yield at 55°/5 mm. or 38°/2 mm.

By rather drastic modifications, this procedure may be adapted to the carbonylation of biscyclopentadienylcobalt at *atmospheric pressure*. The lower yields and the greater ease of carrying out reactions at atmospheric pressure in larger equipment than that used for high-pressure reactions make desirable and convenient the carbonylation of biscyclopentadienylcobalt at atmospheric pressure on a larger scale than the corresponding carbonylation at high pressures.

The atmospheric pressure carbonylation of biscyclopentadienylcobalt is carried out in a well-ventilated hood in a 2-liter three-necked flask equipped with a gas inlet, motor stirrer, reflux condenser, and pressure-equalized dropping funnel. After filling the system with nitrogen, the flask is charged with 46 g. (2 moles) of sodium metal and 1 liter of dry triglyme.[60] The mixture is heated with a heating mantle until the sodium melts (~98°). Vigorous stirring is then begun to convert the molten sodium to sodium sand.[61] The reaction mixture is then cooled to room temperature and treated dropwise with 198 ml. (158 g., 2.4 mole) of cyclopentadiene that has been freshly prepared from dicyclopentadiene and has formed a reddish solution of sodium cyclopentadienide.

The resulting sodium cyclopentadienide solution is treated with 130 g. (1 mole) of anhydrous cobalt(II) chloride.[62] An exothermic reaction

---

[59] Because of the volatility of $C_5H_5Co(CO)_2$, it is inadvisable to heat the flask during solvent removal; otherwise, significant amounts of $C_5H_5Co(CO)_2$ may be lost by codistillation with the solvent.

[60] For brevity, the abbreviation "triglyme" will be used for *tri*ethylene *gly*col *di*methyl ether, $CH_3OCH_2CH_2OCH_2CH_2OCH_2CH_2OCH_3$ as done by most workers in this field (see footnote 1, page 82). This solvent is available from Ansul Chemical Company, Marinette, Wisconsin, and may be dried with sodium or sodium-lead alloy ("Safe-Na") prior to use. Distillation over lithium aluminum hydride may also be used provided the distillation is carried out under reduced pressure (water-aspirator vacuum). However, this preparation of $C_5H_5Co(CO)_2$ has been carried out successfully with triglyme directly as received from Ansul without attempts at purification.

[61] A commercial sodium dispersion in mineral oil may be used instead of this sodium sand. Use of a commercial sodium dispersion in xylene should be avoided due to the similar volatilities of xylene and $C_5H_5Co(CO)_2$.

[62] The pure blue anhydrous cobalt(II) chloride may be obtained by heating hydrated cobalt(II) chloride at ~160°/0.1 mm. until no more water is lost (see footnote 31, page 70).

occurs with the production of purple biscyclopentadienylcobalt. The nitrogen stream is then replaced with a stream of carbon monoxide, and the dropping funnel is replaced with a distillation take-off head equipped with a thermometer. The reaction mixture is heated to $\sim$180° in a stream of carbon monoxide. At this temperature, a dark-red liquid begins to distill over which consists of a mixture of $C_5H_5Co(CO)_2$ and triglyme. The distillation in the carbon monoxide atmosphere is continued until $\sim$400 ml. of the distillate is collected. Toward the end of the distillation, the temperature is raised to the boiling point of triglyme ($\sim$210°).

The resulting distillate of $C_5H_5Co(CO)_2$ and triglyme is diluted to $\sim$1 liter with water, and the $C_5H_5Co(CO)_2$ is extracted with 50-ml. portions of pentane until the extracts are no longer red. The combined pentane extracts are dried several minutes over the anhydrous sulfate of magnesium, sodium, or calcium, and are then filtered from the drying agent washing the latter with several milliliters of pentane. Pentane is removed from the filtrate in a water-aspirator vacuum.[59] The red liquid residue of $C_5H_5Co(CO)_2$ is then distilled at 1 to 5 mm. in a manner similar to the previously described preparation. The yield of the dark-red liquid product is $\sim$12%.

Procedure B:

$$Co_2(CO)_8 + 2C_5H_6 \rightarrow 2C_5H_5Co(CO)_2 + 4CO \uparrow + H_2$$

A mixture of $\sim$30 g. (0.0878 mole) of dicobalt octacarbonyl in 180 ml. of benzene, toluene, pentane, hexane, petroleum ether, or other hydrocarbon solvent[63] and 26 ml. (20.8 g., 0.315 mole) of freshly prepared cyclopentadiene is irradiated under nitrogen for at least 16 hr. with a powerful ultraviolet lamp preferably in quartz apparatus. The resulting reaction mixture[64] is then filtered, and the solvent is removed from the filtrate in a water-aspirator vacuum.[59,65] The residual, dark-red liquid

---

[63] An appropriate quantity of either a commercial solution of dicobalt octacarbonyl in a hydrocarbon solvent or the petroleum ether solution of dicobalt octacarbonyl obtained directly from cobalt(II) carbonate, carbon monoxide, and hydrogen according to I. Wender, H. W. Sternberg, S. Metlin, and M. Orchin, *Inorg. Syn.* 5, 190 (1958), may be used for this reaction. The exact quantity of $Co_2(CO)_8$ introduced in this reaction is not critical. Its quantity may be estimated with sufficient accuracy from the manufacturer's specifications or from the amount of cobalt(II) carbonate used for the preparation and an estimation of the yield.

[64] In order to minimize dimerization of excess cyclopentadiene to dicyclopentadiene which cannot be separated from $C_5H_5Co(CO)_2$ by simple distillation, the reaction mixture should be worked up as soon as possible.

[65] If toluene is used as solvent an oil-pump vacuum of 1 to 5 mm. may be required for removal at an appreciable rate. Some $C_5H_5Co(CO)_2$ may be lost by codistillation during removal of toluene. Therefore, toluene is recommended as solvent for

is distilled at 1 to 5 mm. in a similar manner to the previously described preparation to give ~15 g. (47.5% yield) of crude cyclopentadienyl-cobalt dicarbonyl containing appreciable amounts (~20%) of dicyclo-pentadiene[66] but suitable for many preparative purposes. Chromatography on alumina in pentane, hexane, or petroleum ether solution may be used to obtain a pure product.[67] The $C_5H_5Co(CO)_2$ appears on the chromatogram as a red band.

Cyclopentadienylcobalt dicarbonyl is a dark-red, malodorous liquid, m.p. —22°, b.p. 139–140°/710 mm., that is immiscible with water but readily miscible with all organic solvents. It is probably very toxic and should be handled in a good hood. Its infrared spectrum (CS_2 solution) exhibits very strong metal carbonyl absorptions at 2028 and 1967 cm.$^{-1}$. Its proton n.m.r. spectrum in CS_2 solution exhibits a single sharp resonance at 5.00 τ due to the five equivalent cyclopentadienyl protons. It reacts with various dienes both conjugated and nonconjugated at elevated temperatures to give the orange derivatives C_5H_5Co(diene).[56,68] Treatment with perfluoroalkyl iodides gives the black derivatives $C_5H_5CoR_f(CO)I$ (R_f = perfluoroalkyl group) which contain an asymmetric cobalt atom (four different ligands) but which have not yet been resolved into optical isomers.[56] Treatment of $C_5H_5Co(CO)_2$ with allyl halides gives π-allyl derivatives both of the ionic type $[C_5H_5CoCOC_3H_5]X$[69] and the covalent type $C_5H_5CoC_3H_5X$.[70]

6. Cyclopentadienylnickel Carbonyl Dimer

The only well-established preparations of $[C_5H_5NiCO]_2$ described in the literature are based on the reaction between nickel tetracarbonyl and biscyclopentadienylnickel in benzene first described by Fischer and Palm.[71] The procedure that is described here includes minor improvements introduced by Tilney-Bassett[72] and by the Fellowship sponsored by the International Nickel Company at the Mellon Institute.[73]

---

this reaction only if $Co_2(CO)_8$ is available more readily in toluene solution than in any other form (as was the case at one time with the author).

[66] The amount of dicyclopentadiene present in the $C_5H_5Co(CO)_2$ may be estimated from an integration of the relative intensities of the cyclopentadienyl resonance of $C_5H_5Co(CO)_2$ and one of the dicyclopentadiene resonances in the proton n.m.r. spectrum.

[67] Compare W. McFarlane, L. Pratt, and G. Wilkinson, *J. Chem. Soc.* 2162 (1963).

[68] A. Nakamura and N. Hagihara, *Bull. Chem. Soc. Japan.* 34, 452 (1961).

[69] E. O. Fischer and R. D. Fischer, *Z. Naturforsch.* 16b, 556 (1961).

[70] R. F. Heck, *J. Org. Chem.* 28, 604 (1963)

[71] E. O. Fischer and C. Palm, *Chem. Ber.* 91, 1725 (1958).

[72] J. F. Tilney-Bassett, *J. Chem. Soc.* 577 (1961).

[73] R. D. Feltham and J. T. Carriel, private communications (1962).

Procedure:

$$(C_5H_5)_2Ni + Ni(CO)_4 \rightarrow [C_5H_5NiCO]_2 + 2CO \uparrow$$

The reaction is carried out under nitrogen in an excellent hood in a three-necked flask equipped with a stirrer, reflux condenser, and nitrogen inlet. In order to minimize exposure to the extremely toxic nickel carbonyl vapors, the outlet of the system is connected to a tube inserted into the exhaust system of the hood. The flask is charged with a mixture of 31.2 g. (0.165 mole) of biscyclopentadienylnickel (page 71),[74] 60 ml. (79 g., 0.465 mole) of nickel tetracarbonyl,[75] and 200 ml. of thiophene-free benzene. The reaction mixture is heated for at least 5 hr. under gentle reflux; the green color of the $(C_5H_5)_2Ni$ soon becomes the characteristic blood red of $[C_5H_5NiCO]_2$.

After the reaction period is over, the reaction mixture is cooled to room temperature. Excesses of benzene and nickel tetracarbonyl are then removed in a water-aspirator vacuum (15 to 50 mm.) through a $-78°$ trap (acetone-Dry Ice) to condense at least most of the very toxic nickel tetracarbonyl vapors. After all of the solvent has been removed, nitrogen is admitted to the evacuated flask, and the residue is extracted with 450 ml. of anhydrous diethyl ether in four portions. The extracts are passed through a 2×15 cm. alumina column to remove the trimeric derivative $(C_5H_5)_3Ni_3(CO)_2$. The column is washed with sufficient diethyl ether to remove all of the red $[C_5H_5NiCO]_2$. The solvent is removed from the diethyl ether eluate to give a total of 27 g. (54% yield) of crystalline dichroic $[C_5H_5NiCO]_2$. The $[C_5H_5NiCO]_2$ as thus obtained is pure enough for most preparative purposes but may be purified further by sublimation at $100°/0.1$ mm.

Cyclopentadienylnickel carbonyl dimer forms air-stable crystals, m.p. $136°$ (dec.), which appear red-violet by transmitted light and green by reflected light. It is readily soluble in organic solvents giving characteristic blood-red solutions oxidized slowly by air. It exhibits carbonyl bands at 1880 and 1830 cm.$^{-1}$ in the infrared spectrum (KBr pellet) and a single sharp resonance at 4.70 τ in the proton n.m.r. spectrum due to the equivalent cyclopentadienyl protons. Presence of the paramagnetic biscyclopentadienylnickel as an impurity will broaden the cyclopenta-

---

[74] Available commercially from Arapahoe Chemicals, Inc., Boulder, Colorado.

[75] Nickel tetracarbonyl, available from International Nickel, Inc., 67 Wall Street, New York 5, New York, is a volatile liquid even more toxic than hydrogen cyanide. It should always be handled in a well-ventilated hood. It can be conveniently removed from the steel cylinder by inverting the cylinder, opening the valve and allowing the liquid to run into a pressure-equalized dropping funnel flushed out with nitrogen.

dienyl n.m.r. resonance of $[C_5H_5NiCO]_2$. Like nickel tetracarbonyl and C_5H_5NiNO, $[C_5H_5NiCO]_2$ appears to be very toxic; its solutions in organic solvents irritate the skin.

Cyclopentadienylnickel carbonyl dimer reacts with various acetylenes to form green-black compounds of the type $(C_5H_5)_2Ni_2RC_2R$.[72,76] It is cleaved by iodine to form the very reactive, black-violet C_5H_5NiCOI.[71] On heating or treatment with sodium amalgam in methanol, $[C_5H_5NiCO]_2$ is converted to the green very stable paramagnetic $(C_5H_5)_3Ni_3(CO)_2$.[71]

[76] J. F. Tilney-Bassett and O. S. Mills, *J. Am. Chem. Soc.* **81**, 4757 (1959).

D. Olefin and Acetylene Metal Complexes

1. Bicyclo[2,2,1]heptadiene-Chromium Tetracarbonyl

Bicyclo[2,2,1]heptadiene-chromium tetracarbonyl has been prepared by Bennett, Pratt, and Wilkinson[1] by treatment of chromium hexacarbonyl with bicyclo-[2,2,1]heptadiene[2] at elevated temperatures.

Procedure:

$$C_7H_8 + Cr(CO)_6 \xrightarrow{\Delta} C_7H_8Cr(CO)_4 + 2CO \uparrow$$

A mixture of 5.0 g. (0.0227 mole) of chromium hexacarbonyl (page 84), 8.0 ml. (7.25 g., 0.0787 mole) of bicycloheptadiene, and 40 ml. of methylcyclohexane is heated under reflux at least 40 hr. under nitrogen with magnetic stirring. The colorless reaction mixture soon becomes yellow. After the reaction period is over, the reaction mixture is allowed to cool to room temperature. The methylcyclohexane is then removed at 25°/(1 to 15 mm.) (oil-pump or good water-aspirator vacuum). The residue is transferred to a sublimation apparatus. After subliming out any white unreacted chromium hexacarbonyl at 25–50°/0.1 mm.,[3] the probe is cleaned, and the sublimation is continued at 70–90°/0.1 mm. to give 1.7 g. (29% yield) of bright golden yellow crystalline bicycloheptadiene–chromium tetracarbonyl. If a larger quantity of product is needed, this reaction may be scaled up four times with similar results.

Bicycloheptadiene-chromium tetracarbonyl forms golden yellow crystals, m.p. 92–93°, soluble in organic solvents and readily sublimed at 80°/0.1 mm. Pure crystalline bicycloheptadiene-chromium tetracarbonyl is oxidized slowly by air at room temperature over a period of

---

[1] M. A. Bennett, L. Pratt, and G. Wilkinson, *J. Chem. Soc.* 2037 (1961).

[2] Designated hereafter simply as "bicycloheptadiene." Readily available commercially (e.g., Shell Chemical Company, New York, New York).

[3] This recovered chromium hexacarbonyl may be used for a later preparation of bicycloheptadiene-chromium tetracarbonyl or resublimed and used for other purposes.

months, but even after a year this decomposition is still minor. Its infrared spectrum[1] in solution exhibits strong metal carbonyl bands at 2033, 1959, 1944, and 1913 cm.$^{-1}$, and its proton n.m.r. spectrum[1] (CCl_4 solution) exhibits resonances at 5.58 τ (apparent triplet), 6.27 τ (complex unresolved), and 8.70 τ (triplet, $J = 1.4$ cps) of relative intensities ~4:2:2. Tris(dimethylamino)phosphine displaces the hydrocarbon ligand from bicylcloheptadiene-chromium tetracarbonyl to form $\{[(CH_3)_2N]_3P\}_2Cr(CO)_4$.[4]

2. Cycloheptatriene-Chromium Tricarbonyl

Cycloheptatriene-chromium tricarbonyl was first prepared by Abel et al.[5] by treatment of chromium hexacarbonyl with cycloheptatriene. The procedure given here includes some modifications suggested by work of Munro and Pauson.[6]

Procedure:

$$C_7H_8 + Cr(CO)_6 \xrightarrow{\Delta} C_7H_8Cr(CO)_3 + 3CO \uparrow$$

A mixture of 20.0 g. (0.091 mole) of chromium hexacarbonyl (page 84), 24.0 g. (0.24 mole) of ~92% cycloheptatriene,[7] and 100 ml. of ethylcyclohexane[8] is heated under reflux at least 20 hr. under nitrogen with magnetic stirring. The colorless reaction mixture soon becomes red. After the reaction period is over, the reaction mixture is cooled to room temperature, and the solvent is removed at 25°/(0.1 to 1 mm.) (oil-pump vacuum). After the solvent is removed, the pumping is continued until the residue is as free as possible from oily impurities. The residue is then transferred to a sublimation apparatus and the product is isolated by sublimation at 100°/0.1 mm. for 20 hr. The red crystalline sublimate is washed quickly with two 20-ml. portions of cold pentane to remove oily impurities and is then sucked dry to give cycloheptatriene-chromium tricarbonyl in ~15% yield.

Improved results in the preparation of cycloheptatriene-chromium tricarbonyl can be obtained by carrying out the reaction in a special

[4] R. B. King, *Inorg. Chem.* **2**, 936 (1963).

[5] E. W. Abel, M. A. Bennett, R. Burton, and G. Wilkinson, *J. Chem. Soc.* 4559 (1958).

[6] J. D. Munro and P. L. Pauson, *J. Chem. Soc.* 3475 (1961).

[7] Available commercially from Shell Chemical Company, New York, New York.

[8] If ethylcyclohexane (b.p. 132°) is not available, other saturated aliphatic or alicyclic hydrocarbons of similar boiling point such as 2,2,5-trimethylhexane (b.p. 124°) or *n*-octane (b.p. 136°) may be used as a solvent in this reaction. For reactions of the carbonyls M(CO)₆ (M = Cr, Mo, W), aromatic hydrocarbons cannot be used as solvents due to the tendency to form arene-metal tricarbonyls.

apparatus designed by Strohmeier.[9] This somewhat complicated apparatus permits the automatic return of sublimed unreacted chromium hexacarbonyl into the reaction mixture by means of the refluxing solvent. Construction of this special apparatus is justified if relatively large quantities of cycloheptatriene-chromium tricarbonyl are to be prepared but is not worthwhile for an occasional small-scale preparation.

Cycloheptatriene-chromium tricarbonyl forms red crystals, m.p. 128–130° (dec.), which are soluble in organic solvents and form solutions that oxidize in air over a period of several hours. Its infrared spectrum[5] in solution exhibits strong metal carbonyl bands at 1991, 1921, and 1893 cm.$^{-1}$, and its proton n.m.r. spectrum[5] exhibits resonances at $3.99\,\tau$ (double doublet), $5.17\,\tau$ (complex unresolved), $\sim6.6\,\tau$ (complex), $\sim7.1\,\tau$ (complex), and $8.23\,\tau$ (doublet) of relative intensities $\sim2:2:2:1:1$. Hydride ion is abstracted by the triphenylmethyl cation to form red salts of the cation $[C_7H_7Cr(CO)_3]^+$.[6] The hydrocarbon ligand is displaced from cycloheptatriene-chromium tricarbonyl with many Lewis bases such as phosphines, arsines, and amines to form compounds of the type $L_3Cr(CO)_3$.[10]

3. Bicycloheptadiene-Molybdenum Tetracarbonyl

Bicycloheptadiene-molybdenum tetracarbonyl was first obtained by Pettit[11] and later by Bennett, Pratt, and Wilkinson[1] by treatment of molybdenum hexacarbonyl with bicycloheptadiene at elevated temperatures.

---

[9] For details of this apparatus see W. Strohmeier, *Chem. Ber.* **94**, 2490 (1961). Details of a cycloheptatriene-chromium tricarbonyl procedure using the special apparatus of Strohmeier were kindly supplied to the author by P. L. Pauson and are repeated here.

A 4.4 g. (0.02 mole) sample of freshly sublimed chromium hexacarbonyl and 2.8 g. (0.03 mole) of redistilled cycloheptatriene are refluxed 18 hr. (165° bath temperature) in a mixture of 15 ml. of pure diglyme and 45 ml. of dry, aromatic-free, petroleum ether, b.p. 100–120°, in the Strohmeier apparatus. The mixture is cooled in an ice bath and filtered into 150 ml. of air-free water to remove 0.22 g. of unchanged chromium hexacarbonyl. The filtrates are extracted with ether and the ether extract is washed with water. After filtration through celite, the ethereal solution is dried over anhydrous sodium sulfate for 30 min., out of contact with light. Evaporation to $\sim$15 ml. is followed by addition of 10 ml. of petroleum ether, b.p. 40–60°, and chilling to $-78°$. Deep-red crystals (4.19 g., 96.7% based on unrecovered chromium hexacarbonyl), m.p. 129–130°, are obtained and removed by filtration.

It is essential to use rigorously purified diglyme in this preparation since traces of peroxides can lead to complete decomposition. For this purpose, diglyme is most conveniently purified by refluxing 24 hr. over calcium hydride followed by distillation under an atmosphere of nitrogen and storage over sodium wire.

[10] E. W. Abel, M. A. Bennett, and G. Wilkinson, *J. Chem. Soc.* 2323 (1959).

[11] R. Pettit, *J. Am. Chem. Soc.* **81**, 1266 (1959).

Procedure:

$$C_7H_8 + Mo(CO)_6 \xrightarrow{\Delta} C_7H_8Mo(CO)_4 + 2CO \uparrow$$

The reaction is carried out in a 1-liter three-necked flask fitted with a reflux condenser, stirrer, nitrogen inlet, and pressure-equalized dropping funnel. After filling with nitrogen, the flask is charged with 52.8 g. (0.2 mole) of molybdenum hexacarbonyl and 400 ml. of methylcyclohexane. This mixture is then heated to the boiling point with stirring and then treated dropwise with 75 ml. (67.9 g., 0.74 mole) of bicycloheptadiene.[12] After all of the bicycloheptadiene has been added, the refluxing is continued for about 16 additional hours.

After the reaction period is over, the reaction mixture is cooled to room temperature. The reaction mixture is then filtered through glass wool[13] and the filtrate is collected under nitrogen. The filtrate is cooled in a $-78°$ bath for several hours, a tan precipitate soon forming. This precipitate is filtered, sucked dry, and charged into a sublimer. The light yellow crystalline bicycloheptadiene-molybdenum tetracarbonyl is isolated in yields up to 80% (30% to 50% is more usual) by sublimation at $100°/0.1$ mm.

Bicycloheptadiene-molybdenum tetracarbonyl forms pale yellow crystals, m.p. 76–77°, readily soluble in organic solvents. On standing in air it gradually becomes pale brown but does not readily decompose extensively. Its infrared spectrum exhibits strong metal carbonyl bands at 2030, 1980–1920, and 1870 cm.$^{-1}$, and its proton n.m.r. spectrum (CCl_4 solution) exhibits resonances at 5.15τ (apparent triplet), 6.22τ (broad unresolved), and 8.67τ (triplet, $J = 1.3$ cps) of relative intensities 4:2:2. Tris(dimethylamino) phosphine readily displaces the bicycloheptadiene ligand to form the derivative $\{[(CH_3)_2N]_3P\}_2Mo(CO)_4.$[4]

4. Cycloheptatriene-Molybdenum Tricarbonyl

Cycloheptatriene-molybdenum tricarbonyl was first prepared by Abel, Bennett, Burton, and Wilkinson[5] and later by Dauben and Honnen[14] from molybdenum hexacarbonyl and cycloheptatriene.

Procedure:

$$C_7H_8 + Mo(CO)_6 \xrightarrow{\Delta} C_7H_8Mo(CO)_3 + 3CO \uparrow$$

A mixture of 52.8 g. (0.2 mole) of molybdenum hexacarbonyl, 100 ml. of ~92% cycloheptatriene,[7] and 400 ml. of ethylcyclohexane[8] is heated

---

[12] Dropwise addition of the bicycloheptadiene at the reaction temperature minimizes formation of an insoluble rubbery polymer.

[13] This filtration is very slow because of the presence of some bicycloheptadiene polymer.

[14] H. J. Dauben, Jr., and L. R. Honnen, *J. Am. Chem. Soc.* **80**, 5570 (1958).

under reflux at the boiling point under nitrogen for 16 hr.; the reaction mixture soon becomes red. After the reaction period is over, the reaction mixture is allowed to cool to room temperature and is then filtered by gravity, and the filtrate is collected under nitrogen. The filtrate is cooled in a −78° bath for several hours precipitating red crystals of the crude product. These are filtered and sucked dry. Excess molybdenum hexacarbonyl (generally not present) and other volatile impurities are removed by drying at 50°/0.1 mm. for at least 8 hr. The red solid cycloheptatriene-molybdenum tricarbonyl obtained in 40 to 75% yield is sufficiently pure for many preparative purposes. A purer material may be obtained as red-orange crystals by sublimation at 100°/0.1 mm.

Cycloheptatriene-molybdenum tricarbonyl forms red to red-orange crystals, m.p. 100.5–101.5°, that are readily soluble in organic solvents to give red solutions. Although fairly air-stable in the crystalline state, its solutions begin to oxidize after several minutes. Its infrared spectrum[5] in solution exhibits strong metal carbonyl bands at 2000, 1929, and 1895 cm.$^{-1}$ and its proton n.m.r. spectrum (CS_2 solution) exhibits resonances at 3.96 τ, 5.12 τ, 6.44 τ, and 7.44 τ of equal relative intensities.

Cycloheptatriene-molybdenum tricarbonyl reacts with the triphenylmethyl cation with loss of hydride to form yellow derivatives of the $[C_7H_7Mo(CO)_3]^+$ cation,[14] which are useful intermediates in the preparations of the halides $C_7H_7Mo(CO)_2X$.[15] Treatment of cycloheptatriene-molybdenum tricarbonyl at room temperature with a variety of Lewis bases including certain phosphines, arsines, amines, and sulfides produces derivatives of the general formula $L_3Mo(CO)_3$[10]; the mildness of the reaction conditions makes this synthetic route useful for the preparation of a wide variety of molybdenum carbonyl derivatives.

5. Cyclooctatetraene-Iron Tricarbonyl

Cyclooctatetraene-iron tricarbonyl, discovered independently in at least three different laboratories,[16a,b,c] is readily obtained by heating or irradiating iron pentacarbonyl with cyclooctatetraene. The procedure given here is essentially that of Manuel and Stone.[16a]

[15] D. J. Bertelli, Ph.D. Thesis, University of Washington, 1961 (H. J. Dauben, Jr., Research Adviser).
[16a] T. A. Manuel and F. G. A. Stone, *Proc. Chem. Soc.* 90 (1959); *J. Am. Chem. Soc.* **82**, 366 (1960).
[16b] M. D. Rausch and G. N. Schrauzer, *Chem. Ind.* (*London*) 957 (1959).
[16c] A. Nakamura and N. Hagihara, *Bull. Chem. Soc. Japan* **32**, 881 (1959).

Procedure:

$$C_8H_8 + Fe(CO)_5 \xrightarrow{\Delta} C_8H_8Fe(CO)_3 + 2CO \uparrow$$

A mixture of 6.45 g. (0.062 mole) of cyclooctatetraene,[17] 12 ml. (17.5 g., 0.089 moles) of iron pentacarbonyl, and 150 ml. of ethylcyclohexane[8,18] is heated at the boiling point under reflux 24 hr. under nitrogen with magnetic stirring. The reaction mixture is then allowed to cool to room temperature and the solvent is removed at $25°/(0.1$ to 1 mm.). The red crystalline residue is sublimed at $60-80°/0.1$ mm. to give 9.0 g. (60% yield) of red crystalline $C_8H_8Fe(CO)_3$. The binuclear derivatives $C_8H_8Fe_2(CO)_6$ and $C_8H_8Fe_2(CO)_7$ may be present in the sublimation residue to a limited extent.[16a]

Cyclooctatetraene-iron tricarbonyl forms red air-stable crystals, m.p. $93-95°$, that are soluble in organic solvents to give air-stable red solutions and are readily sublimable in vacuum. Its infrared spectrum[16a] (CS_2 solution) exhibits strong metal carbonyl bands at 2058 and 1992 cm.[-1] and its proton n.m.r. spectrum (CS_2 solution) unexpectedly exhibits a single sharp resonance at 4.82 τ. Cyclooctatetraene-iron tricarbonyl is protonated by strong acids to give salts of the $[C_8H_9Fe(CO)_3]^+$ cation.[19] Treatment with excess iron pentacarbonyl gives the binuclear derivative $C_8H_8Fe_2(CO)_6$ already mentioned.[16b] A 1:1 adduct is formed from $C_8H_8Fe(CO)_3$ and tetracyanoethylene.[20]

Cycloheptatriene-iron tricarbonyl[21] may be prepared in the previously described manner similar to that for $C_8H_8Fe(CO)_3$ using cycloheptatriene rather than cyclooctatetraene. Since cycloheptatriene-iron tricarbonyl is a liquid it is purified by distillation (b.p. $70°$, 0.4 mm.) rather than sublimation. A larger quantity of the polyolefin and iron pentacarbonyl for a given amount of solvent can be used in the preparation of cycloheptatriene-iron tricarbonyl than in the preparation of

---

[17] Available from Badische Anilin- und Soda-Fabrik, Ludwigshafen, Germany. Secondary more expensive sources of cyclooctatetraene include Aldrich and Columbia in the United States and Light in Great Britain.

[18] In the absence of a solvent, no $C_8H_8Fe(CO)_3$ is isolated from the reaction between iron pentacarbonyl and cyclooctatetraene. If ethylcyclohexane is not available, toluene or xylene may be used as the solvent.

[19] G. N. Schrauzer, *J. Am. Chem. Soc.* 83, 2966 (1961); A. Davison, W. McFarlane, and G. Wilkinson, *Chem. Ind. (London)* 820 (1962).

[20] G. N. Schrauzer and S. Eichler, *Angew. Chem.* 74, 585 (1962); A. Davison, W. McFarlane, L. Pratt, and G. Wilkinson, *J. Chem. Soc.* 4821 (1962).

[21] R. Burton, L. Pratt, and G. Wilkinson, *J. Chem. Soc.* 594 (1961); H. J. Dauben, Jr., and D. J. Bertelli, *J. Am. Chem. Soc.* 83, 497 (1961).

cyclooctatetraene-iron tricarbonyl (e.g., 50 ml. each of iron pentacarbonyl and 92% cycloheptatriene to 150 ml. of ethylcyclohexane).

6. Butadiene-Iron Tricarbonyl

Butadiene-iron tricarbonyl $C_4H_6Fe(CO)_3$ was first obtained from
iron pentacarbonyl and butadiene by Reihlen, Gruhl, Hessling, and
Pfrengle in 1930[22] and later investigated in greater detail by Hallam
and Pauson in 1958.[23]

Procedure:

$$C_4H_6 + Fe(CO)_5 \xrightarrow{\Delta} C_4H_6Fe(CO)_3 + 2CO$$

Because of the volatility of butadiene, it is necessary to carry out its
reaction with iron pentacarbonyl in a pressure vessel. Either a stainless
steel Hoke bomb (page 14) of at least 500 ml. internal capacity or an
autoclave of this capacity similar to that recommended for the preparations of various metal carbonyls and cyclopentadienyl-metal carbonyls
in earlier portions of this book may be used.

Butadiene is condensed from a tank into a −78° trap. About 110 ml.
(71.3 g., 1.3 mole) of this liquid butadiene is measured rapidly into a
graduate cooled in a refrigerator, and this liquid is poured immediately
into the pressure vessel containing several pieces of Dry Ice to displace
the air. After immediately adding 100 ml. (146 g., 0.745 mole) of iron
pentacarbonyl,[24] the vessel is closed rapidly, and then heated to 140 ± 5°
for at least 12 hr. After the reaction period is over, the vessel is cooled
to room temperature and butadiene and carbon monoxide are vented.
The autoclave is opened, and the orange liquid product is transferred to
a flask equipped for vacuum distillation. Excess iron pentacarbonyl is
removed by distillation in a water-aspirator vacuum (b.p. 40°/55 mm.).
About 85 g. (61%) of iron pentacarbonyl is recovered. The residue is
then distilled in an oil-pump vacuum. After an intermediate fraction,
~23 g. (17% based on total $Fe(CO)_5$, 42% based on unrecovered

---

[22] H. Reihlen, A. Gruhl, G. v. Hessling, and O. Pfrengle, *Ann. (Liebigs)* **482**, 161 (1930).
[23] B. F. Hallam and P. L. Pauson, *J. Chem. Soc.* 642 (1958).
[24] The iron pentacarbonyl and butadiene may also be charged into the reaction
vessel by vacuum distillation into the evacuated and cooled reaction vessel. However, since traces of water do not significantly affect the reaction, the much faster
procedure of simply pouring the reactants into the reaction vessel is satisfactory.
The toxicity of iron pentacarbonyl and the flammability of butadiene make desirable loading the autoclave in a hood. Since butadiene is so inexpensive and the ratio
of iron pentacarbonyl to butadiene is not critical within wide limits, evaporation of
small amounts of the butadiene during the loading is not serious.

Fe(CO)₅) of butadiene-iron tricarbonyl is collected as a liquid boiling at 47–49°/0.1 mm. freezing to yellow crystals at 19°.

Butadiene-iron tricarbonyl is an air-stable orange liquid, m.p. 19°, immiscible with water but readily miscible with organic solvents. Its infrared spectrum[23] exhibits strong metal carbonyl bands at 2051 and 1978 cm.$^{-1}$, and its proton n.m.r. spectrum exhibits resonances at 4.72 τ (complex triplet), 8.32 τ (double doublet), and 9.78 τ (double doublet) of relative intensities 2:2:2.

7. 1,3-Cyclohexadiene-Iron Tricarbonyl

1,3-Cyclohexadiene-iron tricarbonyl was first prepared by Hallam and Pauson in 1958[23] from 1,3-cyclohexadiene and iron pentacarbonyl. Later, it was discovered that 1,4-dienes react with iron carbonyls to give metal complexes of 1,3-dienes.[25] Since 1,4-cyclohexadiene is less expensive and less prone to form dimers and polymers than 1,3-cyclohexadiene, the preparation of 1,3-cyclohexadiene-iron tricarbonyl from iron pentacarbonyl and 1,4-cyclohexadiene using this rearrangement is recommended.

Procedure:

$$C_6H_8 + Fe(CO)_5 \xrightarrow{\Delta} C_6H_8Fe(CO)_3 + 2CO$$

Since the reaction between iron pentacarbonyl and 1,4-cyclohexadiene is carried out considerably above the boiling point of the olefin, it is necessary to use a closed reaction vessel. A 300-ml. stainless steel Hoke high-pressure bomb is recommended although an autoclave of comparable size or even a heavy glass sealed Carius tube could also be used.

The Hoke bomb or other reaction vessel is charged with 20 ml. (29.2 g., 0.149 mole) of iron pentacarbonyl (Antara) and 15 ml. (12.9 g., 0.161 mole) of 1,4-cyclohexadiene.[26] This mixture is then cooled to —78° and evacuated to at least 1 mm. at this temperature with an oil pump. The bomb is then placed in an oven preheated to 150° and kept there for at least 20 hr. After the reaction period is over, the bomb is allowed to cool to room temperature and the yellow liquid contents are then discharged. This reaction between iron pentacarbonyl and 1,4-cyclohexadiene is repeated in the same manner a total of three times.

---

[25] R. B. King, T. A. Manuel, and F. G. A. Stone, *J. Inorg. Nucl. Chem.* **16**, 233 (1961); J. E. Arnet and R. Pettit, *J. Am. Chem. Soc.* **83**, 2954 (1961).
[26] Available commercially from Columbia Organic Chemicals, Inc., Columbia, South Carolina.

The products from the three reactions (a total of 60 ml. of iron pentacarbonyl and 45 ml. of 1,4-cyclohexadiene)[27] are combined. Excesses of iron pentacarbonyl and 1,4-cyclohexadiene are removed at ~1 mm. (oil-pump vacuum) and collected in a −78° trap to protect the oil pump and to minimize the spread of the toxic iron pentacarbonyl vapors. The liquid residue is distilled in an oil-pump vacuum. The product (~19.2 g., 18.5% conversion) is collected at 50–66°/1 mm. as a yellow liquid freezing in a refrigerator.

1,3-Cyclohexadiene-iron tricarbonyl is a yellow air-stable liquid at room temperature, m.p. 8–9°, immiscible with water but readily miscible with organic solvents. Its infrared spectrum[23] exhibits strong metal carbonyl bands at 2066 and 1978 cm.$^{-1}$, and its proton n.m.r. spectrum (CS_2 solution) exhibits resonances at 4.72 τ (double doublet, $J_1 = 5$ cps, $J_2 = 3$ cps), 6.85 τ (broad, unresolved, and 8.32 τ (singlet) of relative intensities 2:2:4. It reacts with salts of the triphenylmethyl cation in dichloromethane or similar polar nonhydroxylic organic solvents to form salts of the cation $[C_6H_7Fe(CO)_3]^+$.[28]

8. Maleic Anhydride-Iron Tetracarbonyl

Recently olefin-iron tetracarbonyl complexes have been obtained from monoolefins with electronegative substituents such as cyanide, carboxylic acid, ester, anhydride, and aldehyde either by mild heating of $Fe_2(CO)_9$ with the olefin[29] or by irradiating iron pentacarbonyl with the olefin.[30] The preparation of these complexes is exemplified by the preparation of maleic anhydride-iron tetracarbonyl by Weiss et al.[29] as described here.

Procedure:

$$Fe_2(CO)_9 + C_4H_2O_3 \rightarrow C_4H_2O_3Fe(CO)_4 + Fe(CO)_5$$

A mixture of 4.9 g. (0.05 mole) of maleic anhydride,[31] 18.2 g. (0.05 mole) of $Fe_2(CO)_9$ (page 93), and 50 ml. of thiophene-free benzene is heated at 45° for 4 hr. preferably with magnetic stirring. The yellow, sparingly soluble $Fe_2(CO)_9$ is gradually converted to yellow, sparingly

[27] If a 1-liter rather than 300-ml. reaction vessel is used, the 60 ml. of iron pentacarbonyl and 45 ml. of 1,4-cyclohexadiene may be reacted in a single batch rather than in three batches.

[28] E. O. Fischer and R. D. Fischer, *Angew. Chem.* **72**, 919 (1960).

[29] E. Weiss, K. Stark, J. E. Lancaster, and H. D. Murdoch, *Helv. Chim. Acta.* **46**, 288 (1963).

[30] G. O. Schenck, E. Körner von Gustorf, and Mon-Jon-Jun, *Tetrahedron Letters,* 1059 (1962).

[31] The use of freshly sublimed material is recommended by Weiss et al. (Ref. 29).

soluble maleic anhydride-iron tetracarbonyl. After the reaction period is over, the reaction mixture is cooled to room temperature and the product is filtered, washed with benzene, and sucked dry to give 11.2 g. (89% yield) of crude maleic anhydride-iron tetracarbonyl. The crude product may be purified by crystallization from acetone (100 ml./3 g.) to give 78% recovery of pure material.

Maleic anhydride-iron tetracarbonyl forms yellow crystals, m.p. 148° (dec.), sparingly soluble in organic solvents. Its infrared spectrum[29] (KBr pellet) exhibits strong metal carbonyl bands at 2131, 2087, 2055, 2045, 2032, and 2017 cm.$^{-1}$ and strong anhydride carbonyl bands at 1824 and 1746 cm.$^{-1}$. Its proton n.m.r. spectrum ($(CD_3)_2CO$ solution) exhibits a single sharp resonance at 5.63 τ.

9. Cyclopentadienylcobalt-1,5-Cyclooctadiene

Cyclopentadienylcobalt-1,5-cyclooctadiene, $C_5H_5CoC_8H_{12}$, has been obtained by heating cyclopentadienylcobalt dicarbonyl with 1,5-cyclo-octadiene[32] or by hydrogenation of cyclopentadienylcobalt-cycloocta-tetraene.[33] The former method is more convenient and also illustrative of a general synthesis of the complexes C_5H_5Co(diene) from cyclopenta-dienylcobalt dicarbonyl and various diolefins applicable to olefins such as 1,3-cyclohexadiene, 1,3,5-cyclooctatriene, and bicyclo[2,2,1]hepta-diene.[32]

Procedure:

$$C_5H_5Co(CO)_2 + C_8H_{12} \xrightarrow{\Delta} C_5H_5CoC_8H_{12} + 2CO \uparrow$$

A mixture of 1.0 ml. (~1.3 g., 0.00724 mole) of cyclopentadienyl-cobalt dicarbonyl, 2.0 ml. (1.77 g., 0.0164 mole) of 1,5-cyclooctadiene,[34] and 5 ml. of ethylcyclohexane[8] is heated at the boiling point under reflux for at least 16 hr. under nitrogen. The reaction mixture is then cooled to room temperature and poured onto a 2×45 cm. alumina chromatography column made up with pentane. The column is developed with pentane; a single orange band of $C_5H_5CoC_8H_{12}$ appears. This band is eluted with pentane collecting the eluate in a stream of nitrogen to minimize oxidation of the $C_5H_5CoC_8H_{12}$ solution. After filtering the eluate, pentane is removed in a water-aspirator vacuum leaving orange crystals of $C_5H_5CoC_8H_{12}$. The crude product (0.8 g., 48% yield) may be purified

[32] R. B. King, P. M. Treichel, and F. G. A. Stone, *J. Am. Chem. Soc.* **83**, 3593 (1961).
[33] A. Nakamura and N. Hagihara, *Bull. Chem. Soc., Japan* **33**, 425 (1960).
[34] Available commercially from various sources (e.g. Columbian Carbon Co., Commercial Development Dept., P. O. Box 975, Princeton, New Jersey, and L. Light and Co., Colnbrook, Bucks, England).

by sublimation at 50–70°/0.1 mm. with nearly quantitative recovery except for mechanical losses.

Cyclopentadienylcobalt-1,5-cyclooctadiene forms orange fairly air-stable crystals, m.p. 103–105°, that are insoluble in water but soluble in organic solvents to give solutions which are slowly oxidized by air. Its proton n.m.r. spectrum (CS$_2$ solution) exhibits resonances at 5.5 τ (singlet), 6.63 τ (broad), 7.68 τ (complex multiplet), and 8.38 τ (complex multiplet) of relative intensities 5:4:4:4.

10. 1,5-Cyclooctadiene-Rhodium(I) Chloride Dimer

1,5-Cyclooctadiene-rhodium(I) chloride dimer, [C$_8$H$_{12}$RhCl]$_2$, has been prepared by treatment of ethanolic rhodium(III) chloride with 1,5-cyclooctadiene at ~80°.[35,36]

Procedure:

$$2RhCl_3(H_2O)_3 + 2C_8H_{12} + 2C_2H_5OH \rightarrow [C_8H_{12}RhCl]_2 + 2CH_3CHO + 4HCl + 6H_2O$$

A mixture of 2.6 g. (0.01 moles) of "rhodium trichloride trihydrate" (40% rhodium),[37] 5.0 ml. (4.42 g., 0.041 moles) of 1,5-cyclooctadiene,[34] and 50 ml. of 95% ethanol is heated at the boiling point under reflux for ~3 hr. preferably with magnetic stirring.[38] After cooling to room temperature, the yellow precipitate is filtered, washed with two 25-ml. portions of ethanol and two 25-ml. portions of pentane, hexane, or petroleum ether, and sucked dry to give 1,5-cyclooctadiene-rhodium(I) chloride dimer in about 60% yield.

1,5-Cyclooctadiene-rhodium(I) chloride dimer is a yellow air-stable solid that is stable to 250° and soluble in polar organic solvents. Its proton n.m.r. spectrum (C$_6$H$_6$ solution) exhibits resonances at 5.75 τ (unresolved singlet) and ~7.8 τ (broad quadruplet) of relative intensities 4:8. Amines and triphenylphosphine react with [C$_8$H$_{12}$RhCl]$_2$ to form monomeric derivatives of the type C$_8$H$_{12}$RhXL (L = amine or triphenylphosphine). Treatment of [C$_8$H$_{12}$RhCl]$_2$ with bromide, iodide, or acetate ion gives the dimeric derivatives [C$_8$H$_{12}$RhX]$_2$ (X = Br, I, or acetate).[35,36] Treatment of [C$_8$H$_{12}$RhCl]$_2$ with sodium cyclopentadienide

[25] J. Chatt and L. M. Venanzi, *Nature* 177, 852 (1956).

[26] J. Chatt and L. M. Venanzi, *J. Chem. Soc.* 4735 (1957).

[27] Available commercially from Englehard Industries, 113 Astor Street, Newark 2, New Jersey, Johnson Matthey, 78-83 Hatton Garden, London, E. C. 2, England, or Degussa Zweigniederlassung, Hanau, Germany.

[38] Unlike practically all of the other preparations in this book, the use of a nitrogen or other inert atmosphere is not necessary for the preparation of [C$_8$H$_{12}$RhCl]$_2$ since both reactants and products are completely air-stable.

gives monomeric $C_5H_5RhC_8H_{12}$[35,36] completely analogous to the cobalt derivative of which the preparation from $C_5H_5Co(CO)_2$ and 1,5-cyclo-octadiene was described (page 131).

Similar synthetic techniques may be used to obtain the corresponding dimeric rhodium(I) chloride complexes $[(C_2H_4)_2RhCl]_2$[39] and $[C_7H_8RhCl]_2$[40] derived from ethylene and bicyclo[2,2,1]heptadiene, respectively.

11. Diphenylacetylene-Dicobalt Hexacarbonyl

Numerous compounds of the type (acetylene)$Co_2(CO)_6$ have been obtained by workers at the U.S. Bureau of Mines from reactions between dicobalt octacarbonyl and various acetylenes at room temperature.[41] One of the most thoroughly investigated of these complexes is the di-phenylacetylene derivative $(C_6H_5)_2C_2Co_2(CO)_6$, the preparation of which is described below.

Procedure:

$$Co_2(CO)_8 + (C_6H_5)_2C_2 \rightarrow (C_6H_5)_2C_2Co_2(CO)_6 + 2CO \uparrow$$

A solution of 29.6 g. (0.0865 mole) of dicobalt octacarbonyl in 150 ml. of petroleum ether[42] is stirred overnight under nitrogen at room temperature with 14.8 g. (0.0832 mole) of diphenylacetylene.[43] The solvent is then blown off in a rapid stream of nitrogen.[44] The residue is treated with 1 liter of methanol and the mixture is heated under nitrogen until the residue has dissolved. The hot methanol solution is filtered rapidly under nitrogen[45] and the filtrate is allowed to cool to room temperature. Filtering the crystals by suction gives 31.5 g. (82% yield) of deep-purple diphenylacetylene-dicobalt hexacarbonyl. Further purification may be accomplished by a second crystallization from methanol or by sublimation at 90°/1 mm.

Minor variations of this procedure may be used for the preparation

---

[39] R. D. Cramer, *Inorg. Chem.* **1**, 722 (1962).

[40] E. W. Abel, M. A. Bennett, and G. Wilkinson, *J. Chem. Soc.* 3178 (1959).

[41] H. Greenfield, H. W. Sternberg, R. A. Friedel, J. H. Wotiz, R. Markby, and I. Wender, *J. Am. Chem. Soc.* **78**, 120 (1956).

[42] Pentane or isohexane may be used in place of petroleum ether.

[43] Commercially available in the United States and Great Britain. Preparations of diphenylacetylene are given in *Organic Syntheses, Coll. Vol. 3*, 350 (1955), and *Coll. Vol. 4*, 377 (1963).

[44] This technique of solvent removal is used to minimize decomposition of the product.

[45] All manipulations including filtration with diphenylacetylene-dicobalt hexacarbonyl in solution or in the moist state should be carried out under nitrogen.

of $R_2C_2Co_2(CO)_6$ compounds derived from other acetylenes. In some cases, such as $H_2C_2Co_2(CO)_6$ derived from acetylene itself, the product is a liquid and best purified by vacuum distillation.

Diphenylacetylene-dicobalt hexacarbonyl forms deep-purple crystals, m.p. 109.5–110°, that are readily soluble in organic solvents and gradually oxidized on exposure to air. The infrared spectrum exhibits metal carbonyl bands at 2093, 2050, and 2040 cm.$^{-1}$. Certain of the $R_2C_2Co_2(CO)_6$ complexes are converted into complexes of general formula $R_2CHCCo_3(CO)_9$ on treatment with strong mineral acids[46] and into complexes of general formula $R_2C_2Co_2(CO)_9$ on treatment with carbon monoxide at elevated temperatures and pressures.[47]

12. Tetramethylcyclobutadiene-Nickel Dichloride Dimer

Tetramethylcyclobutadiene-nickel dichloride dimer, $[(CH_3)_4C_4Ni\ Cl_2]_2$, is readily obtained in good yield by treating 1,2-dichloro-1,2,3,4,-tetramethylcyclobutene with nickel tetracarbonyl in benzene, acetone, or diethyl ether.[48] The dichlorotetramethylcyclobutene[49] required for this reaction may be obtained from dimethylacetylene (butyne-2[50]) and chlorine under rather critical reaction conditions.[51]

Procedure:

$$2Ni(CO)_4 + 2C_8H_{12}Cl_2 \rightarrow [C_8H_{12}NiCl_2]_2 + 8CO \uparrow$$

A sample of dichlorotetramethylcyclobutene is first prepared according to Criegee and Moschel[51] by passing chlorine gas *slowly*[52] through *well-cooled* dimethylacetylene containing catalytic quantities of boron trifluoride etherate and water ($H[BF_3OH]$).

After obtaining the dichlorotetramethylcyclobutene, 10.0 g. (0.0559 mole) of a recrystallized and preferably freshly sublimed sample of this

[46] R. Markby, I. Wender, R. A. Friedel, F. A. Cotton, and H. W. Sternberg, *J. Am. Chem. Soc.* **80**, 6529 (1958).

[47] H. W. Sternberg, J. G. Shukys, C. D. Donne, R. Markby, R. A. Friedel, and I. Wender, *J. Am. Chem. Soc.* **81**, 2339 (1959).

[48] R. Criegee and G. Schröder, *Ann. Chem.* **623**, 1 (1959).

[49] Hereafter, 1,2-dichloro-1,2,3,4-tetramethylcyclobutene will be designated as "dichlorotetramethylcyclobutene."

[50] Available commercially from Air Reduction Co., 150 East 42nd Street, New York 17, New York.

[51] R. Criegee and A. Moschel, *Chem. Ber.* **92**, 2181 (1959).

[52] The reaction between chlorine and dimethylacetylene is very exothermic and the temperature for formation of dichlorotetramethylcyclobutene very critical ($-20°$). Efficient cooling is therefore mandatory. Slow addition of chlorine may be accomplished by evaporation of liquid chlorine contained in a trap.[51]

material is refluxed under nitrogen for at least 10 hr. in 200 ml. of thiophene-free benzene to which 15 ml. (19.8 g., 0.116 mole) of commercial nickel tetracarbonyl has been cautiously added. The reaction is preferably conducted with magnetic stirring and definitely in an efficient hood to remove the vapors of the extremely toxic nickel tetracarbonyl (see pages 57 and 104).

After the reaction period is over, the reaction mixture is cooled to room temperature. The precipitate of nickel(II) chloride and the desired tetramethylcyclobutadiene-nickel(II) chloride is filtered and washed several times with benzene. It is then transferred to a thimble of a Soxhlet extraction apparatus and is extracted continuously with boiling chloroform until the fresh extracts are no longer colored. The chloroform extracts are then cooled to room temperature, and the chloroform is removed in a water-aspirator vacuum. The resulting dark-purple residue is washed with two 25-ml. portions of pentane and dried several hours at 25°/0.1 mm. to give yields up to ∼70% of [(CH₃)₄C₄NiCl₂]₂. If the drying is incomplete, the product will contain chloroform of crystallization.

Tetramethylcyclobutadiene-nickel dichloride dimer forms purple air-stable crystals that are sparingly soluble in most organic solvents but dissolve readily in water to give red conducting solutions. When heated in vacuum at ∼200°, two isomeric hydrocarbons of the composition $C_{16}H_{24}$ are produced depending on the decomposition conditions.[48] It reacts with sodium cyclopentadienide to form a red nickel compound $C_5H_5NiC_{13}H_{17}$, whose structure has been the cause of much discussion.[53]

---

[53] R. Criegee and P. Ludwig, *Chem. Ber.* **94**, 2038 (1961); R. B. King, *Inorg. Chem.* **2**, 528 (1963); L. F. Dahl, private communication (1963).

E. Arene Metal Complexes

1. Dibenzene-Chromium

Dibenzene-chromium may be obtained by the reduction of chromium (III) chloride with aluminum powder in the presence of aluminum chloride and benzene followed by further reduction with alkaline dithionite[1] (reducing Friedel-Crafts reaction), by the treatment of chromium(III) chloride with phenylmagnesium bromide followed by hydrolysis,[2] and by the reduction of chromium(III) chloride with isopropylmagnesium bromide in the presence of excess 1,3-cyclohexadiene.[3]

The best method for the preparation of dibenzene-chromium in quantity is the reducing Friedel-Crafts reaction developed by Fischer and co-workers. A suitable procedure is described in *Inorganic Syntheses*[4] and will not be repeated here. In other papers, Fischer and co-workers have described suitable preparations of dibenzene-molybdenum[5] and dibenzene-vanadium.[6] Dicumene-chromium is now available commercially in the United States from Union Carbide Chemical Co., South Charleston, West Virginia.

Dibenzene-chromium forms brown-black crystals, m.p. 284–285°, that are sparingly soluble in most organic solvents and are readily oxidized in air to derivatives of the $[(C_6H_6)_2Cr]^+$ cation.

2. Arene-Chromium Tricarbonyls

The very useful reaction between chromium hexacarbonyl and a variety of aromatic hydrocarbons was discovered independently by three research groups: Fischer and co-workers in Germany,[7] Nicholls and Whiting in England,[8] and Natta and co-workers in Italy.[9] This reaction

---

[1] E. O. Fischer and W. Hafner, *Z. Naturforsch.* **10b**, 665 (1955).

[2] M. Tsutsui and H. Zeiss, *J. Am. Chem. Soc.* **81**, 1367 (1959).

[3] E. O. Fischer and J. Müller, *Z. Naturforsch.* **17b**, 776 (1962).

[4] E. O. Fischer, *Inorg. Syn.* **6**, 132 (1960).

[5] E. O. Fischer, F. Scherer, and H. O. Stahl, *Chem. Ber.* **93**, 2065 (1960).

[6] E. O. Fischer and A. Reckziegel, *Chem. Ber.* **94**, 2204 (1961).

[7] E. O. Fischer, K. Öfele, H. Essler, W. Fröhlich, J. P. Mortensen, and W. Semmlinger, *Z. Naturforsch.* **13b**, 458 (1958); *Chem. Ber.* **91**, 2763 (1958).

[8] B. Nicholls and M. C. Whiting, *J. Chem. Soc.* 551 (1959).

[9] G. Natta, R. Ercoli, F. Calderazzo, and S. Santambrogio, *Chim. Ind.* (*Milan*) **40**, 1003 (1958).

permits the preparation of numerous arene-chromium tricarbonyls by simple heating of an aromatic compound with chromium hexacarbonyl either in an open system or an autoclave. Excess aromatic compound may sometimes be used as solvent as in the cases of the preparations of the chromium tricarbonyl derivatives of aniline, mesitylene, methyl benzoate, dimethylaniline, chlorobenzene, and acetophenone; in other cases, an inert organic solvent such as diglyme[10] or decalin[11] is preferably used. The preparation of methyl benzoate-chromium tricarbonyl is given here as an illustration of one of the simpler and more efficient preparations of arene-chromium tricarbonyl derivatives. The preparation of benzene-chromium tricarbonyl itself is more difficult and there is more variation between the recommended procedures of the three research groups[7-9] who discovered its synthesis.

Procedure:

$$Cr(CO)_6 + Arene \xrightarrow{\Delta} (Arene)Cr(CO)_3 + 3CO \uparrow$$

For the preparation of methyl benzoate-chromium tricarbonyl, a mixture of 7.0 g. (0.0318 moles) of chromium hexacarbonyl (page 84) and 40 ml. of methyl benzoate is heated under reflux at the boiling point under nitrogen for at least 12 hr. Chromium hexacarbonyl subliming into the reflux condenser is periodically returned mechanically to the reaction mixture with a wire or rod; for this reason, use of a straight reflux condenser is recommended.[12]

After the reaction period is over, the reaction mixture is cooled to room temperature and excess methyl benzoate removed at 25°/0.5 mm. The residue is transferred to a sublimation apparatus and the product is collected by sublimation at 80–90°/0.1 mm. to give 5.7 g. (66% yield) of orange-red crystalline methyl benzoate-chromium tricarbonyl, m.p. 93–95°.

The arene-chromium tricarbonyl derivatives are yellow to red-orange solids generally stable to air, soluble in organic solvents, insoluble in

---

[10] Diethylene glycol dimethyl ether.

[11] Sometimes when decalin (decahydronaphthalene) is used as a solvent for the preparation of arene-chromium tricarbonyls, the formation of tetralin-chromium tricarbonyl is observed. The tetralin (tetrahydronaphthalene) is present either as an impurity or arises from partial dehydrogenation of some of the decalin.

[12] Improved results in the preparation of arene-chromium tricarbonyls can often be obtained by carrying out the reaction in the special apparatus designed by Strohmeier[13] for automatically returning sublimed unreacted chromium hexacarbonyl to the reaction mixture with the refluxing solvent (page 124).

[13] W. Strohmeier, *Chem. Ber.* 94, 2490 (1961).

water, and volatile in vacuum ($\sim$0.1 mm.) at temperatures from 70°
to 150°. The chromium-tricarbonyl group bonded to the aromatic ring
appears to have a similar effect as a nitro group hindering electrophilic
substitution reactions but facilitating nucleophilic substitution reactions.

3. Cyclopentadienylbenzene-Iron Hexafluorophosphate

Salts of the cyclopentadienylbenzene-iron cation, $[C_5H_5FeC_6H_6]^+$,
were first prepared by treatment of cyclopentadienyliron dicarbonyl
chloride with benzene in the presence of aluminum chloride at elevated
temperatures.[14] The mesitylene analog had previously been prepared by
a similar reaction.[15] Much more recently, it was discovered by Nesmeyanov and co-workers[16] that the cyclopentadienylbenzene-iron cation
could be prepared much more readily by treatment of ferrocene with
benzene in the presence of aluminum powder and aluminum chloride. A
practical preparation of the hexafluorophosphate $[C_5H_5FeC_6H_6][PF_6]$
follows.

Procedure:

(1) $(C_5H_5)_2Fe + C_6H_6 + 2AlCl_3 \xrightarrow[Al]{\Delta} [C_5H_5FeC_6H_6][AlCl_4] + \{C_5H_5AlCl_2\}$

(2) $[C_5H_5FeC_6H_6][AlCl_4] + NH_4PF_6 \xrightarrow{H_2O} [C_5H_5FeC_6H_6][PF_6] \downarrow + NH_4Cl + AlCl_3$

The reaction is carried out under nitrogen in a 1-liter three-necked
flask equipped with a nitrogen inlet, efficient motor stirrer, and reflux
condenser. After filling the flask with nitrogen, it is charged with 55.8 g.
(0.3 mole) of ferrocene, 200 g. (1.5 mole) of anhydrous aluminum
chloride, 13.5 g. (0.5 mole) of aluminum powder, and 500 ml. of thiophene-free benzene. This reaction mixture is heated under reflux 16 hr.
at the boiling point with stirring. After the reaction period is over, the
reaction mixture is allowed to cool to room temperature and is finally
placed in an ice bath. The cold reaction mixture is treated dropwise with
500 ml. of ice water as such a rate that the benzene is kept below its
boiling point by the exothermic reaction. The lower aqueous layer is
separated in a separatory funnel from the upper benzene layer and
washed with three 50-ml. portions of benzene. The washed aqueous layer
is filtered by gravity directly into a concentrated aqueous solution con-

[14] M. L. H. Green, L. Pratt, and G. Wilkinson, *J. Chem. Soc.* 989 (1960).
[15] T. H. Coffield, V. Sandel, and R. D. Closson, *J. Am. Chem. Soc.* 79, 5826 (1957).
[16] A. N. Nesmeyanov, N. A. Vol'kenau, and I. N. Bolesova, *Tetrahedron Letters* 1725 (1963).

taining 48.9 g. (0.3 mole) of ammonium hexafluorophosphate.[17] A yellow precipitate of $[C_5H_5FeC_6H_6][PF_6]$ forms immediately. After standing for 1 hr. the product is filtered, sucked dry, and finally dried in vacuum over phosphorus pentoxide or similar drying agent to give 56.0 g. (54% yield) of yellow solid $[C_5H_5FeC_6H_6][PF_6]$.

Cyclopentadienylbenzene-iron hexafluorophosphate, $[C_5H_5FeC_6H_6]$ $[PF_6]$, is an air-stable yellow solid that is sparingly soluble in water and many polar organic solvents and is insoluble in nonpolar organic solvents. It blackens upon prolonged exposure to light. Its proton n.m.r. spectrum (acetone solution) exhibits singlet resonances at 3.59 τ and 4.83 τ of relative intensities 6:5 due to the protons of the benzene and cyclopentadienyl rings, respectively. On reduction of $[C_5H_5FeC_6H_6]^+$ with lithium aluminum hydride in tetrahydrofuran solution, cyclopentadienyl-cyclohexadienyliron, $C_5H_5FeC_6H_7$, is formed.[14,18] Treatment of $[C_5H_5-FeC_6H_6]^+$ with phenyllithium in diethyl ether solution gives cyclopentadienyl(phenylcyclohexadienyl)iron, $C_5H_5FeC_6H_6C_6H_5$.[19]

---

[17] Available from Ozark-Mahoning Company, 310 West Sixth Street, Tulsa 19, Oklahoma.
[18] G. Winkhaus, L. Pratt, and G. Wilkinson, *J. Chem. Soc.* 3807 (1961).
[19] D. Jones, L. Pratt, and G. Wilkinson, *J. Chem. Soc.* 4458 (1962).

F. Cycloheptatrienyl and Cycloheptadienyl Metal Complexes

1. Cyclopentadienylcycloheptatrienylvanadium

Cyclopentadienylcycloheptatrienylvanadium ($C_5H_5VC_7H_7$) is readily obtained by heating cyclopentadienylvanadium tetracarbonyl with cycloheptatriene.[1]

Procedure:

$$2C_5H_5V(CO)_4 + 2C_7H_8 \xrightarrow{\Delta} 2C_5H_5VC_7H_7 + 8CO \uparrow + H_2$$

A mixture of 2.28 g. (0.01 moles) of cyclopentadienylvanadium tetracarbonyl (page 105) and 30 ml. of commercial 91% cycloheptatriene[2] is heated under reflux at the boiling point under nitrogen for at least 8 hr. After cooling to room temperature, excess cycloheptatriene is removed at 25°/0.1 mm. It may be recovered by condensation into a clean —78° trap.

After all of the cycloheptatriene has been removed, nitrogen is admitted to the evacuated flask, and the black residue is transferred to a sublimation apparatus with a water-cooled probe. The sublimer is heated to 100° at 0.1 mm. Initially, oily material appears on the probe. When purple crystalline $C_5H_5VC_7H_7$ begins to appear on the probe, the sublimation is interrupted, the sublimer is cooled, nitrogen is admitted, and the probe is cleaned. The sublimer is then reassembled, evacuated, and the sublimation continued at 100°/0.1 mm. A purple sublimate of $C_5H_5VC_7H_7$ is collected in 40 to 60% yield (0.82 to 1.23 g). This material is removed and stored under nitrogen. Further purification may be accomplished by a second sublimation at 80°/0.1 mm.

Cyclopentadienylcycloheptatrienylvanadium, $C_5H_5VC_7H_7$, forms purple crystals. It may be handled in air for short periods of time in the solid state, but its purple solutions in organic solvents oxidize rapidly in air. It is one of the most readily available neutral "sandwich" compounds containing two rings of different sizes. Other compounds of this type such as

---

[1] R. B. King and F. G. A. Stone, *J. Am. Chem. Soc.* **81**, 5263 (1959).
[2] Available commercially from Shell Chemical Company, New York, New York.

C$_5$H$_5$CrC$_7$H$_7$,[3] C$_5$H$_5$CrC$_6$H$_6$,[4] and C$_5$H$_5$MnC$_6$H$_6$[5] are only preparable in much lower yield and with greater difficulty.

2. Cycloheptatrienylmolybdenum Tricarbonyl Tetrafluoroborate and Cycloheptatrienylmolybdenum Dicarbonyl Iodide

Cycloheptatrienylmolybdenum tricarbonyl tetrafluoroborate, [C$_7$H$_7$-Mo(CO)$_3$][BF$_4$], has been prepared by Dauben and Honnen by hydride abstraction from cycloheptatriene-molybdenum tricarbonyl with triphenylmethyl tetrafluoroborate.[6a] Treatment of cycloheptatrienylmolybdenum tricarbonyl tetrafluoroborate with iodide ion in acetone solution has been shown by Bertelli and Dauben to give cycloheptatrienylmolybdenum dicarbonyl iodide in good yield.[6b] Scaled-up versions of these preparations follow.

Procedure:

(1)   C$_7$H$_8$Mo(CO)$_3$ + [(C$_6$H$_5$)$_3$C][BF$_4$] $\xrightarrow{\text{CH}_2\text{Cl}_2}$ [C$_7$H$_7$Mo(CO)$_3$][BF$_4$] $\downarrow$ + (C$_6$H$_5$)$_3$CH

(2)   [C$_7$H$_7$Mo(CO)$_3$][BF$_4$] + NaI $\xrightarrow{\text{(CH}_3\text{)}_2\text{CO}}$ C$_7$H$_7$Mo(CO)$_2$I + CO $\uparrow$ + NaBF$_4$

A freshly prepared red solution of 27.2 g. (0.1 mole) of cycloheptatriene-molybdenum tricarbonyl (page 125) in 150 ml. of dichloromethane is treated with 36.5 g. (0.11 mole) of triphenylmethyl tetrafluoroborate.[7] After stirring for 30 minutes at room temperature, the tan precipitate is filtered, washed with five 50-ml. portions of dichloromethane, and sucked dry to give ~90% yield of cycloheptatrienylmolybdenum tricarbonyl tetrafluoroborate.

If cycloheptatrienylmolybdenum dicarbonyl iodide is desired, the entire sample of cycloheptatrienylmolybdenum tricarbonyl tetrafluoroborate thus prepared is stirred with 70 g. (0.467 moles) of sodium iodide[8] in 700 ml. of reagent-grade acetone at room temperature. The solution turns deep green immediately with vigorous gas evolution. The reaction

---

[3] E. O. Fischer and S. Breitschaft, *Angew. Chem.* **75**, 94, 167 (1963); R. B. King and M. B. Bisnette, *Tetrahedron Letters* 1137 (1963).

[4] E. O. Fischer and H. P. Kögler, *Z. Naturforsch.* **13b**, 197 (1958).

[5] T. H. Coffield, V. Sandel, and R. D. Closson, *J. Am. Chem. Soc.* **79**, 5826 (1957).

[6a] H. J. Dauben and L. R. Honnen, *J. Am. Chem. Soc.* **80**, 5570 (1958).

[6b] D. J. Bertelli, Ph.D. Thesis, University of Washington, 1961, (H. J. Dauben, Jr., Research Adviser).

[7] Triphenylmethyl tetrafluoroborate is most conveniently prepared by treatment of triphenylcarbinol with 48% aqueous tetrafluoroboric acid in propionic anhydride solution according to the procedure of H. J. Dauben, L. R. Honnen, and K. M. Harmon, *J. Org. Chem.* **25**, 1442 (1960).

[8] Potassium iodide or lithium iodide may be substituted for the sodium iodide.

mixture is stirred at least 16 hr. to insure complete reaction. The solvent is then removed in a water-aspirator vacuum ($\sim$30 mm.). A black solid residue remains. This residue is ground in a mortar with $\sim$600 ml. of dichloromethane in five portions, and the extracts are filtered by suction. The solvent is removed from the deep-green filtrate in a water-aspirator vacuum. Deep-green crystals remain. These are washed on a filter with five 50-ml. portions of pentane to remove small quantities of dicyclo-heptatrienyl (ditropyl) that are present as impurities and the crystals are sucked dry to give $\sim$27.7 g. (75% yield based on $C_7H_8Mo(CO)_3$) of green-black cycloheptatrienylmolybdenum dicarbonyl iodide.

Cycloheptatrienylmolybdenum tricarbonyl tetrafluoroborate forms orange to brown air-stable crystals (m.p. >270°; gradual darkening >140°) soluble only in the more polar organic solvents due to its ionic nature. Its infrared spectrum (KBr pellet) exhibits metal carbonyl bands at 2030, 1990, and 1950 cm.$^{-1}$

Cycloheptatrienylmolybdenum dicarbonyl iodide forms green-black crystals, m.p. 179–184° (dec.), that are sparingly soluble in nonpolar organic solvents but soluble in polar organic solvents and give green to black solutions. Its infrared spectrum (KBr pellet) exhibits metal carbonyl bands at 1980 and 1930 cm.$^{-1}$ and its proton n.m.r. spectrum (acetone solution) exhibits a single sharp resonance at 4.17 τ. It reacts with sodium cyclopentadienide to form the unusual complex $C_5H_5Mo(CO)_2C_7H_7$[9,10] and with $NaMn(CO)_5$ to form the compound $C_7H_7Mo(CO)_2Mn(CO)_5$.[10]

3. Cycloheptadienyliron Tricarbonyl Tetrafluoroborate and Cycloheptadienyliron Dicarbonyl Iodide

Salts of the cycloheptadienyliron tricarbonyl cation have been prepared either by protonation of cyclohepta*trie*ne-iron tricarbonyl with various strong acids[11,12] or by hydride abstraction from cyclohepta-*di*ene-iron tricarbonyl with the triphenylmethyl cation.[11] As is often true for complex transition metal cations, the tetrafluoroborate salt of the cycloheptadienyliron tricarbonyl cation, $[C_7H_9Fe(CO)_3][BF_4]$, is especially readily prepared and handled. Treatment of cycloheptadienyl-iron tricarbonyl tetrafluoroborate with iodide ion in acetone solution gives red-black cycloheptadienyliron dicarbonyl iodide, $C_7H_9Fe(CO)_2I$.[11] Scaled-up versions of these preparations follow.

[9] R. B. King and M. B. Bisnette, *Tetrahedron Letters* 1137 (1963).
[10] R. B. King and M. B. Bisnette, *Inorg. Chem.* 3, 785 (1964).
[11] H. J. Dauben and D. J. Bertelli, *J. Am. Chem. Soc.* 83, 497 (1961).
[12] R. Burton, L. Pratt, and G. Wilkinson, *J. Chem. Soc.* 594 (1961).

Procedure:

(1)   C$_7$H$_8$Fe(CO)$_3$ + HBF$_4$ $\xrightarrow{\text{(C}_2\text{H}_5\text{CO})_2\text{O}}$ [C$_7$H$_9$Fe(CO)$_3$][BF$_4$] $\downarrow$

(2)   [C$_7$H$_9$Fe(CO)$_3$][BF$_4$] + NaI $\xrightarrow{\text{(CH}_3)_2\text{CO}}$ C$_7$H$_9$Fe(CO)$_2$I + CO $\uparrow$ + NaBF$_4$

Cycloheptatriene and iron pentacarbonyl are converted to cyclo-heptatriene-iron tricarbonyl by boiling under reflux at least overnight in ethylcyclohexane solution (page 127). The product thus obtained after distillation (b.p. 70°/0.4 mm.) may be used for the reaction with tetra-fluoroboric acid. Since cycloheptadiene-iron tricarbonyl, often present as an impurity in cycloheptatriene-iron tricarbonyl, does not react with tetrafluoroboric acid, its presence is not harmful in the preparation of [C$_7$H$_9$Fe(CO)$_3$][BF$_4$].

A 23.2 g. (0.1 mole) sample of cycloheptatriene-iron tricarbonyl is dissolved in 150 ml. of propionic anhydride in a polyethylene beaker[13] equipped with a magnetic stirrer and cooled in an ice bath.[14] Commercial 48% tetrafluoroboric acid (22.1 g., 0.12 mole as HBF$_4$) is added dropwise with magnetic stirring; a yellow precipitate forms. After all of the acid has been added, the reaction mixture is stirred at 0° for an additional 20 minutes. The precipitate is then filtered, washed with five 50-ml. portions of dichloromethane, and sucked dry to give yellow solid [C$_7$H$_9$Fe(CO)$_3$][BF$_4$] in yields up to 91%.

If cycloheptadienyliron dicarbonyl iodide is desired, a 16.0 g. (0.05 mole) sample of [C$_7$H$_9$Fe(CO)$_3$][BF$_4$] is stirred at least 4 hr. at room temperature with a solution of 35 g. (0.233 mole) of sodium iodide[8] in 250 ml. of reagent-grade acetone. Gas evolution occurs, and the reaction mixture becomes a deep red-brown. After the reaction is completed, the solvent is removed from the reaction mixture in a water-aspirator vacuum (~30 mm.). A red-brown residue remains. This residue is extracted with three 100-ml. portions of dichloromethane and the extracts are filtered. The solvent is removed from the filtrate in a water-aspirator vacuum (~30 mm.). The brown crystalline residue is washed with three 50-ml. portions of pentane, hexane, or petroleum ether to give 7.5 g. to 12.4 g. (45 to 75% yield) of cycloheptadienyliron dicarbonyl iodide.

Cycloheptadienyliron tricarbonyl tetrafluoroborate is a yellow solid soluble only in the more polar organic solvents because of its ionic nature. Its infrared spectrum (KBr pellet) exhibits metal carbonyl bands at 2110, 2053, and 1980 cm.$^{-1}$, and its proton n.m.r. spectrum exhibits

---

[13] Glass apparatus may also be used but with danger of minor amounts of etching.

[14] A nitrogen atmosphere is not necessary for this reaction since both reactants and products are sufficiently air-stable.

resonances at 3.1 τ (triplet), 4.2 τ (double doublet), 5.1 τ (unresolved multiplet), 7.5 τ (unresolved multiplet), and 8.5 τ (unresolved multiplet).

Cycloheptadienyliron dicarbonyl iodide forms red-brown crystals, m.p. 86–89° (dec.), that are sparingly soluble in nonpolar organic solvents but soluble in polar organic solvents to give red-brown solutions. Its infrared spectrum (dichloromethane solution) exhibits metal carbonyl bands at 2033 and 1960 cm.$^{-1}$, and its proton n.m.r. spectrum (hexachloroacetone solution) displays resonances at 3.1 τ (apparent doublet), 4.3 τ (apparent triplet), 6.1 τ (broad, unresolved), 7.7 τ (broad unresolved), and 8.5 τ (apparent doublet) of relative intensities 1:2:2:2:2.

G. Alkyl, Acyl, and Perfluoroalkyl Metal Carbonyls

1. σ-Methyl-π-Cyclopentadienylmolybdenum Tricarbonyl

σ-Methyl-π-cyclopentadienylmolybdenum tricarbonyl, $CH_3Mo(CO)_3C_5H_5$, has been synthesized by Piper and Wilkinson by treatment of the sodium salt, $NaMo(CO)_3C_5H_5$, with methyl iodide.[1] The necessary $NaMo(CO)_3C_5H_5$ may be obtained either by treatment of molybdenum hexacarbonyl with sodium cyclopentadienide in refluxing tetrahydrofuran[1] or by reaction of molybdenum hexacarbonyl with dicyclopentadiene to form $[C_5H_5Mo(CO)_3]_2$ followed by reduction of this material with sodium amalgam in tetrahydrofuran.[2] The preparation of $NaMo(CO)_3C_5H_5$ from molybdenum hexacarbonyl and sodium cyclopentadienide is more practical for the larger-scale preparations and is used for the preparation of $CH_3Mo(CO)_3C_5H_5$ that follows.

Procedure:

$$(1) \quad Mo(CO)_6 + NaC_5H_5 \xrightarrow[C_4H_8O]{\Delta} Na[Mo(CO)_3C_5H_5] + 3CO \uparrow$$

$$(2) \quad Na[Mo(CO)_3C_5H_5] + CH_3I \rightarrow CH_3Mo(CO)_3C_5H_5 + NaI$$

The reaction is carried out under nitrogen in a 500-ml. three-necked flask equipped with a pressure-equalized dropping funnel, motor stirrer, reflux condenser, and nitrogen inlet. After filling the system with nitrogen either by passing a rapid stream of nitrogen through the apparatus for several minutes or preferably by evacuating the apparatus and refilling with nitrogen, the flask is charged with 2.76 g. (0.12 mole) of sodium metal and ~150 ml. of dry toluene or xylene. The mixture is heated to the boiling point and the sodium is dispersed into fine sand-like granules by vigorous stirring at the boiling point.[3] After cooling to room tempera-

[1] T. S. Piper and G. Wilkinson, *J. Inorg. Nucl. Chem.* 3, 104 (1956).

[2] R. G. Hayter, *Inorg. Chem.* 2, 1031 (1963).

[3] A commercial sodium dispersion in xylene may be used. Sodium dispersions in mineral oil are also available. The use of such sodium dispersions in mineral oil however results in a less pure product in cases in which the product is isolated by direct vacuum sublimation (as in the $CH_3Mo(CO)_3C_5H_5$ preparation) because of the tendency for the mineral oil to volatilize and contaminate the product during the sublimation.

ture, the xylene is siphoned off, and 250 ml. of redistilled tetrahydrofuran[4] is added. The suspension of sodium in tetrahydrofuran is treated dropwise with sufficient cyclopentadiene (freshly prepared by thermal dedimerization of commercial dicyclopentadiene) in order to dissolve all of the sodium to form a pink to dark red-violet sodium cyclopentadienide solution. Generally 11.4–14.8 ml. (9.2–11.9 g., 0.14–0.18 mole) of cyclopentadiene are necessary.

This resulting sodium cyclopentadienide solution is then treated with 26.4 g. (0.1 mole) molybdenum hexacarbonyl,[5] and the reaction is heated under reflux at least 12 hr. at the boiling point and forms a yellowish solution of the sodium salt $NaMo(CO)_3C_5H_5$.

This $NaMo(CO)_3C_5H_5$ solution is allowed to cool to room temperature and is then treated dropwise with 7.5 ml. (17 g., 0.12 mole) of methyl iodide. After all of the methyl iodide has been added, the reaction mixture is stirred at room temperature for at least 5 hr. to insure complete reaction. After replacing the stirrer with a stopper, the solvent is removed from the reaction mixture in a water-aspirator vacuum at room temperature until a dry solid residue remains. Nitrogen is then admitted to the evacuated flask, and the residue is transferred under nitrogen[6] to a large sublimation apparatus.[7] The $CH_3Mo(CO)_3C_5H_5$ is isolated as yellow crystals from this residue by sublimation at 80°/0.1 mm. A yield of 85% has been reported for this reaction.[1]

σ-Methyl-π-cyclopentadienylmolybdenum tricarbonyl is a yellow solid, m.p. 124° (dec.), that is readily soluble in organic solvents, readily purified by vacuum sublimation, and slowly oxidized by air. Its infrared spectrum (CS_2 solution) exhibits strong metal carbonyl bands at 2020 and 1937 cm.$^{-1}$.

A similar general technique may be used to prepare other $RMo(CO)_3C_5H_5$ derivatives such as the ethyl,[1] isopropyl,[1] and allyl[8] compounds. In certain cases, extraction of the product from the evaporated

[4] Tetrahydrofuran may be purified by redistillation over lithium aluminum hydride or sodium metal or by passage through a column of molecular sieves (Linde Air Products, Morristown, New Jersey.

[5] In order to insure complete reaction of the molybdenum hexacarbonyl to avoid its contamination of the product, the ratio $C_5H_5Na:Mo(CO)_6$ is 1:1.2 rather than the theoretical 1:1.

[6] Evaporated sodium cyclopentadienide residues may be pyrophoric especially after sublimation. Therefore, the residue should be transferred to the sublimer under nitrogen. After the sublimation, the residue should be discarded into a place where it can safely burn.

[7] If a sufficiently large sublimer is not available, the sublimation may be carried out in several portions in a smaller sublimer.

[8] M. Cousins and M. L. H. Green, J. Chem. Soc. 889 (1963).

reaction mixture with pentane or dichloromethane may be preferable to immediate sublimation of the product from the residue. Tungsten hexacarbonyl also reacts with sodium cyclopentadienide in tetrahydrofuran or 1,2-dimethoxyethane solution to form the salt $NaW(CO)_3C_5H_5$; this reacts with methyl iodide and other alkyl halides to form $RW(CO)_3C_5H_5$ derivatives which are even more stable than their molybdenum analogs.

2. Methylmanganese Pentacarbonyl

Methylmanganese pentacarbonyl, $CH_3Mn(CO)_5$, may be prepared by treatment of the anion $Mn(CO)_5^-$ with methyl iodide or methyl sulfate[9,10] or, less conveniently from diazomethane and $HMn(CO)_5$.[9] The anion $Mn(CO)_5^-$ may be obtained from dimanganese decacarbonyl and a base or alkali metal in an appropriate solvent. Special precautions are necessary for the preparation of $CH_3Mn(CO)_5$ because of its high volatility.

Procedure:

(1) $$13Mn_2(CO)_{10} + 40NaOH \xrightarrow[CH_3OH]{H_2O} 24NaMn(CO)_5 + 2MnCO_3 \downarrow + 8Na_2CO_3$$
$$+ 20H_2O$$

(2) $$NaMn(CO)_5 + CH_3I \rightarrow CH_3Mn(CO)_5 \downarrow + NaI$$

The reaction is conducted in a 100-ml. flask fitted with a nitrogen-inlet, reflux condenser, and magnetic stirrer. After filling with nitrogen, the flask is charged with 2.0 g. (0.0051 mole) of dimanganese decacarbonyl (page 89) and a methanolic solution of sodium hydroxide obtained by dissolving 1.3 g. (0.024 mole) of commercial sodium methoxide or an equivalent quantity of metallic sodium in 25 ml. of methanol and adding 5 ml. of water. The reaction mixture is heated for 30 minutes at the boiling point. During this process, the dimanganese decacarbonyl is attacked and a light colored precipitate is formed.

The resulting basic solution is cooled to $\sim 0°$ in an ice bath and treated with a mixture of 0.9 ml. (2.0 g., 0.0142 mole) of methyl iodide, 15 ml. of methanol, and 15 ml. of water. A voluminous white precipitate of $CH_3Mn(CO)_5$ soon forms. This is removed by filtration after an hour and is sucked dry for a few seconds. Prolonged suction is to be avoided because of the high volatility of $CH_3Mn(CO)_5$.

For further purification, the crude product is dissolved in diethyl ether, and excess anhydrous magnesium or sodium sulfate is added as a

[9] W. Hieber and G. Wagner, *Ann. Chem.* **618**, 24 (1958).
[10] R. D. Closson, J. Kozikowski, and T. H. Coffield, *J. Org. Chem.* **22**, 598 (1957).

drying agent. After about 30 minutes of drying at room temperature, the ether solution is filtered from the drying agent which has been washed twice with ether. The filtrate is then evaporated in a water-aspirator vacuum ($\sim$30 mm.). The flask must be allowed to cool from the heat of vaporization of the diethyl ether, and pumping should be discontinued promptly upon removal of the diethyl ether to prevent volatilization losses of $CH_3Mn(CO)_5$.

The crystalline residue of $CH_3Mn(CO)_5$ may finally be purified by sublimation at 25°/0.1 mm. onto a probe cooled to 0° or −78° in a closed system[11] to prevent volatilization into the vacuum system or pump. Yields of 60 to 90% of $CH_3Mn(CO)_5$ may be expected for this preparation.

Methylmanganese pentacarbonyl forms white air-stable crystals m.p. 95°, that are insoluble in water but readily soluble in organic solvents. Its volatility (v.p. 2 mm. at 20°) is so great that samples placed in an open container soon evaporate. Caution is therefore needed during its preparation to prevent losses from volatilization. Methylmanganese pentacarbonyl exhibits carbonyl bands at 2085, 2000, and 1960 cm.$^{-1}$ in its infrared spectrum and a single sharp resonance at $\sim$9.95 τ in its proton n.m.r. spectrum. It reacts with carbon monoxide to form the acetyl derivative $CH_3COMn(CO)_5$ more readily obtained from $NaMn(CO)_5$ and acetyl chloride in an inert ethereal solvent.[10] Treatment with certain amines such as cyclohexylamine converts methylmanganese pentacarbonyl into acetyl amminemanganese tetracarbonyls.[12]

3. Trifluoroacetylmanganese Pentacarbonyl and Trifluoromethylmanganese Pentacarbonyl

Trifluoroacetylmanganese pentacarbonyl, $CF_3COMn(CO)_5$, has been prepared by McClellan[13] by treatment of $LiMn(CO)_5$ with trifluoroacetyl fluoride and by Coffield, Kozikowski, and Closson[14] by treatment of $NaMn(CO)_5$ with trifluoroacetic anhydride. The latter procedure uses more readily available and handled reagents and is therefore recommended.

---

[11] After charging the sublimer, it is evacuated and the stopcock leading to the pump is then closed. Continuous pumping on the sublimer during sublimation of a compound as volatile as $CH_3Mn(CO)_5$ is likely to lead to losses due to volatilization of the compound beyond the sublimer.

[12] K. A. Keblys and A. H. Filbey, *J. Am. Chem. Soc.* **82**, 4204 (1960).

[13] W. R. McClellan, *J. Am. Chem. Soc.* **83**, 1598 (1961).

[14] T. H. Coffield, J. Kozikowski, and R. D. Closson, *Abstr. 5th Intern. Conf. Coordination Chem. London,* The Chemical Society Special Publication 13, London, p. 126 (1959).

Procedure:

$$(1) \quad Mn_2(CO)_{10} + 2Na \xrightarrow[C_4H_8O]{Hg} 2NaMn(CO)_5$$

$$(2) \quad NaMn(CO)_5 + (CF_3CO)_2O \rightarrow CF_3COMn(CO)_5 + Na[CF_3CO_2]$$

$$(3) \quad CF_3COMn(CO)_5 \rightarrow CF_3Mn(CO)_5 + CO \uparrow$$

The reaction is conducted in a 1-liter three-necked flask with a stop-cock fused to the bottom (Fig. 23) for removal of mercury and excess amalgam and fitted with a nitrogen inlet, efficient motor stirrer, pressure-equalized dropping funnel, and reflux condenser. After filling with nitrogen, the flask is charged with 23 ml. (~310 g.) of mercury and 3.0 g. (0.13 mole) of sodium metal is added in ~0.2-g. portions with stirring. After an induction period of several seconds depending on the

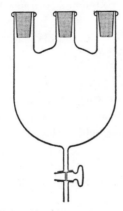

Fig. 23. Diagram of a special three-necked flask for reactions with amalgams.

crust on the sodium and the rate of stirring, each piece of sodium will suddenly react exothermically with the mercury to form the amalgam with a hissing sound. After all of the sodium has reacted, the liquid amalgam is allowed to cool to room temperature and is then treated with 20.0 g. (0.051 mole) of dimanganese decacarbonyl (page 89)[15] and 300 ml. of tetrahydrofuran.[4] This mixture is stirred vigorously[16] for at least 1 hr. During this period, the yellow color of the $Mn_2(CO)_{10}$ should

---

[15] This preparation may be readily scaled down to use less dimanganese decacarbonyl if a smaller quantity of product is desired.

[16] The stirring should be efficient and vigorous enough not only to agitate the tetrahydrofuran solution but also to agitate the liquid amalgam at the bottom of the flask and fresh surfaces should be exposed continually.

completely disappear because of reduction to the colorless $Mn(CO)_5^-$ anion; the reaction mixture, however, will appear gray due to suspended finely divided mercury.

When the formation of the $Mn(CO)_5^-$ anion is complete, excess mercury and amalgam are removed through the stopcock at the bottom.[17] The $NaMn(CO)_5$ solution is then treated dropwise with 14.1 ml. (21.0 g., 0.1 mole) of trifluoroacetic anhydride. After all of the trifluoroacetic anhydride is added, the reaction mixture is stirred at least 1 additional hr. at room temperature to insure complete reaction. The solvent is then removed from the reaction mixture in a water-aspirator vacuum ($\sim$30 mm.). The residue is transferred to a sublimer, and product is sublimed from the residue at 50–55°/1.5 mm. to give white crystalline $CF_3COMn(CO)_5$ in $\sim$75% yield.

The preparation of $CF_3Mn(CO)_5$ is carried out in a 250-ml. round-bottom flask with the neck connected to a gas bubbler filled with mercury or mineral oil and heated with an oil bath.[18] After filling with nitrogen, the flask is charged with 10 g. (0.0342 moles) of the trifluoroacetyl derivative $CF_3COMn(CO)_5$ and heated to 110° for 1 hr. and 40 minutes. The rate of carbon monoxide evolution is readily determined by the flow through the gas bubbler. Initially, at 110° the carbon monoxide evolution should be very vigorous, but, toward the end of the reaction period, little or no gas evolution should occur. After the reaction period is complete, the bubbler is disconnected while the flask is hot[19] and the flask is allowed to cool to room temperature. The solid residue is transferred to a sublimer and the trifluoromethylmanganese pentacarbonyl is isolated in $\sim$92% yield (8.3 g.) by sublimation at 70°/20 mm. (water-aspirator vacuum).

Trifluoroacetylmanganese pentacarbonyl, $CF_3COMn(CO)_5$, is a white air-stable volatile solid, m.p. 55–56°, that is soluble in organic solvents. Its infrared spectrum exhibits strong metal carbonyl bands at 2150 and 2040 cm.[-1] and a single strong acyl carbonyl band at 1625 cm.[-1]. Its most

---

[17] The mercury may be recovered for another dilute sodium amalgam reaction by washing first with methanol or ethanol to destroy any remaining sodium and then with water. If still dirty, dilute nitric acid may be used but the mercury should not be allowed to stand in the nitric acid any longer than necessary because of the tendency for some mercury to dissolve. Since the solubility of water in mercury is negligible, the washed mercury may be used immediately for another sodium amalgam reaction without requiring any special drying to remove the water.

[18] It is advisable to evacuate the flask containing the $CF_3COMn(CO)_5$ and refill it with nitrogen before carrying out the heating. Otherwise, it is not necessary to provide an inert atmosphere for this reaction.

[19] The bubbler must be disconnected from the flask before cooling in order to prevent sucking of the oil in the bubbler back into the flask upon cooling.

characteristic reaction is the decarbonylation reaction that has been described.

Trifluoromethylmanganese pentacarbonyl, $CF_3Mn(CO)_5$, is a white air-stable extremely volatile solid, m.p. 82–83°; it is less soluble in organic solvents than $CF_3COMn(CO)_5$. Its infrared spectrum exhibits strong metal carbonyl bands at 2155, 2050, and 2015 cm.$^{-1}$ and its F^{19} n.m.r. spectrum exhibits a single sharp resonance at —9.3 ϕ due to the CF_3 group.

4. σ-Methyl-π-Cyclopentadienyliron Dicarbonyl

The methyl derivative $CH_3Fe(CO)_2C_5H_5$ is readily obtained by treatment of the sodium salt $NaFe(CO)_2C_5H_5$ with methyl iodide.[1] The sodium salt in turn is obtained from $[C_5H_5Fe(CO)_2]_2$ and dilute sodium amalgam.[1]

Procedure:

$$(1) \quad [C_5H_5Fe(CO)_2]_2 + 2Na \xrightarrow[C_4H_8O]{Hg} 2Na[Fe(CO)_2C_5H_5]$$

$$(2) \quad Na[Fe(CO)_2C_5H_5] + CH_3I \rightarrow CH_3Fe(CO)_2C_5H_5 + NaI$$

The preparation of $CH_3Fe(CO)_2C_5H_5$ is carried out in a 1-liter three-necked flask with a stopcock fused to the bottom (Fig. 23) and fitted with a nitrogen-inlet, efficient motor stirrer, pressure-equalized dropping funnel, and reflux condenser. After filling with nitrogen, the flask is charged with 23 ml. (~310 g.) of mercury and 3.0 g. (0.13 mole) of sodium metal added in ~0.2 g. portions with stirring. After an induction period of several seconds, each piece of sodium suddenly reacts exothermically with the mercury to form the amalgam with a hissing sound. After all of the sodium has reacted, the liquid amalgam is allowed to cool to room temperature and then treated with 17.7 g. (0.05 mole) of $[C_5H_5Fe(CO)_2]_2$ (page 114) and 300 ml. of tetrahydrofuran.[4] The reaction mixture is stirred vigorously[16] for at least 1 hr.; the red-brown color of the $[C_5H_5Fe(CO)_2]_2$ in solution becomes the orange-brown color of $NaFe(CO)_2C_5H_5$.

When the formation of $NaFe(CO)_2C_5H_5$ is complete, excess mercury and amalgam are removed through the stopcock at the bottom.[17] The $NaFe(CO)_2C_5H_5$ solution is then treated dropwise with 17.0 g. (0.12 mole) of methyl iodide; a slightly exothermic reaction occurs.

After stirring for at least 8 hr. at room temperature, the stirrer is replaced with a stopper to minimize leakage and solvent is removed in a water-aspirator vacuum (~30 mm.). When a dry residue remains, nitrogen is admitted, and the residue is transferred to a large sublimation apparatus.[7] Sublimation at 60°/0.1 mm. to a water-cooled probe gives 10.0 to 13.4 g. (52% to 70% yield) of orange waxy $CH_3Fe(CO)_2$-C_5H_5.

σ-Methyl-π-cyclopentadienyliron dicarbonyl is a volatile orange waxy material, m.p. 78–82°, that is readily soluble in organic solvents. Exposure to air slowly oxidizes the solid material, but rapidly oxidizes its solutions. Its infrared spectrum (CS_2 solution) exhibits strong metal carbonyl bands at 2010 and 1955 cm.$^{-1}$, and its proton n.m.r. spectrum (CS_2 solution) exhibits sharp resonances at 5.35 τ and 9.85 τ due to the cyclopentadienyl and methyl protons, respectively.

Numerous other compounds of the type $RFe(CO)_2C_5H_5$ ($R = C_2H_5$, C_6H_5, RCO, R_2NCO, C_6F_5, $CH_2=CHCH_2$, $NCCH_2$, $HC\equiv CCH_2$, etc.) may be obtained in similar ways from $NaFe(CO)_2C_5H_5$ and halides such as ethyl iodide,[1] iodobenzene,[1] several acyl and perfluoroacyl chlorides[14,20,21] dialkylcarbamyl chlorides,[20] hexafluorobenzene,[22] allyl chloride,[23] chloroacetonitrile,[24] and propargyl chloride.[25] In addition, $NaFe(CO)_2C_5H_5$ reacts similarly with polymethylene dibromides of the general formula $Br(CH_2)_nBr$ ($n = 3, 4, 5,$ and 6) to give binuclear derivatives of the type $(CH_2)_n[Fe(CO)_2C_5H_5]$ ($n = 3, 4, 5,$ and 6).[26] Isolation and purification of these compounds depending on the individual case utilizes the techniques of sublimation, chromatography on alumina in pentane or benzene solution, and/or crystallization from hydrocarbon solvents sometimes mixed with chloroform or dichloromethane.

5. Heptafluoropropylcobalt Tetracarbonyl

Heptafluoropropylcobalt tetracarbonyl may be prepared by treatment of the $Co(CO)_4^-$ anion with heptafluorobutyryl chloride; spontaneous decarbonylation occurs.[13]

Procedure:

$$(1) \quad Co_2(CO)_8 + 2Na \xrightarrow[C_4H_8O]{Hg} 2NaCo(CO)_4$$

$$(2) \quad NaCo(CO)_4 + C_3F_7COCl \rightarrow C_3F_7Co(CO)_4 + CO\uparrow + NaCl$$

The preparation of $C_3F_7Co(CO)_4$ like the preparations of CF_3COMn-$(CO)_5$ and $CH_3Fe(CO)_2C_5H_5$ that have been described is conveniently

[20] R. B. King, *J. Am. Chem. Soc.* 85, 1918 (1963).
[21] R. B. King and M. B. Bisnette, *J. Organometal. Chem.* 2, 15 (1964).
[22] R. B. King and M. B. Bisnette, *J. Organometal. Chem.* 2, 38 (1964).
[23] M. L. H. Green and P. L. I. Nagy, *J. Chem. Soc.* 189 (1963).
[24] J. K. P. Ariyaratne and M. L. H. Green, *J. Chem. Soc.* 2976 (1963).
[25] J. K. P. Ariyaratne and M. L. H. Green, *J. Organometal. Chem.* 1, 90 (1963).
[26] R. B. King, *Inorg. Chem.* 2, 531 (1963).

carried out in a special 1-liter three-necked flask with a stopcock fused to the bottom (Fig. 23) and fitted with a nitrogen inlet, efficient motor stirrer, pressure-equalized dropping funnel, and reflux condenser. After filling with nitrogen, the flask is charged with 23 ml. ($\sim$310 g.) of mercury, and 3.0 g. (0.13 mole) of sodium metal is added in $\sim$0.2-g. portions with stirring as in the previously described preparations. After all of the sodium has reacted, the liquid amalgam is allowed to cool to room temperature and is treated with 17.1 g. (0.05 mole) of dicobalt octacarbonyl (page 98). The reaction mixture is stirred vigorously[16] at room temperature for at least 3 hr.; the dark orange color of the $Co_2(CO)_8$ soon becomes a gray to yellow-gray.

When the formation of the $NaCo(CO)_4$ is complete, excess mercury and amalgam are removed through the stopcock at the bottom.[17] The $NaCo(CO)_4$ solution is treated dropwise with a freshly prepared mixture of 18.0 ml. (23.2 g., 0.1 mole) of heptafluorobutyryl chloride[27] and 30 ml. of tetrahydrofuran.[4] Vigorous gas evolution occurs.

After stirring the reaction mixture at room temperature for at least 3 hr., volatile materials are removed from the reaction mixture first in a water-aspirator vacuum ($\sim$30 mm.), and when this is no longer effective in an oil-pump vacuum ($\sim$1 mm.). All volatile materials are collected in a trap cooled to $-78°$.

Tetrahydrofuran is removed from the combined volatile materials by distillation at $\sim$25°/$\sim$100 mm. through a 40-cm. Vigreux column. After all of the tetrahydrofuran has been removed, the residue is transferred into a smaller flask with the aid of several milliliters of pentane. After removing this pentane, the product is distilled in a water-pump vacuum to give 11 g. (32% yield) of a yellow liquid, b.p. 44°/16 mm.

Heptafluoropropylcobalt tetracarbonyl is a yellow, fairly air-stable liquid readily miscible with organic solvents but immiscible with water and readily purified by distillation. Its infrared spectrum exhibits metal carbonyl bands at 2130 and 2050 cm.$^{-1}$.

6. Methinyltricobalt Enneacarbonyl Derivatives

Substituted methinyltricarbonyl enneacarbonyls of the general type $RCCH_2CCo_3(CO)_9$ were first obtained by treatment of acetylene-dicobalt hexacarbonyls of the general type $(RC_2H)Co_2(CO)_6$ with strong mineral

---

[27] Heptafluorobutyryl chloride, a malodorous toxic liquid, b.p. 38°/$\sim$760 mm., may be obtained commercially (e.g., Columbia Organic Chemicals, Inc., Columbia, South Carolina) or prepared from heptafluorobutyric acid and phosphorus pentachloride [J. H. Simons, W. T. Black, and R. F. Clark, *J. Am. Chem. Soc.* **75,** 5621 (1953)].

acids.[28] Later, a more general synthesis of these compounds and other compounds of the type $YCCo_3(CO)_9$ (Y = halogen, methyl, phenyl, hydrogen, trifluoromethyl, etc.) was discovered by Dent and co-workers in England; they treated dicobalt octacarbonyl with various polyhalomethanes generally in a polar solvent.[29] This synthesis was developed further by Bor and co-workers in Hungary[30] and Ercoli and co-workers in Italy.[31] This method of preparation of $YCCo_3(CO)_9$ compounds is illustrated by the preparation of chloromethinyltricobalt enneacarbonyl, $ClCCo_3(CO)_9$, from dicobalt octacarbonyl and carbon tetrachloride that follows.

Procedure:

$$9Co_2(CO)_8 + 4YCX_3 \rightarrow 4YCCo_3(CO)_9 + 36CO \uparrow + 6CoX_2 \qquad (X = Y = Cl)$$

The reaction is carried out under nitrogen in a 500-ml. flask fitted with a nitrogen inlet, reflux condenser, and magnetic stirrer. After filling with nitrogen, the flask is charged with 10.3 g. (0.03 moles) of dicobalt octacarbonyl (page 98) and 200 ml. of pure carbon tetrachloride. This mixture is heated to $57 \pm 3°$ for 1 hr. with stirring. It is then allowed to cool to room temperature and treated with 150 ml. of water. The lower organic layer is separated and evaporated to dryness in a water-aspirator vacuum ($\sim$30 mm.) at room temperature using a rotary evaporator if available to speed up the process. The dry residue is transferred to a sublimation apparatus, and the product is isolated in 71% yield (4.5 g.) as purple crystals by sublimation at 35–40°/0.05 mm.

Chloromethinyltricobalt enneacarbonyl, $ClCCo_3(CO)_9$, forms purple volatile crystals, m.p. 131–133° (dec.), that are moderately stable in air and give purple solutions in organic solvents. Its infrared spectrum (hexane solution) exhibits metal carbonyl bands at 2109 (w), 2062 (vs), 2046 (s), and 2030 (w) cm.$^{-1}$. Upon heating with the alcohols ROH (R = methyl or ethyl), it is converted to the esters $Co_3(CO)_9CCO_2R$.[31]

The bromine analog, $BrCCo_3(CO)_9$ may readily be obtained by treatment of dicobalt octacarbonyl with carbon tetrabromide in benzene solution at room temperature.[31] The methyl derivative $CH_3CCo_3(CO)_9$ may be obtained by treatment of dicobalt octacarbonyl with 1,1,1-trichloro-

[28] R. Markby, I. Wender, R. A. Friedel, F. A. Cotton, and H. W. Sternberg, *J. Am. Chem. Soc.* **80**, 6529 (1958).

[29] W. T. Dent, L. A. Duncanson, R. G. Guy, H. W. B. Reed, and B. L. Shaw, *Proc. Chem. Soc.* 169 (1961).

[30] G. Bor, L. Markó, and B. Markó, *Chem. Ber.* **95**, 333 (1962).

[31] R. Ercoli, E. Santambrogio, and G. Tettamanti Casagrande, *Chim. Ind.* (*Milan*) **44**, 1344 (1962).

ethane in refluxing methanol or ethanol. All of these cobalt compounds are isolated by evaporation of the solution followed by vacuum sublimation of the residue; the purple derivatives are noted for their stability to air (unusual for a cobalt carbonyl derivative), solubility in organic solvents to give purple solutions, and, above all, unusual volatility especially for a trinuclear derivative. Some of the $YCCo_3(CO)_9$ complexes are even reported to be steam-distillable.[29]

H. Metal Carbonyl Hydride Derivatives

1. Cyclopentadienylmetal Tricarbonyl Hydrides of Molybdenum and Tungsten

The hydrides $C_5H_5M(CO)_3H$ (M = molybdenum or tungsten) are readily obtained by acidification of solutions of the anions $[M(CO)_3$-$C_5H_5]^-$, which are prepared by heating the hexacarbonyls with solutions of sodium cyclopentadienide (page 145).[1] The preparation of the molybdenum compound, $C_5H_5Mo(CO)_3H$, follows.

Procedure:

(1) $M(CO)_6 + NaC_5H_5 \xrightarrow[C_4H_8O]{\Delta} Na[M(CO)_3C_5H_5] + 3CO \uparrow$

(2) $Na[M(CO)_3C_5H_5] + CH_3CO_2H \rightarrow HM(CO)_3C_5H_5 + Na[CH_3CO_2]$

$$(M = Mo \text{ and } W)$$

The reaction is carried out under nitrogen in a 500-ml. three-necked flask equipped with a pressure-equalized dropping funnel, motor stirrer, reflux condenser, and nitrogen inlet. After filling with nitrogen, the flask is charged with 2.76 g. (0.12 mole) of sodium metal and 150 ml. of dry toluene or xylene. The sodium is dispersed into fine sand-like granules by vigorous stirring at the boiling point.[2] After cooling to room temperature, the xylene or toluene is siphoned off, and 250 ml. of tetrahydrofuran[3] is added. The suspension of sodium in tetrahydrofuran is treated dropwise with sufficient freshly prepared cyclopentadiene (12.3–14.8 ml., 9.9–11.9 g.,

---

[1] T. S. Piper and G. Wilkinson, *J. Inorg. Nucl. Chem.* **3**, 104 (1956).

[2] A commercial sodium dispersion in xylene may be used. Sodium dispersions in mineral oil are also available. The use of such sodium dispersions in mineral oil, however, results in a less pure product in cases in which the product is isolated by direct vacuum sublimation (as in the $C_5H_5Mo(CO)_3H$ preparation); this is caused by the tendency of the mineral oil to volatilize and contaminate the product during the sublimation.

[3] Tetrahydrofuran may be purified by redistillation over lithium aluminum hydride or sodium metal or by passage through a column of molecular sieves (Linde Air Products, Morristown, New Jersey).

0.15–0.18 mole) to dissolve all of the sodium to form a pink to dark red-violet sodium cyclopentadienide solution.

This sodium cyclopentadienide solution is then heated under reflux at least 12 hr. at the boiling point with 26.4 g. (0.1 mole) of molybdenum hexacarbonyl to form a yellowish solution of the sodium salt NaMo(CO)$_3$C$_5$H$_5$.[4]

After cooling to room temperature, the NaMo(CO)$_3$C$_5$H$_5$ solution is treated with 12 ml. (12.6 g., 0.21 mole) of glacial (99.8%) acetic acid. After stirring for 2 hr. at room temperature, the solvent is removed from the reaction mixture at ~30 mm. (water-aspirator vacuum). Nitrogen is then admitted, and the resulting purple residue is broken up under nitrogen with a spatula. The pulverized residue is transferred to a large sublimation apparatus,[5] and the pale yellow crystalline C$_5$H$_5$Mo(CO)$_3$H is sublimed out of the residue at 40–80°/0.1 mm. onto a probe cooled with running water or ice. After the sublimation is complete, nitrogen is admitted to the sublimer, and the product is removed from the probe under nitrogen and stored in the absence of air. Yields of up to 90% may be obtained in this reaction. The residue from the sublimation is pyrophoric.

Cyclopentadienylmolybdenum tricarbonyl hydride forms pale yellow volatile crystals, m.p. 50–52° (dec.), that are insoluble in water, soluble in organic solvents and aqueous bases, and rapidly darken on exposure to air. Its infrared spectrum (CS$_2$ solution) exhibits strong metal carbonyl bands at 2030 and 1949 cm.$^{-1}$ and its proton n.m.r. spectrum (toluene solution) exhibits a sharp cyclopentadienyl resonance at 4.6 τ and a sharp metal hydride resonance at 15.4 τ of relative intensities 5:1. Cyclopentadienylmolybdenum tricarbonyl hydride is a weak acid, pK ~7.[1,6] On heating, it loses hydrogen to form [C$_5$H$_5$Mo(CO)$_3$]$_2$.[1,6] It reacts with diazomethane to form the methyl derivative CH$_3$Mo(CO)$_3$-C$_5$H$_5$ in low yield.[1] On dissolving in carbon tetrachloride, it is rapidly converted to the chloride C$_5$H$_5$Mo(CO)$_3$Cl.[1] The corresponding bromide and iodide are obtained by treatment of C$_5$H$_5$Mo(CO)$_3$H with N-bromosuccinimide and methyl iodide, respectively.[1] Treatment of C$_5$H$_5$Mo-(CO)$_3$H with N-methyl-N-nitroso-p-toluenesulfonamide ("Diazald") gives the nitrosyl derivative C$_5$H$_5$Mo(CO)$_2$NO.[1] Treatment of C$_5$H$_5$Mo-(CO)$_3$H with dimethyldisulfide gives the sulfur derivative [C$_5$H$_5$Mo-

---

[4] In order to insure complete reaction of the molybdenum hexacarbonyl to avoid its contamination of the product, the ratio C$_5$H$_5$Na/Mo(CO)$_6$ is 1.2:1 rather than the theoretical 1:1.

[5] If a sufficiently large sublimer is not available, the sublimation may be carried out in several portions in a smaller sublimer.

[6] E. O. Fischer, W. Hafner, and H. O. Stahl, Z. Anorg. Allgem. Chem. **282**, 47 (1955).

$(CO)_2SCH_3]_2$.[7] Treatment of $C_5H_5Mo(CO)_3H$ with tetrafluoroethylene gives the tetrafluoroethyl derivative $HCF_2CF_2Mo(CO)_3C_5H_5$.[7]

The tungsten derivative, $C_5H_5W(CO)_3H$, may be prepared in a manner similar to $C_5H_5Mo(CO)_3H$, but using 35.4 g. of tungsten hexacarbonyl instead of the 26.4 g. of molybdenum hexacarbonyl required for the preparation of $C_5H_5Mo(CO)_3H$ that was described. Because of the lower reactivity of tungsten hexacarbonyl, it is preferable but not essential to prepare the sodium cyclopentadienide and carry out its reaction with tungsten hexacarbonyl in 1,2-dimethoxyethane (b.p. 82°)[3] rather than tetrahydrofuran (b.p. 66°).

Cyclopentadienyltungsten tricarbonyl hydride is a volatile, very pale, yellow crystalline solid, m.p. 66–67°, that is insoluble in water but soluble in aqueous alkali and organic solvents. It is much less readily oxidized by air than the molybdenum analog. Although storage under nitrogen especially for longer periods of time is definitely recommended, $C_5H_5W(CO)_3H$ may be transferred and weighed in air for brief periods without significant oxidation. The reactions of $C_5H_5W(CO)_3H$ are similar to those of $C_5H_5Mo(CO)_3H$ that have been described except that they occur much less readily. The infrared spectrum (CS_2 solution) of $C_5H_5W(CO)_3H$ exhibits strong metal carbonyl bands at 2020 and 1929 cm.$^{-1}$; its proton n.m.r. spectrum (CS_2 solution) exhibits a sharp cyclopentadienyl resonance at 4.53 τ and a sharp tungsten hydride resonance at 17.30 τ of relative intensities 5:1. The hydride resonance is flanked by two satellites due to W^{183} —H coupling ($J_{WH} = 36$ cps).

2. Manganese Pentacarbonyl Hydride

Manganese pentacarbonyl hydride may be obtained by reaction of dimanganese decacarbonyl with hydrogen under pressure at 200° in the presence of carbon monoxide pressure,[8] by reduction of dimanganese decacarbonyl with magnesium metal in aqueous methanolic hydrochloric acid,[8] or by acidification of $Mn(CO)_5^-$ (preferably the dry sodium salt) with phosphoric acid.[8] The latter method is the most convenient and efficient. Its description in detail follows.

Procedure:

$$(1) \quad Mn_2(CO)_{10} + 2Na \xrightarrow[C_4H_8O]{Hg} 2NaMn(CO)_5$$

$$(2) \quad NaMn(CO)_5 + H_3PO_4 \rightarrow HMn(CO)_5 + Na[H_2PO_4]$$

The reaction is conducted in a 300-ml. three-necked flask with a stopcock fused to the bottom (Fig. 23, page 149) for removal of mercury

---

[7] P. M. Treichel, J. H. Morris, and F. G. A. Stone, *J. Chem. Soc.* 720 (1963).

[8] W. Hieber and G. Wagner, *Z. Naturforsch.* **12b**, 478 (1957); **13b**, 339 (1958).

and excess amalgam and fitted with a nitrogen inlet, efficient motor stirrer, pressure-equalized dropping funnel, and reflux condenser. After filling with nitrogen, the flask is charged with 4 ml. (54 g.) of mercury, and 0.45 g. (0.0195 mole) of sodium metal is added in several portions with stirring. After an induction period of several seconds depending on the crust on the sodium and the rate of stirring, each piece of sodium will suddenly react exothermically with the mercury to form the amalgam with a hissing sound. After all of the sodium has reacted, the liquid amalgam is allowed to cool to room temperature and then treated with 3.0 g. (0.0077 mole) of dimanganese decacarbonyl (page 89) and 60 ml. of tetrahydrofuran.[3] The reaction mixture is stirred vigorously[9] for at least 1 hr. During this period, the yellow color of the $Mn_2(CO)_{10}$ should completely disappear because of reduction to the colorless $Mn(CO)_5^-$ anion; the reaction mixture, however, will appear gray due to suspended finely divided mercury.

When the formation of the $Mn(CO)_5^-$ is complete, excess mercury and amalgam are removed through the stopcock at the bottom.[10] The reflux condenser, and motor stirrer are replaced by stoppers and solvent is removed from the $NaMn(CO)_5$ solution in a water-aspirator vacuum (∼30 mm.) leaving a grayish residue. After admitting nitrogen to the evacuated flask, a dropping funnel containing 30 ml. of 85% aqueous orthophosphoric acid is added to the flask which is then connected through a −196° trap containing ∼20 g. of dry "phosphorus pentoxide" (P_4O_{10}) to a vacuum system. During these operations, the flask containing air-sensitive $NaMn(CO)_5$ should always be kept under nitrogen.

The system is evacuated and the phosphoric acid is then added gradually to the solid $NaMn(CO)_5$ over a period of 1 hr. During the addition of the phosphoric acid, the $HMn(CO)_5$ and water from the acid distill into the external trap containing the phosphorus pentoxide where the water is removed. Toward the end of the phosphoric acid addition, the reaction flask is heated to ∼50° with a warm water bath to insure complete removal of the $HMn(CO)_5$.

The manganese pentacarbonyl hydride is then distilled from the external trap into the vacuum system and fractionated in the vacuum system to remove traces of tetrahydrofuran and finally distilled a second time over phosphorus pentoxide in the vacuum system to give 2.5 g. (83% yield) of slightly yellow liquid manganese pentacarbonyl hydride.

---

[9] The stirring should be efficient and vigorous enough not only to agitate the tetrahydrofuran solution but also to agitate the liquid amalgam at the bottom of the flask exposing fresh surfaces continually.

[10] The mercury may be recovered for another dilute sodium amalgam reaction by washing with an alcohol followed by water and possibly dilute nitric acid as indicated in footnote 17, page 150.

Manganese pentacarbonyl hydride, $HMn(CO)_5$, when pure is a colorless, malodorous liquid, m.p. $-24.6°$, b.p. (extrap.) $111°$, that is rapidly oxidized by air to yellow dimanganese decacarbonyl; normally, samples of $HMn(CO)_5$ will appear yellow because of the presence of small quantities of $Mn_2(CO)_{10}$. It is a weak acid $(K = 0.8 \times 10^{-7})$. In general, it is best handled by transfer in a vacuum system.

The reactions of $HMn(CO)_5$ correspond in many cases to those of the hydrides $C_5H_5M(CO)_3H$ discussed previously. Thus, $HMn(CO)_5$ is readily converted to $Mn_2(CO)_{10}$. It reacts with diazomethane to form $CH_3Mn(CO)_5$.[11] Treatment of $HMn(CO)_5$ with N-methyl-N-nitroso-p-toluenesulfonamide gives the nitrosyl derivative $Mn(CO)_4NO$.[12] Dimethyldisulfide and tetrafluoroethylene give the compounds $[CH_3SMn(CO)_4]_2$[7] and $HCF_2CF_2Mn(CO)_5$[13] when treated with $HMn(CO)_5$. Recently, $HMn(CO)_5$ was found to react with germane, GeH_4, to give $H_2Ge[Mn(CO)_5]_2$.[14]

3. Cobalt Tetracarbonyl Hydride

Cobalt tetracarbonyl hydride, $HCo(CO)_4$, is readily obtained by acidification of the anion $Co(CO)_4^-$ with sulfuric acid.[15,16] An alternative but less convenient preparation is the reaction of dicobalt octacarbonyl with hydrogen under pressure at elevated temperatures in the presence of carbon monoxide pressure.[17] Details for an excellent preparation of $HCo(CO)_4$ are given in *Inorganic Syntheses*[16]; in this preparation, dicobalt octacarbonyl is reacted first with pyridine to form $[Co(C_5H_5N)_6]$ $[Co(CO)_4]_2$ which is then acidified with sulfuric acid. The description of this preparation will not be repeated in this book.

Cobalt tetracarbonyl hydride is a toxic malodorous gas that decomposes at room temperature to hydrogen and dicobalt octacarbonyl or cobalt metal and carbon monoxide depending upon the conditions. Despite this instability, it may readily be transferred in a stream of carbon monoxide at atmospheric pressure.

[11] W. Hieber and G. Wagner, *Ann. Chem.* **618**, 24 (1958).

[12] P. M. Treichel, E. Pitcher, R. B. King, and F. G. A. Stone, *J. Am. Chem. Soc.* **83**, 2593 (1961).

[13] P. M. Treichel, E. Pitcher, and F. G. A. Stone, *Inorg. Chem.* **1**, 511 (1963).

[14] A. G. Massey, A. J. Park, and F. G. A. Stone, *J. Am. Chem. Soc.* **85**, 2021 (1963).

[15] H. W. Sternberg, I. Wender, R. A. Friedel, and M. Orchin, *J. Am. Chem. Soc.* **75**, 2717 (1953).

[16] H. W. Sternberg, I. Wender, and M. Orchin, *Inorg. Syn.* **5**, 192 (1957).

[17] M. Orchin, L. Kirch, and I. Goldfarb, *J. Am. Chem. Soc.* **78**, 5450 (1956).

I. Metal Nitrosyl Derivatives

1. Cyclopentadienylchromium Dinitrosyl Chloride

Cyclopentadienylchromium dinitrosyl chloride, $C_5H_5Cr(NO)_2Cl$, may be obtained by treatment of cyclopentadienylchromium dichloride dimer[1] with nitric oxide.[2-4] The cyclopentadienylchromium dichloride dimer need not be isolated in the pure state for this preparation but instead it may be prepared *in situ* either by reaction between biscyclopentadienyl chromium and hydrogen chloride[3] or by reaction of chromium(III) chloride with sodium cyclopentadienide in a 1:1 mole ratio.[2,4] The preparation given here is based on a procedure worked out by Fischer and Kuzel[4] with a few minor modifications developed by the author.

Procedure:

$$(1) \quad CrCl_3 + NaC_5H_5 \rightarrow C_5H_5CrCl_2 + NaCl$$
$$(2) \quad C_5H_5CrCl_2 + 3NO \rightarrow C_5H_5Cr(NO)_2Cl + \{NOCl\}$$

The reaction is carried out in a 2-liter three-necked flask fitted out with a reflux condenser, motor stirrer, pressure-equalized dropping funnel, and gas inlet. After filling with nitrogen, the flask is charged with 23.5 g. (1.02 mole) of sodium metal and 300 ml. of dry toluene or xylene. The sodium is dispersed into fine sand-like granules by vigorous stirring at the boiling point.[5] The stirring is then stopped, and the mixture is allowed to cool to room temperature. The xylene or toluene is siphoned off, and 1000 ml. of tetrahydrofuran[6] is added. The suspension of sodium sand in tetrahydrofuran is treated dropwise with sufficient freshly prepared cyclopentadiene (~125 ml., 101 g., 1.52 moles) to dissolve all of the sodium to form a pink to dark-red-violet sodium cyclopentadienide solution.

[1] E. O. Fischer, K. Ulm and P. Kuzel, *Z. Anorg. Allgem. Chem.* **319**, 253 (1963).

[2] T. S. Piper and G. Wilkinson, *J. Inorg. Nucl. Chem.* **2**, 38 (1956).

[3] T. S. Piper and G. Wilkinson, *J. Inorg. Nucl. Chem.* **3**, 104 (1956).

[4] E. O. Fischer and P. Kuzel, *Z. Anorg. Allgem. Chem.* **317**, 226 (1962).

[5] An equivalent quantity of a commercial sodium dispersion in mineral oil or xylene may be used.

[6] Tetrahydrofuran may be purified by redistillation over lithium aluminum hydride or sodium metal or by passage through a column of molecular sieves (Linde Air Products, Morristown, New Jersey).

This sodium cyclopentadienide solution is treated with 80.0 g. (0.5 mole) of anhydrous chromium(III) chloride.[7] An exothermic reaction occurs. The reaction mixture is refluxed at the boiling point for at least 2 hr. to insure complete reaction.

After cooling to room temperature, the green-black reaction mixture is treated with purified[8] nitric oxide until about 30 g. have been introduced [about a 12-atmosphere drop in the pressure of a No. 4 ($\sim$14 $\times$ 35.5 cm) tank]. The solvent is then removed from the reaction mixture in a water-aspirator vacuum (15 to 50 mm.).

Nitrogen is admitted to the evacuated flask, and the black residue is extracted with ten 100-ml. portions of dichloromethane. The extracts are filtered by suction through about 100 g. of alumina,[9] and the alumina is washed with 50-ml. portions of dichloromethane until the washings are no longer colored. To insure removal of all suspended matter (which would contaminate the final product), the filtered extracts are refiltered by gravity, and the final dark-yellow-green filtrate is collected under nitrogen. The solvent is then removed from this filtrate in a water-aspirator vacuum (15 to 50 mm.). The residue is washed on a filter with at least five 50-ml. portions of pentane and sucked dry to give 35.0 g. (33% yield) of olive-green crystalline $C_5H_5Cr(NO)_2Cl$ sufficiently pure for preparative purposes.

If a purer sample of $C_5H_5Cr(NO)_2Cl$ is desired, the crude product is dissolved in dichloromethane or chloroform. Hexane is then added to the filtered solution, and the solvent is slowly removed in a water-aspirator vacuum (15 to 50 mm.). The crystals of $C_5H_5Cr(NO)_2Cl$ which separate are removed by filtration, washed with several portions of pentane, hexane, or petroleum ether, and sucked dry.

Cyclopentadienylchromium dinitrosyl chloride forms olive-green crystals, dec. 140° without melting, that are sparingly soluble in water and nonpolar organic solvents and give yellow solutions in water; they are very soluble in polar organic solvents and give brown solutions. Its infrared spectrum ($CHCl_3$ solution) exhibits strong metal nitrosyl bands

---

[7] Anhydrous chromium(III) chloride is readily available commercially in the United States from companies such as Diamond Alkali Corp., Painesville, Ohio. It may also be obtained by treatment of the commercially available hydrated chromium(III) chloride with thionyl chloride. [A. R. Pray, *Inorg. Syn.* **5**, 153 (1957)].

[8] For the preparation of metal nitrosyls, it is advisable to purify the nitric oxide (from NO_2, etc.) by passing it through a −78° trap preferably charged with Linde molecular sieves.[6]

[9] The addition of alumina at this stage facilitates the rather slow filtration process. Chromatography-grade alumina is recommended for this purpose.

at 1823 and 1715 cm.⁻¹, and its proton n.m.r. spectrum (CHCl₃ solution) exhibits a single sharp cyclopentadienyl resonance at 4.33 τ. Treatment of $C_5H_5Cr(NO)_2Cl$ or the corresponding bromide or iodide with Grignard reagents gives the fairly stable alkyl derivatives $C_5H_5Cr(NO)_2R$.[10] Reduction of an aqueous solution of $C_5H_5Cr(NO)_2Cl$ with sodium borohydride gives the nitrosyl derivative $[C_5H_5Cr(NO)_2]_2$ which is suggested by its infrared spectrum to contain bridging nitrosyl groups.[11]

2. Cyclopentadienylmanganese Dicarbonyl Nitrosyl Hexafluorophosphate

The cyclopentadienylmanganese dicarbonyl nitrosyl cation, $[C_5H_5Mn(CO)_2NO]^+$, is readily obtained on treatment of cyclopentadienylmanganese tricarbonyl with sodium nitrite and hydrochloric acid at elevated temperatures.[12] This cation is particularly conveniently isolated as the hexafluorophosphate.[11]

Procedure:

$$C_5H_5Mn(CO)_3 + NaNO_2 + 2HCl + NH_4PF_6 \rightarrow [C_5H_5Mn(CO)_2NO][PF_6]$$
$$+ NaCl + H_2O + CO \uparrow + NH_4Cl$$

The reaction is carried out in a 2-liter three-necked flask equipped with a reflux condenser, nitrogen inlet, motor stirrer, and pressure-equalized dropping funnel. After flushing out the system with nitrogen, the flask is charged with 900 ml. of 95% ethanol, 180 ml. of concentrated ($\sim$12N) hydrochloric acid, and 60 g. (0.294 mole) of cyclopentadienylmanganese tricarbonyl (page 111). This mixture is heated to the boiling point and at this temperature is treated dropwise with a solution of 21.0 g. (0.304 mole) of sodium nitrite in 50 ml. of water. After all of the sodium nitrite solution has been added, the reaction mixture is kept at the boiling point for an additional 5 minutes and then is rapidly filtered hot by suction. The white precipitate of sodium chloride may be discarded. The filtrate is treated immediately with a solution of 60 g. (0.368 mole) of ammonium hexafluorophosphate in 100 ml. of water (or an equivalent quantity of a concentrated aqueous solution of sodium or potassium hexafluorophosphates). The reaction mixture is then allowed to cool to room temperature; a yellow precipitate of $[C_5H_5Mn(CO)_2NO]$ [PF₆] forms. After standing for at least 30 minutes to insure complete precipitation, the yellow precipitate is filtered through a fine filter. Any

[10] T. S. Piper and G. Wilkinson, *J. Inorg. Nucl. Chem.* **3**, 104 (1956).
[11] R. B. King and M. B. Bisnette, *J. Am. Chem. Soc.* **85**, 2527 (1963); *Inorg. Chem.* **3**, 791 (1964).
[12] T. S. Piper, F. A. Cotton, and G. Wilkinson, *J. Inorg. Nucl. Chem.* **1**, 165 (1955).

unreacted $C_5H_5Mn(CO)_3$ is removed by washing with 75-ml. portions of dichloromethane until the dichloromethane washings are no longer colored. The product is then dried in a vacuum desiccator at $25°/1$ mm. to remove water and ethanol. About 50 g. (47% yield) of bright yellow crystalline $[C_5H_5Mn(CO)_2NO][PF_6]$, sufficiently pure for most preparative purposes, is obtained. If a purer product is desired, the crude product may be dissolved in acetone and reprecipitated from the filtered acetone solution with diethyl ether.

Cyclopentadienylmanganese dicarbonyl nitrosyl hexafluorophosphate, $[C_5H_5Mn(CO)_2NO][PF_6]$, is a yellow air-stable solid that blackens gradually without melting on heating above $230°$; it is insoluble in all except very polar organic solvents and sparingly soluble in water. On treatment with dimethylformamide or dimethylsulfoxide, it gives deep-blue unstable solutions. Its infrared spectrum (KBr pellet) exhibits strong metal carbonyl bands at 2125 and 2075 cm.$^{-1}$ and a strong metal nitrosyl band at 1840 cm.$^{-1}$, and its proton n.m.r. spectrum (acetone solution) shows a single sharp cyclopentadienyl resonance at 3.86 τ. Treatment of an aqueous suspension of $[C_5H_5Mn(CO)_2NO][PF_6]$ with aqueous sodium borohydride gives the dimeric nitrosyl derivative $[C_5H_5MnCONO]_2$.[11]

3. Manganese Tetracarbonyl Nitrosyl

Manganese tetracarbonyl nitrosyl, $Mn(CO)_4NO$, has been obtained by reaction of N-nitroso-N-methyl-p-toluenesulfonamide ("Diazald") with either the $Mn(CO)_5^-$ anion[13] or the hydride $HMn(CO)_5$.[14] Because of the rarity of manganese carbonyl derivatives, the preparation of $Mn(CO)_4NO$ from Diazald and $HMn(CO)_5$ is recommended since the purification of the product from this preparation can readily be carried out by vacuum-line techniques that are adaptable to relatively small quantities of this rather unstable material.

Procedure:

$$HMn(CO)_5 + C_7H_7SO_2N(CH_3)(NO) \xrightarrow{(C_2H_5)_2O} Mn(CO)_4NO + CO + C_7H_7SO_2NHCH_3$$

A 1-liter reaction flask or bulb equipped with a stopcock is charged with 4.0 g. (0.02 moles) of N-nitroso-N-methyl-p-toluenesulfonamide ("Diazald")[15] and 20 ml. of anhydrous diethyl ether. This system is

---

[13] T. H. Coffield, U. S. Patent 2,967,087 (Ethyl Corporation).

[14] P. M. Treichel, E. Pitcher, R. B. King, and F. G. A. Stone, *J. Am. Chem. Soc.* **83**, 2593 (1961).

[15] N-methyl-N-nitroso-p-toluenesulfonamide under the name "Diazald" is available from the Aldrich Chemical Co., 2369 North 30th Street, Milwaukee 10, Wisconsin. Other similar N-nitroso derivatives should be satisfactory for this reaction.

cooled to $-196°$ (liquid nitrogen) and evacuated on the vacuum system. A 1.6-g. sample (0.00817 moles) of manganese pentacarbonyl hydride (page 158) is distilled into the reaction vessel from the vacuum line. The stopcock connecting the reaction vessel to the vacuum line is then closed, and the reaction mixture is allowed to stand at least 16 hr. at room temperature. During this time, the originally yellow reaction mixture becomes deep red. After the reaction period is over, volatile materials are removed into the vacuum system through $-35°$, $-78°$, and $-196°$ traps (1,2-dichloroethane partially frozen with liquid nitrogen, Dry Ice–acetone, and liquid nitrogen, respectively). Much noncondensable carbon monoxide is thus removed. The desired product $Mn(CO)_4NO$ collects as red crystals in the $-35°$ trap. It is purified by several distillations in the vacuum system from room temperature to a $-35°$ trap. A 60% yield of $Mn(CO)_4NO$ is thus obtained.

Manganese tetracarbonyl nitrosyl, $Mn(CO)_4NO$, is a dark-red liquid at room temperature that freezes to a red solid at $\sim 0°$ and resembles bromine in appearance. It is volatile (vapor pressure ~ 8 mm. at 25°), insoluble in water, but readily miscible with organic solvents. Upon exposure to air, it is readily oxidized. Upon exposure to light, it is converted to a mixture of $Mn_2(CO)_{10}$, $MnCO(NO)_3$, and $Mn_2(CO)_7(NO)_2$.[14] Its infrared spectrum exhibits metal carbonyl bands at 2095 (m), 2019 (s), and 1972 (s) cm.⁻¹, and a single metal nitrosyl band at 1759 (s) cm.⁻¹.

4. Bis(Iron Tricarbonyl Nitrosyl)mercury

Bis(iron tricarbonyl nitrosyl)mercury, $Hg[Fe(CO)_3NO]_2$, is readily obtained by treating an aqueous methanolic solution of the anion $Fe(CO)_3NO^-$ with mercuric cyanide.[16] The anion $Fe(CO)_3NO^-$ is obtained from iron pentacarbonyl and nitrite ion in methanolic solution. Although the yields of $Fe(CO)_3NO^-$ are higher in the presence of a base such as sodium hydroxide or sodium methoxide,[16] the presence of this base appears to complicate isolation of pure $Hg[Fe(CO)_3NO]_2$ after addition of the mercuric cyanide. Therefore, $Fe(CO)_3NO^-$ prepared without added base is used in the synthesis of $Hg[Fe(CO)_3NO]_2$ that follows.

Procedure:

(1) $\quad Fe(CO)_5 + KNO_2 \xrightarrow{CH_3OH} K[Fe(CO)_3NO] + CO \uparrow + CO_2 \uparrow$

(2) $\quad 2K[Fe(CO)_3NO] + Hg(CN)_2 \rightarrow Hg[Fe(CO)_3NO]_2 \downarrow + 2KCN$

The reaction is carried out in a good hood in a 2-liter three-necked flask fitted with a stirrer, nitrogen inlet, reflux condenser and thermom-

---

[16] W. Hieber and H. Beutner, *Z. Anorg. Allgem. Chem.* **320**, 101 (1963).

eter, and equipped with a water bath. After filling the system with nitrogen, the flask is charged with 500 ml. of methanol, 85 g. (1.0 mole) of potassium nitrite, and 140 ml. (204.5 g., 1.04 mole) of iron penta-carbonyl. The reaction mixture is maintained with stirring for at least 16 hr. at 35° with the aid of a water bath gently warmed with an immersion heater or hot plate. After cooling to room temperature, the reaction mixture is treated with a solution of 70 g. (0.278 mole) of mercury (II) cyanide in 700 ml. of water. After stirring for at least 30 minutes, the brown precipitate is filtered by suction and is sucked on the filter for several minutes to remove most of the water.

The crude, still moist product is extracted with a total of 1000 ml. of dichloromethane in about six portions. The red extracts are filtered by suction leaving behind a brownish residue containing $[HgFe(CO)_4]_n$ and iron (III) oxide. After a second filtration by gravity to remove final traces of suspended matter, the solvent is removed from the red filtrate in a water-aspirator vacuum (15 to 50 mm.). Red crystals of $Hg[Fe(CO)_3NO]_2$, are left behind. These are washed on a filter with two 40-ml. portions of cold pentane and sucked dry for several minutes to give about 70 g. (46.6% yield based on $Hg(CN)_2$) of $Hg[Fe(CO)_3-NO]_2$. The product should be stored in the dark at $-15°$ or below to minimize gradual decomposition.

Bis (iron tricarbonyl nitrosyl) mercury, $Hg[Fe(CO)_3NO]_2$, is a red crystalline solid, m.p. 110°, that is insoluble in water but soluble in many organic solvents to give red to orange solutions. It decomposes gradually at room temperature and forms yellow insoluble $[HgFe(CO)_4]_n$ and various gases; closed containers of $Hg[Fe(CO)_3NO]_2$ at room temperature may develop considerable pressure (*caution*). Storage at low temperatures is therefore recommended. On heating $Hg[Fe(CO)_3NO]_2$ to $\sim80°/0.1$ mm., a small fraction sublimes intact giving a red sublimate, but the bulk of the material decomposes into yellow nonvolatile $[HgFe(CO)_4]_n$ and red volatile $Fe(CO)_2(NO)_2$. The infrared spectrum of $Hg[Fe(CO)_3NO]_2$ (cyclohexane solution) exhibits metal carbonyl bands at 2071, 2051, 2014, 2007, and 1988 cm.$^{-1}$ and metal nitrosyl bands at 1785 and 1770 cm.$^{-1}$. Treatment of $Hg[Fe(CO)_3NO]_2$ with many Lewis bases such as pyridine gives derivatives of the type $[Fe(base)_6][Fe(CO)_3NO]_2$.[17] Nevertheless, triphenylphosphine and tris (dimethyl-amino) phosphine under certain conditions give derivatives of the types $Hg[Fe(CO)_2NO(R_3P)]_2$, $(R_3P)_2Fe(NO)_2$, and $[(R_3P)_2Fe(CO)_2NO][Fe(CO)_3NO]$.[17,18]

[17] W. Hieber and W. Klingshirn, *Z. Anorg. Allgem. Chem.* **323**, 292 (1963).
[18] R. B. King, *Inorg. Chem.* **2**, 1275 (1963).

5. Iron Dicarbonyl Dinitrosyl

Iron dicarbonyl dinitrosyl, $Fe(CO)_2(NO)_2$, may be prepared by the following methods: (a) treatment of $Fe_3(CO)_{12}$ or $Fe_2(CO)_9$ with nitric oxide[19]; (b) acidification of a mixture of $HFe(CO)_4^-$ and nitrite ion[20]; (c) treatment of iron pentacarbonyl with nitrosyl chloride[21]; (d) acidification of a mixture of $Fe(CO)_3NO^-$ and nitrite ion[16]; and (e) pyrolysis of $Hg[Fe(CO)_3NO]_2$ (see foregoing).[16] Although the pyrolysis of $Hg[Fe(CO)_3NO]_2$ prepared as previously described is a convenient method for obtaining small quantities of $Fe(CO)_2(NO)_2$, the acidification of a mixture of nitrite ion with either $HFe(CO)_4^-$ of $Fe(CO)_3NO^-$ provides a more economical preparation of larger quantities of $Fe(CO)_2$-$(NO)_2$. The second of these two methods as developed by Hieber and Beutner[16] follows.

Procedure:

(1) $Fe(CO)_5 + NaNO_2 + 2NaOH \xrightarrow{H_2O} Na[Fe(CO)_3NO] + CO \uparrow + Na_2CO_3 + H_2O$

(2) $Na[Fe(CO)_3NO] + NaNO_2 + 2CH_3CO_2H \rightarrow Fe(CO)_2(NO)_2 + CO \uparrow$
$$+ 2Na[CH_3CO_2] + H_2O$$

The reaction is carried out in a 250- to 300-ml. three-necked flask equipped with a nitrogen inlet, reflux condenser, stirrer, and pressure-equalized dropping funnel. After filling the system with nitrogen, the flask is charged with 5.0 ml. (7.3 g., 0.0373 mole) of iron pentacarbonyl, 6.0 g. (0.087 mole) of sodium nitrite, 10.0 g. (0.25 mole) of sodium hydroxide, and 80 ml. of water and the mixture refluxed for 3 hr. at the boiling point with stirring under nitrogen. The reaction mixture is then cooled to 30–40° and a strong nitrogen stream passed through the system and then through a reversed trap[22] containing 20 g. of anhydrous calcium chloride and cooled to −78° (acetone-Dry Ice bath). A 1:1 solution of glacial acetic acid in water is added dropwise from the dropping funnel until brown fumes of $Fe(CO)_2(NO)_2$ begin to form. The acetic acid addition is discontinued and a nitrogen stream is passed through the

[19] R. L. Mond and A. E. Wallis, *J. Chem. Soc.* **121**, 32 (1922); J. S. Anderson, *Z. Anorg. Allgem. Chem.* **208**, 238 (1932).

[20] F. Seel, *Z. Anorg. Allgem. Chem.* **269**, 40 (1952).

[21] D. W. McBride, S. L. Stafford, and F. G. A. Stone, *Inorg. Chem.* **1**, 386 (1962).

[22] Normally traps are connected so that the inlet reaches almost to the bottom and the outlet is at the top. However, if a trap connected in this manner is used to collect $Fe(CO)_2(NO)_2$, the inlet tube is likely to become clogged with crystalline $Fe(CO)_2(NO)_2$ because of its relatively high melting point. To avoid this problem, the inlet and outlet connections should be reversed, i.e. the inlet is the tube ending at the top of the trap and the outlet is the tube reaching nearly to the bottom of the trap.

system in order to drive all of the $Fe(CO)_2(NO)_2$ formed into the trap. On a run of this scale, about 1 hr. should be required for this process. After all of the $Fe(CO)_2(NO)_2$ has been collected, the trap containing it is warmed under nitrogen to the melting point ($\sim +18°$). The red product is then distilled at room temperature in an oil-pump vacuum (<1 mm.) into a second reversed trap containing about 20 g. of phosphorus pentoxide for final drying. The product may then be transferred to a suitable storage vessel by distillation in a vacuum line. Yields of up to 60% of $Fe(CO)_2(NO)_2$ based on iron pentacarbonyl may be expected for this reaction.

Iron dicarbonyl dinitrosyl, $Fe(CO)_2(NO)_2$, is a red crystalline solid melting slightly above room temperature (m.p. $+18°$) to a deep red liquid. It is very volatile [b.p. $110°/760$ mm. (extrap.)], and, thus is readily transferred in a vacuum system. It is sensitive to air oxidation and decomposes gradually at room temperature. Storage of $Fe(CO)_2$-$(NO)_2$ under nitrogen in the dark as a solid below $0°$ is therefore recommended. The infrared spectrum of $Fe(CO)_2(NO)_2$ (cyclohexane solution) exhibits strong metal carbonyl bands at 2083 and 2034 cm.$^{-1}$ and strong metal nitrosyl bands at 1810 and 1756 cm.$^{-1}$

6. Cobalt Tricarbonyl Nitrosyl

Cobalt tricarbonyl nitrosyl, $Co(CO)_3NO$, may be prepared either by treatment of dicobalt octacarbonyl with nitric oxide[23] or by treatment of aqueous $Co(CO)_4^-$ with nitric oxide or nitrous acid.[24,25] A procedure based on the preparation of $Co(CO)_4^-$ from aqueous cobalt(II) salts, carbon monoxide, and sodium dithionite in the presence of ammonia as developed by Hieber and co-workers[26] (compare page 101) followed by treatment of this $Co(CO)_4^-$ solution with sodium nitrite and glacial acetic acid as recommended by Seel[25] appears to be particularly convenient and efficient and is described here.

Procedure:

(1) $2[Co(H_2O)_6](NO_3)_2 + 8CO + 3Na_2S_2O_4 \xrightarrow[H_2O]{NH_3} 2NaCo(CO)_4 + 6SO_2$
$$+ 4NaNO_3 + 12H_2O$$

(2) $NaCo(CO)_4 + NaNO_2 + 2CH_3CO_2H \rightarrow Co(CO)_3NO + CO\uparrow$
$$+ H_2O + 2Na[CH_3CO_2$$

[23] R. L. Mond and A. E. Wallis, *J. Chem. Soc.* **121**, 34 (1922); R. Reiff, *Z. Anorg. Allgem. Chem.* **202**, 375 (1931).

[24] G. Bor and B. Mohai, *Acta Chim. Acad. Sci. Hung.* **8**, 335 (1956); *Chem. Abs.* **50**, 13643 (1956).

[25] F. Seel, *Z. Anorg. Allgem. Chem.* **269**, 40 (1952).

[26] W. Hieber, E. O. Fischer, and E. Böckly, *Z. Anorg. Allgem. Chem.* **269**, 308 (1952).

The reaction is carried out in an efficient hood in a 2-liter three-necked flask fitted with an efficient motor stirrer, pressure-equalized dropping funnel, reflux condenser, and carbon monoxide inlet. The flask is charged with a mixture of 160 ml. of concentrated (~30%) aqueous ammonia and 240 ml. of water. A solution of 17.5 g. (0.06 mole) of cobalt(II) nitrate hexahydrate[27] in 40 ml. of water is added. The air in the flask is replaced with carbon monoxide and the flask cooled to 10–15° in an ice bath. While maintaining the cooling and stirring, a solution of 20 g. (0.092 moles) of 80% sodium dithionite ($Na_2S_2O_4$) in a mixture of 95 ml. of concentrated (~30%) aqueous ammonia and 135 ml. of water is added dropwise (1 drop per 10–15 seconds). After all of the sodium dithionite solution has been added, the resulting solution of $Co(CO)_4^-$ is treated with 4.2 g. (0.061 mole) of sodium nitrite dissolved in 15 ml. of water. After cooling this reaction mixture to −10° in an ice-salt bath and adding a trap cooled to −80° (acetone + Dry Ice) to the outlet of the system, the reaction mixture is treated with a mixture of 60 ml. of glacial acetic acid and 60 ml. of water.[28] The $Co(CO)_3NO$ is driven out of the reaction mixture into the trap as it is formed by the stream of carbon monoxide. Passage of carbon monoxide is continued until no more brown fumes of $Co(CO)_3NO$ are observed. The $Co(CO)_3NO$ having been collected in the trap as orange crystals in about 50% yield may be purified further by trap-to-trap distillation in a vacuum.

Cobalt tricarbonyl nitrosyl, $Co(CO)_3NO$, is a dark red extremely volatile liquid, m.p. −1°, b.p. 50°/760 mm. Although immiscible with water, it is readily miscible with organic solvents. It is probably very toxic and should be handled in a good hood. Its infrared spectrum (gas phase) exhibits strong metal carbonyl bands at 2109 and 2047 cm.⁻¹ and a strong metal nitrosyl band at 1825 cm.⁻¹. On treatment with tertiary phosphines and arsines, derivatives of the types $Co(CO)_2NOER_3$ and $CoCONO(ER_3)_2$ (E = P, As, etc.) are obtained.[29]

7. Cyclopentadienylnickel Nitrosyl

Cyclopentadienylnickel nitrosyl, C_5H_5NiNO, has been obtained either by treatment of biscyclopentadienylnickel (nickelocene) with nitric

---

[27] An equivalent amount of cobalt(II) sulfate heptahydrate or cobalt(II) acetate tetrahydrate may be used in place of the cobalt(II) nitrate hexahydrate.

[28] Instead of decomposing the reaction mixture with acetic acid and driving out the $Co(CO)_3NO$ with a stream of carbon monoxide, a vigorous stream of carbon *dioxide* may be bubbled into the reaction mixture to serve both as a weak acid to generate the $Co(CO)_3NO$ and also as a gas to drive the $Co(CO)_3NO$ vapors into the trap [F. Seel and H. Koss, Z. *Naturforsch.* **17b**, 129 (1962)].

[29] L. Malatesta and A. Araneo, *J. Chem. Soc.* 3803 (1957).

oxide[30,31] or by the reaction between nickel tetracarbonyl, diethylamine, cyclopentadiene, and nitric oxide.[32] Although the last method is well suited for efficient industrial preparation of C_5H_5NiNO, it is scarcely suited for a safe and convenient laboratory preparation of this material. A variation of the reaction between nickelocene and nitric oxide will be described in which the nickelocene is prepared *in situ* and reacted with the nitric oxide without isolation and purification.

Procedure:

(1) $Ni + Br_2 \rightarrow NiBr_2$

(2) $NiBr_2 + 2C_5H_6 + 2(C_2H_5)_2NH \rightarrow (C_5H_5)_2Ni + 2[(C_2H_5)_2NH_2]Br$

(3) $(C_5H_5)_2Ni + NO \rightarrow C_5H_5NiNO + \{C_5H_5\cdot\}$

As in the preparation of nickelocene described earlier in this book (page 71), the preparation of C_5H_5NiNO is carried out in a 1-liter three-necked flask fitted with a motor stirrer, reflux condenser, nitrogen inlet, and pressure-equalized dropping funnel. After filling the system with nitrogen, the flask is charged with 500 ml. of 1,2-dimethoxyethane[33] and 29.4 g. (0.5 mole) of nickel powder. From the dropping funnel, 27.3 ml. (80.0 g., 0.5 mole as Br_2) of undiluted liquid bromine is added dropwise to form a yellow etherate of nickel(II) bromide in an exothermic reaction. After the formation of nickel(II) bromide is complete and the reaction mixture has cooled back to room temperature, the solvent is removed from the reaction mixture in a water-aspirator vacuum. Nitrogen is admitted to the flask, and the yellow residue is treated with 400 ml. of diethylamine to give a blue solution with heat evolution. The reaction mixture is then treated dropwise with 98.5 ml. (79 g., 1.2 mole) of freshly prepared cyclopentadiene; the reaction mixture becomes somewhat more greenish. After stirring overnight at room temperature, the stirrer is replaced with a stopper, and the solvent is removed from the reaction mixture in a water-aspirator vacuum leaving a greenish solid residue of a mixture of diethylammonium chloride and nickelocene. Nitrogen is admitted to the flask, and the stirrer is reconnected.

The solid residue is treated with 500 ml. of pentane or low-boiling petroleum ether and a nitric oxide inlet reaching below the liquid level

[30] T. S. Piper, F. A. Cotton, and G. Wilkinson, *J. Inorg. Nucl. Chem.* **1**, 165 (1955).

[31] E. O. Fischer, O. Beckert, W. Hafner, and H. O. Stahl, *Z. Naturforsch.* **10b**, 598 (1955).

[32] R. D. Feltham and J. T. Carriel, *Inorg. Chem.* **3**, 121 (1964).

[33] 1,2-Dimethoxyethane may be purified by redistillation over lithium aluminum hydride or sodium metal or by passage through a column of Linde molecular sieves.

is then added to the system.[34] Purified[8] nitric oxide is then bubbled through the nickelocene solution at room temperature with stirring. The green color of the nickelocene becomes a red to red-brown characteristic of C_5H_5NiNO. After no further color change occurs,[35] the nitric oxide treatment is discontinued, and the reaction mixture is filtered by suction. The discolored diethylammonium chloride is washed with 50-ml. portions of pentane or low-boiling petroleum ether until the washings are colorless. The solvent is removed from the filtrate by distillation at atmospheric pressure heating the distilling flask with an oil bath to minimize overheating. The red-liquid residue is then distilled in a water-aspirator vacuum to give dark-red liquid C_5H_5NiNO, b.p. 59°/27 mm. in about 50% yield.

Cyclopentadienylnickel nitrosyl, C_5H_5NiNO, is a dark-red, fairly air-stable, malodorous liquid, m.p. −41°, b.p. 144–145°/715 mm., that is immiscible with water but readily miscible with organic solvents. Toxicity tests with rats, mice, etc., indicate C_5H_5NiNO to be one of the most toxic known organometallic compounds surpassing even such well-known poisons as tetraethyllead and nickel tetracarbonyl.[36] Although the survival of the several investigators who have studied C_5H_5NiNO indicates its human toxicity not to be as extreme, caution in handling this compound is nevertheless indicated. The infrared spectrum of C_5H_5NiNO exhibits a strong metal nitrosyl band at 1833 cm.[-1].

---

[34] If desired, the preparation of the C_5H_5NiNO may be started at this stage using an equivalent quantity of pure nickelocene rather than preparing the nickelocene *in situ.*

[35] Since C_5H_5NiNO is moderately stable to attack by excess nitric oxide under these conditions, reasonable excesses of nitric oxide are not harmful.

[36] R. D. Feltham and J. T. Carriel, private communications (1962).

J. Metal Carbonyl Halide Derivatives

1. N-Methylpyridinium Iodopentacarbonylmetallates of Chromium, Molybdenum, and Tungsten

The hexacarbonyls of chromium, molybdenum, and tungsten react with iodide ion in ethereal solvents at elevated temperatures to form the anions $M(CO)_5I^-$ (M = Cr, Mo, and W).[1-3] Especially suitable for these reactions is N-methylpyridinium iodide because of its relatively high solubility in various ethers. The preparation of the N-methylpyridinium derivatives, $[C_5H_5NCH_3][M(CO)_5I]$, (M = Cr, Mo, and W), from the hexacarbonyls follows.

Procedure:

$$M(CO)_6 + [C_5H_5NCH_3]I \xrightarrow{\Delta} [C_5H_5NCH_3][M(CO)_5I] + CO\uparrow \quad (M = Cr, Mo, W)$$

The reaction is carried out under nitrogen in a 100-ml. flask equipped with a magnetic stirrer, nitrogen inlet, and reflux condenser. After filling the system with nitrogen, the flask is charged with 4.4 g. (0.02 mole) of N-methylpyridinium iodide,[4] 50 ml. of dioxane[5,6] or tetrahydrofuran,[5,7]

[1] E. O. Fischer and K. Öfele, *Z. Naturforsch.* **14b,** 736 (1959); *Chem. Ber.* **93,** 1156 (1960).

[2] E. W. Abel, M. A. Bennett, and G. Wilkinson, *Chem. Ind. (London)* 442 (1960).

[3] E. W. Abel, I. S. Butler, and J. G. Reid, *J. Chem. Soc.* 2068 (1963).

[4] N-Methylpyridinium iodide may be prepared by allowing the calculated quantities of pyridine and methyl iodide to react in pentane or hexane solution at room temperature. The white precipitate of N-methylpyridinium iodide after filtration and washing with pentane or hexane may be used for the reactions with the metal hexacarbonyls without further purification.

[5] Dioxane and tetrahydrofuran may be purified for this reaction by distillation over lithium aluminum hydride or sodium.

[6] Dioxane should be used for the reaction of N-methylpyridinium iodide with chromium or tungsten hexacarbonyls.

[7] Tetrahydrofuran may be used for the reaction of N-methylpyridinium iodide with the more reactive molybdenum hexacarbonyl.

and 0.02 mole of the metal hexacarbonyl [i.e., 4.4 g. of Cr(CO)$_6$, 5.3 g. of Mo(CO)$_6$, or 7.4 g. of W(CO)$_6$]. The reaction mixture is boiled under reflux at least 16 hr. under nitrogen with magnetic stirring. It soon becomes yellow or orange.

After the reaction period is over, the reaction mixture is cooled to room temperature. Any insoluble matter present is removed by filtration. The residue is washed with a few milliliters of tetrahydrofuran or dioxane. The solvent is evaporated from the combined filtrate and washings at 25–40° in a vacuum.[8]

The residue from the evaporation which should be solid is transferred to a sublimer and heated at 50–70°/0.1 mm. to insure removal of any unreacted metal hexacarbonyl. Nitrogen is then admitted to the evacuated sublimer, and the residue is extracted with 30-ml. portions of tetrahydrofuran until the extracts are no longer yellow or orange. These extracts are then filtered by gravity and the filtrate is collected under nitrogen. The filtrate is treated with about 40 ml. of hexane, and the solvent is removed in a water-aspirator vacuum (10 to 50 mm.) until the volume is about 20 ml. The yellow to orange crystals that separate during the hexane addition and the solvent removal are filtered, washed with three 25-ml. portions of a 1:2 diethyl ether-pentane mixture, and sucked dry to give the yellow to orange [C$_5$H$_5$NCH$_3$][M(CO)$_5$I] (M = Cr, Mo or W) in about 40–70% yield. The products, although sufficiently stable to be handled in air, should be stored under nitrogen for prolonged periods of time.

The compounds [C$_5$H$_5$NCH$_3$][M(CO)$_5$I] are solids which are yellow in the cases of the molybdenum and tungsten derivatives but orange in the case of the chromium derivative. Treatment of the chromium derivative with mild oxidizing agents such as triiodide ion, ferric ion, or hydrogen peroxide converts it to the deep-blue Cr(CO)$_5$I, which is insoluble in water but soluble in organic solvents.[9] Although the molybdenum and tungsten analogs are not oxidized in a similar manner, a dichloromethane solution of these compounds precipitates yellow [C$_5$H$_5$-NCH$_3$][M(CO)$_4$I$_3$] (M = Mo or W) on treatment with a dichloromethane solution of iodine.[10]

---

[8] Tetrahydrofuran (b.p. 65°) may be readily removed in a water-aspirator vacuum (15 to 50 mm.). The less volatile dioxane (b.p. 101°) requires either an unusually good water-aspirator vacuum (15 mm. or better) or an oil-pump vacuum for removal below 40° at a reasonable rate. Use of a rotary evaporator will also expedite removal of the dioxane.

[9] H. Behrens and H. Zizlsperger, *Z. Naturforsch.* **16b**, 349 (1961).

[10] R. B. King, *Inorg. Chem.* **3**, 1039 (1964).

2. Manganese Pentacarbonyl Bromide

Manganese pentacarbonyl bromide, $Mn(CO)_5Br$, may be prepared by treatment of manganese decacarbonyl with bromine.[11] It is also formed by treatment of certain organomanganese compounds of the type $RMn(CO)_5$ (R = methyl, acetyl, etc.) with bromine,[12] but this method is of no preparative value.

Procedure:

$$Mn_2(CO)_{10} + Br_2 \xrightarrow{CCl_4} 2Mn(CO)_5Br$$

A freshly prepared solution of 6.9 g. (0.0177 mole) of dimanganese decacarbonyl (page 89) in 80 ml. of reagent-grade carbon tetrachloride is treated dropwise with a solution of 1.26 ml. (3.7 g., 0.0231 mole as Br_2) of bromine in 25 ml. of reagent-grade carbon tetrachloride. After standing at room temperature for 1 hr. after all of the bromine has been added, the solvent is removed from the reaction mixture in a water-aspirator vacuum.

In order to remove any manganese(II) bromide, the yellow residue is shaken with 100 ml. of water and the suspension is filtered by suction. The residue is washed in turn with two 50-ml. portions of water and 20 ml. of methanol. After sucking dry, the residue is transferred to a sublimer and manganese pentacarbonyl bromide is sublimed at 50–60°/0.1 mm. onto a water-cooled probe to give 5.75 g. (59% yield) of yellow-orange crystals.

Manganese pentacarbonyl bromide, $Mn(CO)_5Br$, forms air-stable, volatile, yellow-orange crystals that are insoluble in water, sparingly soluble in saturated hydrocarbons, but readily soluble in most other organic solvents. Its infrared spectrum (CCl_4 solution) exhibits metal carbonyl bands at 2133 (w), 2050 (s), 2019 (w), and 2001 (m) cm.$^{-1}$. Reaction of $Mn(CO)_5Br$ with various amines, sulfides, and tertiary phosphines gives either the covalent derivatives of the types $Mn(CO)_4$-LBr or $Mn(CO)_3L_2Br$ or the ionic derivatives $[Mn(CO)_4L_2]Br$ depending on the ligand and the reaction conditions.[11,13] Upon heating, $Mn(CO)_5Br$ loses 1 mole of carbon monoxide to form the dimeric derivatives $[Mn(CO)_4Br]_2$ with bridging halogen atoms.[11] Treatment of $Mn(CO)_5Br$ with certain organomagnesium and organolithium compounds such as C_6H_5Li, C_6F_5MgBr, or $C_6H_5CH_2MgCl$ gives $RMn(CO)_5$ derivatives (R = C_6H_5, C_6F_5, or $C_6H_5CH_2$) as well as much reduction to Mn_2-

[11] E. W. Abel and G. Wilkinson, *J. Chem. Soc.* 1501 (1959).

[12] R. D. Closson, J. Kozikowski, and T. H. Coffield, *J. Org. Chem.* **22**, 598 (1957).

[13] R. J. Angelici, F. Basolo, and A. J. Poë, *Nature* **195**, 993 (1962).

$(CO)_{10}$.[14] Treatment of $Mn(CO)_5Br$ with benzene in the presence of aluminum chloride at elevated temperatures gives the benzene complex $[C_6H_6Mn(CO)_3]^+$.[15]

Manganese pentacarbonyl chloride, $Mn(CO)_5Cl$, may be prepared in a manner similar to the preparation of $Mn(CO)_5Br$ but using chlorine instead of bromine.[11] The iodide, $Mn(CO)_5I$, may be obtained from dimanganese decacarbonyl and iodine but elevated temperatures are necessary[16]; alternatively, the reaction between $NaMn(CO)_5$ and iodine at room temperature in tetrahydrofuran solution may be used.

3. Cyclopentadienyliron Dicarbonyl Iodide

Cyclopentadienyliron dicarbonyl iodide, $C_5H_5Fe(CO)_2I$, has been obtained either by treatment of the corresponding chloride $C_5H_5Fe(CO)_2Cl$ with iodide ion[17] or by treatment of $[C_5H_5Fe(CO)_2]_2$ with iodine.[18] The latter method, which will be described, is more suitable for the preparation of large quantities of $C_5H_5Fe(CO)_2I$.

Procedure:

$$[C_5H_5Fe(CO)_2]_2 + I_2 \xrightarrow{\text{CHCl}_3} 2C_5H_5Fe(CO)_2I$$

After filling with nitrogen, a 1-liter flask is charged with 200 g. (0.0565 mole) of $[C_5H_5Fe(CO)_2]_2$ (page 114) and 650 ml. of chloroform followed by 200 g. (0.788 mole as I_2) of iodine. The black mixture is boiled under reflux for 30 minutes. After cooling to room temperature, the reaction mixture is washed in a large separatory funnel with a solution of 400 g. of sodium thiosulfate 5-hydrate in 1 liter of water in two or three portions to remove excess iodine. The solvent is then removed from the lower black chloroform layer in a water-aspirator vacuum (15–50 mm.). The black crystalline residue is washed with three 150-ml. portions of pentane, hexane, or petroleum ether on a filter and sucked dry to give 287 g. (83% yield) of $C_5H_5Fe(CO)_2I$.

Cyclopentadienyliron dicarbonyl iodide, $C_5H_5Fe(CO)_2I$, is a black crystalline solid, m.p. 120°, that is sparingly soluble in nonpolar organic solvents, more readily soluble in polar organic solvents, and insoluble in

[14] W. Hieber and G. Wagner, *Ann.* (*Liebigs*) **618**, 24 (1958); W. Hieber and E. Lindner, *Chem. Ber.* **95**, 273 (1962); P. M. Treichel, M. A. Chaudhuri, and F. G. A. Stone, *J. Organometallic Chem.* **1**, 98 (1963); M. D. Rausch, *Inorg. Chem.* **3**, 300 (1964).
[15] G. Winkhaus, L. Pratt, and G. Wilkinson, *J. Chem. Soc.* 3807 (1961).
[16] E. O. Brimm, M. A. Lynch, Jr., and W. J. Sesny, *J. Am. Chem. Soc.* **76**, 3831 (1954).
[17] T. S. Piper, F. A. Cotton, and G. Wilkinson, *J. Inorg. Nucl. Chem.* **1**, 165 (1955).
[18] T. S. Piper and G. Wilkinson, *J. Inorg. Nucl. Chem.* **2**, 38 (1956).

water. Although air-stable in the solid state, its solutions are gradually oxidized in air with deposition of brown iron(III) oxide. It may be sublimed at $90°/0.1$ mm. Its infrared spectrum ($CHCl_3$ solution) exhibits strong metal carbonyl bands at 2044 and 2000 cm.$^{-1}$, and its proton n.m.r. spectrum ($CHCl_3$ solution) displays a single sharp cyclopentadienyl resonance at 4.93 τ. On treatment with alkylmagnesium halides or sodium cyclopentadienide, $C_5H_5Fe(CO)_2I$ forms alkyl derivatives of the type $C_5H_5Fe(CO)_2R$ (R = methyl,[19] ethyl,[19] phenyl,[19] cyclopentadienyl,[19] pentafluorophenyl,[20] etc.). Treatment of $C_5H_5Fe(CO)_2I$ with hexafluorophosphoric acid and carbon monoxide under pressure in a propionic acid-propionic anhydride solvent system gives the salt $[C_5H_5Fe(CO)_3]$ $[PF_6]$.[21] A substitution product of this cation, $[C_5H_5Fe(CO)_2\{(CH_3)_2-N\}_3P]I$, is obtained by treatment of $C_5H_5Fe(CO)_2I$ with tris(dimethylamino)phosphine in refluxing benzene.[22]

The analogous chloride, $C_5H_5Fe(CO)_2Cl$, may be prepared by air oxidation of $[C_5H_5Fe(CO)_2]_2$ in the presence of hydrochloric acid, ethanol, and chloroform.[17] The bromide, $C_5H_5Fe(CO)_2Br$, is best obtained by treatment of $[C_5H_5Fe(CO)_2]_2$ with bromine.[17,23]

4. Allyliron Tricarbonyl Iodide

Allyiron tricarbonyl iodide has been prepared by Plowman and Stone[24] by treatment of iron pentacarbonyl with allyl iodide at a carefully controlled temperature or by Murdoch and Weiss from $Fe_2(CO)_9$ and allyl iodide.[25]

Procedure:

$$Fe(CO)_5 + C_3H_5I \rightarrow C_3H_5Fe(CO)_3I + 2CO \uparrow$$

The reaction is carried out in a good hood in a 100-ml. flask equipped with a nitrogen inlet and reflux condenser and heated with an oil bath equipped with a thermometer. After filling with nitrogen, the flask is charged with 16.8 g. (0.1 mole) of allyl iodide and 20 ml. (29.2 g., 0.149 mole) of iron pentacarbonyl. The flask is heated to $40 \pm 5°$ (bath temperature)[26] for at least 50 hr. by means of the oil bath. After cooling to

[19] T. S. Piper and G. Wilkinson, *J. Inorg. Nucl. Chem.* **3**, 104 (1956).

[20] M. D. Rausch, *Inorg. Chem.* **3**, 300 (1962).

[21] R. B. King, *Inorg. Chem.* **1**, 964 (1962).

[22] R. B. King, *Inorg. Chem.* **2**, 936 (1963).

[23] B. F. Hallam and P. L. Pauson, *J. Chem. Soc.* 3030 (1956).

[24] R. A. Plowman and F. G. A. Stone, *Z. Naturforsch.* **17b**, 575 (1962).

[25] H. D. Murdoch and E. Weiss, *Helv. Chim. Acta.* **45**, 1927 (1962).

[26] It is important that the mixture of allyl iodide and iron pentacarbonyl not be heated above this temperature. Above about 50° the major product of the reaction becomes iron(II) iodide rather than allyliron tricarbonyl iodide.

room temperature, volatile materials (unreacted iron pentacarbonyl and allyl iodide) are removed from the reaction mixture in a water-aspirator vacuum (15 to 50 mm.) and collected in a −78° trap to minimize spread of the toxic iron pentacarbonyl vapors. The brown solid residue is transferred to a sublimer with a probe cooled by running cold water. The product is isolated by sublimation at 40–50°/0.1 mm. for at least 24 hr.[27] The yield of dark brown crystalline allyliron tricarbonyl iodide is 20 to 23 g. (65 to 75%).

Allyliron tricarbonyl iodide forms dark brown volatile fairly air-stable crystals, m.p. 98°, that are soluble in organic solvents but insoluble in water. Its infrared spectrum (cyclohexane solution) exhibits metal carbonyl bands at 2077, 2031, 2012, and 2008 cm.$^{-1}$. Its proton n.m.r. spectrum (chloroform solution) exhibits resonances at 4.25 τ (weak and broad), 6.2 τ (intense and complex), and 7.85 τ (doublet, $J = 13$ cps) indicating a complex equilibrium mixture of species in solution with σ-allyl and π-allyl groups. On reaction with tris(dimethylamino)phosphine both the allyl group and the iodine are displaced to give $\{[(CH_3)_2N]_3P\}_2Fe(CO)_3$.[22]

5. Heptafluoropropyliron Tetracarbonyl Iodide

Heptafluoropropyliron tetracarbonyl iodide, $C_3F_7Fe(CO)_4I$, is readily obtained from iron pentacarbonyl and heptafluoropropyl iodide either in benzene solution at atmospheric pressure[28] or in a closed system (Hoke bomb) in the absence of solvent.[29] The latter method, although less convenient, gives an appreciably better yield and is therefore described.

Procedure:

$$Fe(CO)_5 + C_3F_7I \rightarrow C_3F_7Fe(CO)_4I + CO \uparrow$$

A 300-ml. stainless steel Hoke bomb[30] is charged with 20.5 ml. (29.9 g., 0.153 mole) of iron pentacarbonyl and 10.7 ml. (22.0 g., 0.0745 mole) of heptafluoropropyl iodide.[31] The bomb is then cooled to −78° in a Dry

---

[27] This sublimation is a rather slow process.

[28] T. A. Manuel, S. L. Stafford, P. M. Treichel, and F. G. A. Stone, *J. Am. Chem. Soc.* 83, 249 (1961).

[29] R. B. King, S. L. Stafford, P. M. Treichel, and F. G. A. Stone, *J. Am. Chem. Soc.* 83, 3604 (1961).

[30] If a Hoke bomb is not available, an autoclave of comparable size may be used. Another possible reaction vessel is a thick-walled Carius tube.

[31] Heptafluoropropyl iodide, C_3F_7I, may be purchased in the United States from Columbia Organic Chemicals, Inc., Columbia, South Carolina, or from Peninsular Chem. Research, Inc., Gainesville, Florida and in Great Britain from L. Light and

Ice-acetone bath, evacuated, sealed, and heated in an oven at 65–75° for at least 16 hr.

After cooling the bomb to room temperature, it is opened and the contents are washed into a flask with several 50-ml. portions of dichloromethane until the washings are no longer colored. The dichloromethane is removed from the washings in a water-aspirator vacuum (15 to 50 mm.). Nitrogen is admitted to the evacuated flask, and the brown residue is transferred to a sublimer with a probe cooled by running water. The product is sublimed out of the residue at 30–35°/0.1 mm. to give 16 to 28 g. (46 to 80% yield) of red crystalline $C_3F_7Fe(CO)_4I$.

Heptafluoropropyliron tetracarbonyl iodide, $C_3F_7Fe(CO)_4I$, is a red, air-stable, crystalline solid, m.p. 69–70°, that is readily soluble in organic solvents and gives red solutions that oxidize gradually in air. It possesses a characteristic sharp penetrating odor. It is extremely volatile subliming readily at even 25°/0.1 mm. Its infrared spectrum (C_2Cl_4 solution) exhibits metal carbonyl bands at 2145 (m), 2111 (vw), 2088 (vs), and 2054 (m) cm.$^{-1}$, and its F^{19} n.m.r. spectrum (CH_2Cl_2 solution) exhibits resonances at 54.9 ϕ (quartet, J = 11 cps), 78.6 ϕ (triplet, J = 11 cps), and 114.4 ϕ (singlet) of relative intensities 2:3:2. Treatment of C_3F_7Fe-$(CO)_4I$ with certain Lewis bases gives complexes of the type C_3F_7Fe-$(CO)_2L_2I$ (L = triphenylphosphine, L_2 = o-phenanthroline, etc.).[32] On heating, $C_3F_7Fe(CO)_4I$ gives the dimeric complex $[C_3F_7Fe(CO)_3I]_2$[29]; a related dimeric complex $[C_3F_7Fe(CO)_3SCF_3]_2$ is obtained from C_3F_7Fe-$(CO)_4I$ and the silver derivative $[CF_3SAg]_n$ in benzene solution.[33]

Co., Colnbrook, Bucks. It is best prepared from iodine and silver heptafluorobutyrate [E. A. Nodiff, A. V. Grosse, and M. Hauptschein, *J. Org. Chem.* 18, 235 (1953)].

[32] R. A. Plowman and F. G. A. Stone, *Inorg. Chem.* 1, 518 (1962).

[33] R. B. King. *J. Am. Chem. Soc.* 85, 1584 (1963).

K. Metal Carbonyl Derivatives with Phosphorus and Sulfur Ligands

1. 2,5-Dithiahexane-Molybdenum Tetracarbonyl

2,5-Dithiahexane-molybdenum tetracarbonyl, $(CH_3SCH_2CH_2SCH_3)$-Mo$(CO)_4$, has been prepared by Mannerskantz and Wilkinson[1] by treatment of 2,5-dithiahexane with molybdenum hexacarbonyl. The procedure described here uses stoichiometric quantities of the two reactants to avoid handling an excess of the obnoxious 2,5-dithiahexane.

Procedure:

$$Mo(CO)_6 + C_4H_{10}S_2 \xrightarrow{\Delta} C_4H_{10}S_2Mo(CO)_4 + 2CO \uparrow$$

A mixture of 26.4 g. (0.1 mole) of molybdenum hexacarbonyl, 12.2 g. (0.1 mole) of 2,5-dithiahexane,[2] and 100 ml. of methylcyclohexane is boiled under reflux in a 250-ml. flask under nitrogen at the boiling point preferably with magnetic stirring. During the reaction period, yellow crystals of the product separate. After at least 16 hr., the heating is discontinued, and the reaction mixture is allowed to cool to room temperature. The resulting pale yellow solid is filtered (preferably in the hood), washed with at least three 75-ml. portions of pentane, hexane, or petroleum ether, and sucked dry. Although the crude product as thus obtained should contain no molybdenum hexacarbonyl, complete absence of molybdenum hexacarbonyl may be assured by heating the product several hours at 50–60°/0.1 mm. A yield of 33.0 g. (100%) of 2,5-dithiahexane-molybdenum tetracarbonyl is readily obtained from this reaction.

2,5-Dithiahexane-molybdenum tetracarbonyl, $(CH_3SCH_2CH_2SCH_3)$-Mo$(CO)_4$, forms pale-yellow crystals, m.p. 148° (dec.), possessing the

---

[1] H. C. E. Mannerskantz and G. Wilkinson, *J. Chem. Soc.* 4454 (1962).

[2] 2,5-Thiahexane may be purchased from Aldrich Chemical Company, 2371 North 30th Street, Milwaukee, Wisconsin, or from L. Light and Co., Colnbrook, Bucks, England. It has an obnoxious odor. Inhalation may cause headaches and other unpleasant symptoms.

characteristic vile odor of the free ligand. It is insoluble in nonpolar organic solvents, and only sparingly soluble in polar organic solvents. Its infrared spectrum (chloroform solution) exhibits strong metal carbonyl bands at 2030 (s), 1919 (s), 1905 (s), and 1868 (s) cm.$^{-1}$. On treatment with iodine, 2,5-dithiahexane-molybdenum tetracarbonyl forms the tricarbonyl derivative $(CH_3SCH_2CH_2SCH_3)Mo(CO)_3I_2$, which readily loses additional carbon monoxide to form the dimeric dicarbonyl derivative $[(CH_3SCH_2CH_2SCH_3)Mo(CO)_2I_2]_2$.[1]

2. Methylthioiron Tricarbonyl Dimer

Methylthioiron tricarbonyl dimer, $[Fe(CO)_3SCH_3]_2$, has been obtained by treatment of triiron dodecacarbonyl with dimethylsulfide[3] or dimethyldisulfide.[4]

Procedure:

$$2Fe_3(CO)_{12} + 3(CH_3)_2S_2 \xrightarrow{\Delta} 3[CH_3SFe(CO)_3]_2 + 6CO \uparrow$$

A mixture of 84 g. (0.167 mole) of triiron dodecacarbonyl (page 95), 150 ml. of dimethyldisulfide,[5] and 1000 ml. of thiophene-free benzene is heated under reflux at the boiling point under nitrogen with magnetic stirring in a 2-liter flask for at least 5 hr. The green color of the triiron dodecacarbonyl soon becomes the characteristic red color of $[Fe(CO)_3$-$SCH_3]_2$. After the reaction period is over, the reaction mixture is allowed to cool to room temperature and then filtered. The black pyrophoric residue is washed with 50-ml. portions of benzene until the benzene washings are no longer red and is then discarded in a safe place. The solvent is removed from the combined benzene filtrate and washings in a water-aspirator vacuum (15 to 50 mm.)[6] leaving behind about 28 g. (27% yield) of crude red crystalline $[Fe(CO)_3SCH_3]_2$.

In order to purify the $[Fe(CO)_3SCH_3]_2$, it is dissolved in a minimum of pentane or hexane and the solution is filtered. The filtrate is cooled in a $-78°$ bath (Dry Ice mixed with acetone). Red, air-stable crystals of purified $[Fe(CO)_3SCH_3]_2$ separate. These are removed by suction filtration and sucked dry. The product may be purified further by sublimation at $50°/0.1$ mm.

Methylthioiron tricarbonyl dimer, $[Fe(CO)_3SCH_3]_2$, as thus obtained

[3] W. Hieber and C. Scharfenberg, *Chem. Ber.* 73, 1012 (1940).

[4] R. B. King, *J. Am. Chem. Soc.* 84, 2460 (1962).

[5] Available from Crown-Zellerbach, Inc., Camas, Washington or L. Light and Co., Colnbrook, Bucks, England.

[6] This evaporation should be carried out in a hood since the vapors from the benzene and dimethyldisulfide are obnoxious.

consists of at least two isomers.[4] At least 80% of the mixture consists of the so-called "Isomer A", m.p. 65–67.5°, with characteristic methyl proton resonances at 7.87 τ and 8.38 τ of equal intensities. The melting point of the mixture should be close to the melting point of pure Isomer A. In addition, a second isomer of $[Fe(CO)_3SCH_3]_2$, m.p. 101.5–103.5°, known as "Isomer B" may be separated from the much larger quantities of Isomer A present by chromatography on alumina in pentane solution. Isomer B exhibits a single sharp methyl proton n.m.r. peak at 7.93 τ. It is thus apparent that samples of $[Fe(CO)_3SCH_3]_2$ can be analyzed for relative amounts of Isomers A and B by n.m.r. spectroscopy.

3. Bis(triphenylphosphine)nickel Dicarbonyl

Bis(triphenylphosphine)nickel dicarbonyl, $[(C_6H_5)_3P]_2Ni(CO)_2$, is readily obtained by reaction of nickel tetracarbonyl with triphenylphosphine.[7,8]

Procedure:

$$Ni(CO)_4 + 2(C_6H_5)_3P \rightarrow [(C_6H_5)_3P]_2Ni(CO)_2 + 2CO \uparrow$$

The reaction is conducted in an efficient hood in a 250-ml. flask fitted with a nitrogen inlet, reflux condenser, and pressure-equalized dropping funnel. After filling with nitrogen, the flask is charged with 13.1 g. (0.05 mole) of triphenylphosphine and 100 ml. of diethyl ether. This mixture is heated to the boiling point of the ether and 3.2 ml. (4.2 g., 0.0246 mole) of nickel tetracarbonyl added dropwise from the dropping funnel. The reaction mixture is then heated at the boiling point for an additional 30 minutes. It is then cooled. The pale-cream precipitate of bis(triphenylphosphine)nickel dicarbonyl is filtered and sucked dry. The yield should be nearly quantitative.

Bis(triphenylphosphine)nickel dicarbonyl forms a nearly white solid, m.p. 210–215° (dec.), that is sparingly soluble in organic solvents. Its infrared spectrum exhibits strong metal carbonyl bands at 2007 and 1952 cm.⁻¹. Bis(triphenylphosphine)nickel dicarbonyl is a useful catalyst for certain cyclic condensation reactions of acetylene.[7]

---

[7] W. Reppe and W. J. Schweckendiek, *Ann. Chem.* **560**, 104 (1948).

[8] J. D. Rose and F. S. Statham, *J. Chem. Soc.* 69 (1950).

Author Index